MEN *and* ATOMS

*The Discovery, the Uses
and the Future of Atomic Energy*

by

William L. Laurence

SIMON AND SCHUSTER

NEW YORK

1959

Permission has been granted to reprint the following material:

From Madame Curie *by Eve Curie,*
copyright 1937 by Doubleday & Co. Inc.
Reprinted by permission of Doubleday & Co., Inc.

From Einstein—His Life and Times *by Dr. Phillip Frank,*
copyright 1953 by Alfred A. Knopf, Inc.
Reprinted by permission of Alfred A. Knopf, Inc.

From Atomic Quest *by Arthur Holly Compton,*
copyright 1956 by Oxford University Press, Inc.
Reprinted by permission of Oxford University Press.

From The Decision to Use the Atomic Bomb *by Henry L. Stimson,*
copyright 1947 by Harper's *Magazine.*
Reprinted by permission of Harper & Brothers.

From Von der Uranspaltung Bis Calder Hall *by Professor Erich Bagge,*
from Rowohlts Deutsche Enzyklopädie.
Reprinted by permission of Rowohlt Verlag G. M. B. H., Hamburg.

*Grateful acknowledgment is made to Alfred A. Knopf for permission to re-use, in
revised form, some of the material from* Dawn Over Zero.

LIBRARY OF CONGRESS CATALOG CARD NUMBER: 59–13135
MANUFACTURED IN THE UNITED STATES OF AMERICA
BY H. WOLFF BOOK MANUFACTURING CO., INC.

To Florence

CONTENTS

CONTENTS

ACKNOWLEDGMENTS

My profound thanks for their invaluable assistance in the preparation of this manuscript to:

    My sister-in-law, Mrs. Ernest P. Postlethwaite, and

    My editorial assistant, Mrs. Marie Mossoba Berlinghoff.

PROLOGUE

That Night the Atom
Came to Live with Us

by

FLORENCE D. LAURENCE

THAT FOGGY EVENING in February 1939 will remain forever in
my memory.

We were walking north on Sutton Place toward the Queensboro
Bridge with our little brown dachshund, Einstein. The bridge was
barely visible through a thick haze. From the East River came the
sound of foghorns. An endless procession of lights kept moving
across the bridge in both directions. The flickering of the neon
signs across the river and the frequent bursts of flames from gas
tanks and factory chimneys gave the atmosphere a reddish tinge.

Bill's voice sounded as if it came from a great distance, and the
words that I heard soon gave substance to what had been only vague
forebodings.

He had just returned from a meeting of the American Physical
Society at Columbia University, where Niels Bohr and Enrico
Fermi, two of the greatest names in physics, had presented their
interpretations of one of the most remarkable discoveries of all time
—the splitting of the uranium atom. That discovery, called
uranium fission, was first reported in Germany early in January

1939, but its true significance was not realized until it was interpreted by two exiles from Germany then working in Sweden and in Denmark. So far it had been believed to be a small-scale phenomenon, serving only as a new laboratory tool for probing deeper into the mysteries of the atom. But a closer look by Bohr and Fermi had radically changed the picture. There were very cogent reasons for believing, they had said at the meeting, that fission might involve what they called a "chain reaction," which, in nontechnical language, meant that man might at last harness the vast energy in the atom.

In normal times this would have meant the promise of an immense new source of power for raising mankind's standard of living everywhere to heights undreamed of, transforming the earth into a veritable paradise. Alas, in view of the state of the world, what might have been the miracle of the near future seemed likely to become the nightmare of the immediate present. For it was by then quite certain that war was inevitable, and the key to the atom could, therefore, mean that Hitler might have at his disposal the greatest destructive force the world had ever known, millions of times more explosive than TNT.

And while neither Bohr nor Fermi, nor anyone else at the meeting, had even remotely hinted at the possibility of an atomic bomb, it was evident to anyone familiar with the facts that if Bohr and Fermi were right in their conjectures uranium fission would give the Germans an apocalyptic weapon.

"The splitting of the atoms of only one kilogram of uranium would equal twenty thousand tons of TNT as an explosive," I heard Bill say. "A single bomb could destroy the heart of any city in the world. And the nation that gets it first may dominate the world."

As a newspaperman and a veteran member of the staff of *The New York Times,* Bill felt it would be his duty to tell the free world of the danger facing it. If the free world were sufficiently aroused, the atom might be forged into a shield of freedom rather than a weapon of enslavement. But would it be aroused? Would it wake in time?

As we stopped at the iron fence at the dead end of East Fifty-seventh Street, Bill revealed a story which gave me the distinct feeling that our world and our way of life were about to be transformed.

A little more than five months had passed since Munich. Unless the free world were to surrender completely, a second world war appeared inevitable in the near future. With our strict cash-and-carry Neutrality Law we had given the world notice that if war broke out the Yanks were not coming. It was therefore extremely unlikely that Congress could be persuaded to authorize any funds on a fantastic weapon that no layman could believe possible and that most scientists looked upon with skepticism.

Under the circumstances it appeared highly probable that Hitler would be the first to possess an atomic bomb. The world's only choice would then lie between surrender and destruction.

We came home in deep gloom.

The atom had come to live with us from that night on.

PART ONE

The Second Coming
of Prometheus

CHAPTER ONE

"An Informal Meeting"

THE MEETING at Columbia University took place on the afternoon of Friday, February 24, 1939, in Lecture Hall 401 of Pupin Hall, the headquarters of the university's physics department. It was an informal meeting, held at the close of the regular program of the annual New York meeting of the American Physical Society, "for the discussion of the splitting of uranium atoms." That informal meeting was one of the most momentous in the history of the society and of science in general.

The speakers, Niels Bohr of Denmark and Enrico Fermi of Italy, were the two men in the entire world best qualified to discuss the subject. Bohr was the father of the modern concept of the atom's structure. Fermi had performed the series of epoch-making experiments that led directly to the discovery of uranium fission. By a most fortunate coincidence, they happened to be in the United States at the same time.

Both men, who were not scheduled on the program [I reported in *The New York Times* of Saturday, February 25, 1939], held their audience of 200 distinguished physicists fascinated by their reports on what is being hailed as "the most sensational discovery in modern physics since the discovery of radioactivity more than forty years ago."

This refers to the discovery . . . that by bombarding uranium with a slow neutral particle (neutron) of an energy of only one thirtieth of

3

a volt, the uranium atom is split into two elements, each constituting a gigantic radioactive atomic "cannonball" of 100,000,000 volts. This is the greatest amount of atomic energy so far to be liberated by man on earth.

The work on the newest "fountain of atomic energy" is going on feverishly in many laboratories both here and in Europe, it was reported by Professors Bohr and Fermi. It constitutes the biggest "big game hunt" in modern physics, opening up a new milestone in man's mastery over the elements and marking the most important step yet made by science toward the transmutation of the elements and the utilization of the vast stores of energy locked up within the nucleus of the atom.

The new method for the release of atomic energy and the transmutation of the elements is regarded as the nearest approach yet to be made to the finding of the modern version of the "Philosophers' Stone" of the alchemists. Its discussion by two of the greatest authorities in the field came as a surprise to the physicists attending the joint meeting of the American Physical Society and the Optical Society of America, as the official program gave no hint of the event.

So recent is the discovery and so feverish is the research going on that most of it still remains to be correlated and explained, Prof. Bohr said. The find has been so startling that it has left the scientists in a state of breathless wonder, and the general feeling prevails that physics is now on the eve of epoch-making discoveries.

The atmosphere of Lecture Hall 401 in Pupin Hall was tense. We were experiencing the rare privilege of watching genius in action, a magnificent spectacle of the human intellect challenging nature to yield secrets it had hidden from man ever since he first began to wonder and to think.

One of these secrets was the law of the chain reaction. This law decreed that just one split atom of uranium would serve as a cosmic match to light an atomic fire, or—in a bomb—as a fuse to set off an atomic explosion.

The second basic law of uranium fission (coauthored by Bohr and his former pupil, Professor John A. Wheeler of Princeton), was that only the very rare and elusive type of uranium, known as uranium 235, or U 235 for short, could be used.

The mathematical symbols that Bohr and Fermi were scribbling on the large blackboard, translated into words, meant that man

4

had found the means to light a new kind of fire, millions of times more powerful than any of the sun-derived fires until then lighted on earth. Indeed, it was a fire that came from the very same source of cosmic energy that enables the sun, and the myriads of luminous stars and supersuns that make up our cosmos, to radiate light and heat for billions of years without any outward signs of diminution.

A famous formula by Einstein has given us the key to the enormous amount of energy locked up in even a minute quantity of matter. On the basis of this formula it has been calculated that one thirtieth of a gram of water (there are 453.59 grams per pound), converted entirely into pure energy, would yield enough heat to turn one thousand tons of water into steam. In one whole gram of water there is a sufficient store of energy to raise a load of one million tons to the top of a mountain six miles high. A breath of air could operate a powerful airplane continuously for a year; a handful of snow could heat a large apartment house for a year; the pasteboard in a small railroad ticket could run a heavy passenger train several times around the globe; a cup of water could supply the power of a generating station of 100,000 kilowatt capacity for a year; the energy frozen in one dime (2.5 grams) could yield an explosive force equal to fifty thousand tons of TNT.

While the existence of this cosmic treasure house had been known for some decades, it had also been thought that it would remain forever beyond the reach of man. Only the sun and the giant stars, it was thought, could draw energy from the cosmic fountain. The stars alone possessed the key to the treasure house, a key that appeared much too large to be contained on earth, a tiny insignificant bit of cosmic dust in the hinterland of space.

Only a few months before that meeting at Columbia I had asked Einstein whether the time might ever come when man would find this key.

"No," he answered. "We are poor marksmen, shooting at birds in the dark in a country where there are very few birds!"

He was referring to the fact that at that time it was necessary to fire billions upon billions of atomic bullets, at a vast expenditure of energy, to force just a few atoms to yield a minute part of their energy content. These experiments were designed to yield new knowledge about the constitution of the atom and the inner structure of matter; they offered no hint of man's ability to tap the energy in the atom on a practical scale. Never in their wildest dreams did scientists dare hope that it would ever be possible to make the atom yield the enormous quantities of energy released in the splitting of uranium.

For, just as an ordinary fire needs oxygen to burn, the splitting of uranium can be done only with neutrons, one of the two basic building blocks in the nucleus of all atoms but one. The trouble was that all the neutrons in the universe were tightly bound inside the nuclei of the atoms, and there was no known power on earth to dislodge them in the quantities required to split uranium on a large scale. All that could be done was to dislodge an infinitesimal number of these neutrons. They would split a few uranium atoms, but this would be no more than striking an atomic match that would be extinguished just as quickly as an ordinary match in an environment lacking oxygen.

It looked hopeless. But that evening at Columbia I heard Fermi say two simple words that were destined to change man's destiny forever:

"Chain reaction!"

It took some time—it seems an eternity in retrospect—before the true meaning of those two simple words penetrated my consciousness. And then, suddenly, my conscious mind came to life and their meaning was revealed to me. Each uranium atom, as it splits, Fermi and Bohr were saying, would automatically release at least two neutrons to split two more atoms. The two, in turn, would release four neutrons, to split four atoms, and that would release eight neutrons, and so on, in geometric progression.

Simple arithmetic shows that a number multiplied by 2 at every successive step will reach a thousand (in round numbers) in the first ten steps, and will continue to multiply itself by a thousand at every ten steps thereafter, reaching a million in twenty steps, a billion in thirty, a trillion in forty, and so on. In eighty steps, the number of atoms that would be split in a chain reaction would reach the astronomical total of a trillion trillion, a figure represented by the numeral 1 followed by twenty-four zeros.

This figure represents the number of atoms in about one pound of uranium.

Man had found a way to create an atmosphere of neutrons, in

6

which he could build an atomic fire more powerful than any fire ever built before on earth. With it he could create a new civilization, transform the earth into a paradise of plenty, abolish poverty and disease, and return to the Eden he had lost.

I remember saying to myself, "This is the Second Coming of Prometheus, unbound at last after some half a million years, bringing down a fire from the original flame that had lighted the stars from the beginning."

I looked with fascination at the strange symbols and hieroglyphics Fermi was writing on the blackboard, interrupted here and there by Bohr. I was still daydreaming about what the "Second Coming of Prometheus" would mean for the future when I came to with a start.

This new Promethean fire, I found myself thinking, could be used by Hitler as the most destructive weapon in history. And, since the discovery of uranium fission had been made in Germany more than a month before, the Nazi scientists might already be working on this very project.

I asked my good friend and mentor, Professor John R. Dunning of Columbia, who was seated next to me, how the energy released by the fission of any given amount of uranium compared with the energy released by an equal amount of TNT.

"The energy is twenty million times the energy released in TNT," he replied. The splitting of one kilogram of uranium thus meant the release of an energy equal to the explosion of twenty million kilograms, or twenty thousand tons, of TNT.

"Supposing a chain reaction could be started," I asked, "how fast would such a reaction go? How long would it take, for example, for such a chain reaction to split a kilogram of uranium?"

Professor Dunning smiled. "My guess would be," he said, "that it would take a millionth of a second or thereabouts. The trouble is that there's no way at present to produce pure uranium 235 in amounts even as small as a millionth of a gram. A kilogram of uranium 235 is, in the present state of our knowledge, 'way beyond reach."

Uranium as found in nature is a mixture of two main variants, or isotopes. By far the most abundant, constituting 99.3 per cent of all natural uranium, is uranium 238, so called because its nucleus is composed of 238 fundamental building blocks of matter. The

7

second variety, uranium 235 (U 235), which has a nucleus composed of 235 fundamental particles (92 positively charged protons and 143 electrically neutral neutrons), constitutes only 0.7 of one per cent of all the uranium in nature.

It is this rare variety of uranium, Bohr had told the physicists, that would sustain a self-perpetuating chain reaction and thus serve as the element for the large-scale release of atomic energy, either at a controlled rate for use as a vast source of power, three million times the energy of coal, or at an uncontrolled rate as an explosive twenty million times the force in TNT.

On the other hand, Bohr continued, the heavy U 238 not only would be useless as an atomic fuel or explosive, it would actually serve as an atomic-fire extinguisher that would prevent an atomic fire from igniting in the light uranium. What he was saying in more technical terminology was that the uranium 238 would swallow a large percentage of the neutrons needed by the U 235 to maintain the chain reaction.

This was at the same time both bad and good news. It was bad news because it was then impossible to isolate U 235 in pure form, free from the atomic-fire extinguisher, which meant that atomic energy for power was still very theoretical. On the other hand, it was also reassuring news, since the impossibility of separating the 0.7 per cent of U 235 from the 99.3 per cent of U 238 meant that an atomic explosive was equally theoretical.

I wondered whether a simple method might not soon be found for separating U 235 from U 238. The progress of science was built on someone's doing what had been universally regarded as "impossible." Suppose Hitler's scientists could find a way to concentrate U 235!

I decided to ask guidance from Fermi and Bohr. As soon as the meeting was over, after asking Professor Dunning for an introduction, I put the question bluntly to the two great men: "Could not a small quantity of uranium 235, say just one kilogram, be used as a bomb equal to thousands of tons of TNT?"

Only some years later did I learn from Fermi the impact my question had made upon him and Bohr. For I could not even have suspected at the time that, in their secret counsels, they and other leading scientists among the exiles from Nazi and Fascist lands were already discussing plans for alerting the American government to this peril that was facing the free world.

Nor could I have known that Bohr, Fermi and others in that group of atomic pioneers were already considering the need to impose upon themselves a voluntary code of secrecy.

Fermi was the first to speak, after a pause long enough to give me the distinct feeling that I had asked a rather embarrassing question.

"We must not jump to hasty conclusions," he said, slowly and deliberately. "This is all so new. We will have to learn a lot more before we know the answer. It will take many years."

"How many years would it take, in your opinion?" I asked.

His answer, as he told me six years later, was intended to discourage me.

"At least twenty-five, possibly fifty years."

Remembering the impetus that the First World War gave to the development of aviation and radio, I felt that his estimate was much too conservative.

"Supposing Hitler decides that this may be the very weapon he needs to conquer the world," I persisted, "is it not conceivable that the time could be greatly shortened?"

"Nothing is impossible," he answered, "but it is highly improbable. There is still too much to learn."

"It may turn out to be easier than you think," I argued. "All that may be needed is an efficient method for concentrating uranium 235 in kilogram quantities."

"That may take many years. And we must also find proof that a chain reaction would actually take place."

I asked Fermi how it could be proved experimentally whether or not a chain reaction was actually possible, in view of the fact that it was impossible to isolate U 235 in practical quantities. He thought for a while and smiled in his characteristically impish manner.

"Maybe we could do it in a rather simple way, without isolating the U 235 at all. First, we get a large block of natural uranium, which will contain seven tenths of one per cent of U 235. Next we bore a large hole in the block and fill it with a radium-beryllium source. That will supply us with neutrons to start the process. We will then place the block in an open field, far from any inhabited locality, say somewhere in Kansas, and then wait for the rain to come." (Water slows down neutrons to energies that can split only atoms of uranium 235.)

What Fermi was describing, as we know today, was actually a crude prototype of the nuclear reactor, or atomic furnace, the power plant of the atomic age. The atomic furnace would be lighted as follows: The bullets (nuclei of helium atoms) fired naturally by the radium would knock out neutrons from the nuclei of the beryllium atoms. The rain water would slow down the neutrons to the proper speeds, at which they would be attracted only by the uranium 235, in the same manner as iron filings scattered in a pile of sand would be attracted to a powerful magnet.

The slow-speed neutrons would split the uranium-235 atoms, which would release more neutrons, which, in turn, would be slowed down by the falling raindrops and would split more U-235 atoms and release more neutrons, in a self-perpetuating chain reaction that would start a tremendous atomic conflagration.

We all laughed. But life from that night on was never to be the same for any of us.

CHAPTER TWO

The Miracle That Saved the World

THERE IS AN ANCIENT TALE about three princes of Serendip who in their travels were always discovering, by chance or by wisdom, things they did not seek. In allusion to this tale, Horace Walpole coined the word "serendipity," meaning "the gift of finding valuable or agreeable things not sought for."

The history of science is studded with dramatic examples of serendipity, many of the very greatest discoveries being the result of clues provided by chance. The rise of the water in his bathtub gave Archimedes the clue to the discovery of the law of floating bodies, the basic principle underlying the design of all ships. A falling apple led Isaac Newton to the discovery of the law of universal gravitation, one of the greatest discoveries of all time, which enabled him to formulate the laws of motion governing the revolution of the planets and of all celestial bodies in space. When Michael Faraday observed that an electric current is induced in a wire moved across the lines of magnetic force, he came upon the wonderful discovery that it is possible to transform mechanical energy directly into electrical energy, the fundamental discovery that made possible the modern age of cheap electricity.

While the clues that led to these and many other great scientific discoveries came by chance, it required the inspiration of genius to follow these chance clues to their ultimate meaning. As the great Pasteur said, "Chance favors the prepared mind!" Many an important discovery was missed because the mind of the observer was not prepared to recognize what he was looking at. And in nearly all such cases, the lack of the mind's preparedness—in some instances even minds of men of recognized genius—was the direct result of preconceived ideas.

The most famous example of serendipity in which the discoverer's mind was not prepared to recognize what he had discovered was, of course, that of Columbus. Having set out to find a short cut to India, with the preconceived idea that the course he was taking would lead him there, his mind was not prepared to recognize the fact that he had actually discovered a new continent.

The discovery of nuclear fission is the most famous modern example of a discovery of tremendous importance—perhaps the greatest in recorded history—made by serendipity. Here also, as in the case of the discovery of America, the minds of the original discoverers, and of many others who continued their explorations, were completely unprepared. And here once again it was the case of preconceived ideas that blocked the recognition of revolutionary facts.

As we shall presently relate, this unpreparedness on the part of many of the world's most brilliant minds was, indeed, very fortunate for mankind's future. The world does not yet realize—and it is recorded here for the first time—the vital role that this unprecedented manifestation of collective intellectual blindness played in the preservation of all the cherished values of Western civilization.

For had it not been for this collective intellectual blindness, Hitler would have had the atom bomb at the beginning of World War II, and it is practically certain that he would have been the only one to possess it.

The fact of the matter is that the splitting of the uranium atom, which made the atomic bomb possible, first took place in the spring of 1934, more than five years before the beginning of World War II. It was done at the University of Rome. And the head of the team that split the uranium atom was none other than Enrico Fermi.

But according to all the laws of physics universally accepted at the time, there was no power on earth that could split an atom. None of the world's most illustrious physicists, including Einstein, Planck, Rutherford and Bohr, believed that it would ever be possible to split an atom. So Fermi and his brilliant team watched uranium atoms being split and failed to recognize what they saw.

For nearly five years brilliant nuclear physicists and nuclear chemists in many lands, including Irène Joliot-Curie, Nobel Prize-winning daughter of the famous Marie and Pierre Curie, discoverers of radium and polonium, repeated the Fermi experiments with uranium thousands of times. They all saw the same phenomena, which, had their minds been prepared, they could not have failed to recognize as the results of the splitting of the uranium atom into two lighter elements, accompanied by the release of vast quantities of nuclear energy. But so great is the power of preconceived ideas, even when false, that they failed to arrive at the only logical conclusion that could have explained what was happening before their eyes.

One shudders to think how close the world came to disaster in those days when young Fermi and his small crew of four—Eduardo Amaldi, Oscar d'Agostino, Franco Rasetti and Emilio Segrè—stood gazing in wonder at a brood of strange products created in their crucible following their bombardment of a tiny amount of uranium with their neutron gun, a glass tube barely more than half an inch long from which neutrons streamed, knocked out from beryllium atoms by powerful nuclear "bullets" from radium. Had they become aware of what was actually taking place in their rather simple experimental chamber, the secret of the atomic bomb, and of the hydrogen bomb as well, would have been revealed as far back as May 1934, which would have given Hitler more than five years in which to develop these ultimate weapons.

The fact that Fermi, and the host of brilliant nuclear physicists and chemists throughout the world, failed to recognize the nature and significance of the world-shaking phenomena they were looking at must go down in history as the Great Five-Year Miracle.

It was the great miracle that saved the world.

In 1925 Ida Noddack had collaborated with her husband in the discovery of the element rhenium. In the paper she published in 1934 she suggested the possibility that Fermi had actually split the uranium atom.

One may equally well accept [she speculated] that in this new type of nuclear disintegration brought about by neutrons, important nuclear reactions take place other than those hitherto observed . . . It is conceivable that in the bombardment of heavy nuclei [such as uranium] with neutrons, these nuclei break up into several large fragments which are actually isotopes [twins] of known elements, but are not neighbors of the irradiated elements.

She was, of course, absolutely right, as was learned five years later in a roundabout way after scores of false clues had been followed. But no one considered her suggestion worth even the slightest consideration.

Here we have one of the great paradoxes of history. All human progress is the result of the open mind searching the unknown. Yet here we have a most dramatic illustration of the tightly closed, prejudiced mind saving civilization. Does that mean that the closed mind may sometimes be desirable to serve as a brake against too rapid progress? That we should deliberately slow down the pace of advance of our knowledge of nature to prevent its misuse by brutes and madmen in power? That we should tame the creative mind?

Most certainly not. The events of 1934 prove just the opposite. Instead of the creative mind slowing down, the leaders of civilized nations should recognize the need to speed up their pace to keep in step with the rapid, breathtaking advances of science.

Had that been the case in 1934, there would have been no danger of Hitler's being the first possessor of nuclear weapons. On the contrary, had the discovery of nuclear fission been recognized in 1934, when Fermi first split the uranium atom, and had the political and military leaders recognized the vast potentialities of the discovery, the free world, with its much greater industrial and scientific resources would have been the first to produce nuclear weapons. Under such circumstances Hitler, faced with the possibility of nuclear devastation, might well have been deterred from launching the war.

It was only because the political and military leaders of the free world would most certainly have failed to recognize the danger of an atomic arsenal in the hands of Hitler, just as they had failed to recognize the danger to the free world of the vast conventional German war machine, that the failure of the world's top scientists to keep an open mind became a distinct advantage. For the open mind can become a danger only when it functions in a social and political climate of tightly closed minds.

When one contemplates the events from 1934 to the end of 1938, one can only surmise that a benevolent destiny stood watch over the free world and protected it against the forces of evil. It kept the atomic bomb away from the free world's archenemy by blinding the keenest eyes of mankind.

"How come you missed it?" I asked Fermi in 1945, in his laboratory at Los Alamos, New Mexico.

And as he replied I realized for the first time the full extent of the miracle that kept the atomic bomb from Hitler—and gave us a four-year lead over the Soviet Union.

"It was a thin piece of aluminum foil, three mils [thousandths of an inch] thick, that stopped us all from seeing what actually took place," was his answer.

The reason for the aluminum foil was logical enough. Fermi, and the other atomic explorers who repeated his experiment, believed that they were creating new elements out of the uranium in their chamber, elements heavier than uranium. Such transuranium elements, they had calculated, would give off powerful radiations of a certain range. The thin strip of aluminum foil was to serve as a "radiation sieve," holding back the short-range radiations from the uranium but allowing the long-range radiations from the new elements to pass through.

But the three-mil aluminum foil was thick enough to stop Fermi from seeing an altogether new dimension of radiation energy, so great that only the splitting of the uranium atom could have accounted for its appearance.

Had it not been for the shield of three mils of aluminum foil, Fermi would have seen those radiations on the television screen connected to his apparatus, manifesting themselves in the form of jagged high peaks on a vibrating green line. From the height of these peaks, serving as an atomic thermometer, he would have recognized that the energy of the radiations was greater by far than the energy of any radiation ever before observed.

The unprecedented height of the green peaks on the atomic thermometer would have told Fermi that a great cosmic eruption was taking place in his uranium chamber. The height of the jagged peaks on the green line of his television screen would have revealed to him the vast amount of energy carried by these radiations—something on the order of 200 million electron volts.

This astonishing eruption of an atomic volcano could have led to only one conclusion: The splitting of the uranium atom was taking place.

Thus it came to pass that a tiny strip of aluminum foil, three thousandths of an inch thick, interposed itself between the flying fragments of the split uranium atoms and the television screen, hiding from the eyes of man the awesome vision of nuclear power.

Years later I asked Fermi if he regretted having missed making one of the greatest discoveries of all time.

"I am glad I missed," he answered quietly.

Disaster almost came in 1936 in the laboratory of two Swiss physicists, who, like many others, were trying to clear up some of the strange phenomena that were being observed when Fermi's original experiment with uranium was repeated.

One day they forgot to place the three mils of aluminum foil in their uranium chamber. And as they turned their gaze on the television screen they were dazzled by jagged green peaks rising to unbelievable heights. They looked, and the more they looked the more incredible it all seemed to be.

"The damned instrument is sparking," they agreed.

So they discarded their "faulty instrument" and proceeded to set up the experiment with another one of "normal" behavior. This time, and ever after, they remembered to place the three mils of aluminum foil in the proper place inside their chamber.

CHAPTER THREE

The Impurity That Changed History

On the morning of Monday, January 2, 1939, Enrico Fermi stood on the deck of the *Franconia* and looked at the skyline of New York and the Statue of Liberty. Beside him stood his wife, Laura, and their two children, Nella and Giulio, eight and three years old.

"We have founded the American branch of the Fermi family," said Fermi.

He could not have come at a more opportune time, nor could he have even remotely suspected the transcendent role he was to play in the history of America and of the free world.

He had just received the Nobel Prize in physics, on December 10, 1938, for his "disclosure of new radioactive elements produced by neutron irradiation and for his related discovery of nuclear reactions brought about by slow neutrons." Mussolini's aping of Hitler's anti-Semitic laws had made life intolerable for the Fermi family, as Laura Fermi is of Jewish origin, a member of a distinguished family that had lived in Italy for generations. So when Fermi left for Sweden to receive his Nobel Prize he took his family with him, determined not to return to Fascist Italy.

American universities were, of course, proud to invite a physicist of Fermi's distinction to join their faculties. Of the several offers made to him, he chose to join the teaching staff of Columbia Uni-

17

versity in New York, one of the world's major centers of research in atomic physics.

Fermi was one of the scores of great scientists, artists, writers and scholars who had come to our shores to carry on their work in an atmosphere of freedom. The best known of these was Albert Einstein, who had come in 1933. All, without exception, contributed greatly to our heritage, material and spiritual. They brought to us, a young nation, cultural treasures that will continue to enrich our country for generations to come.

On that Monday morning Fermi was looking forward to the opportunity of continuing his basic studies of the nucleus of the atom. But destiny decreed otherwise. He had been in America less than three months when he found himself called upon to serve as the master builder of the world's most fearful weapon.

Unbeknown to him when he landed here, one of the most significant scientific discoveries in history had just been made in Germany. In the great chemical laboratories of the Kaiser Wilhelm Institute in Berlin, epoch-making experiments had been completed a few days before Christmas of 1938. They were essentially the very same experiments first performed by Fermi and his team in 1934—the transmutation of uranium by the firing of neutrons into its nucleus. But the procedures employed now included the highly refined techniques of radiochemistry, a newly developed scientific field.

The experiments came as the climax of one of the world's great scientific struggles for supremacy, though neither of the protagonists even remotely suspected the magnitude of the prize. At stake was the prestige not only of individuals but of two nations as well. Once again it was Germany against France; this time a team of two distinguished German scientists was challenging a distinguished French scientist. And to add even more grandeur to the struggle, two of the principal protagonists were women, recognized at the time as the two outstanding women scientists in the world.

On the German team were Otto Hahn, the world's foremost radiochemist, and Lise Meitner, a world-renowned nuclear physicist. On the French side was the equally renowned Irène Joliot-Curie. Like her mother, Irène had won the Nobel Prize for chemistry, which she shared with her husband, Frédéric Joliot-Curie, for their discovery of artificial radioactivity—the creation of a great variety of radiumlike elements, similar to the natural radium discovered by

Irène's parents, out of ordinary stable elements. This outstanding discovery opened the way to the synthesis of a host of radioactive isotopes, many of which play a vital role in the chemistry of living things. These provided mankind with the most powerful tools for the study of the living process since the discovery of the microscope.

As a child of famous parents, Irène Curie strove desperately to surpass them. In the words of Lise Meitner, "she seemed to be afraid of being regarded rather as the daughter of her mother than as a scientist on her own account." She wanted above all to equal her mother's achievement of two Nobel Prizes, one in chemistry and another in physics, an honor achieved only once in the entire history of the Nobel Prize awards. And, as we shall presently see, she came very close to winning not only two, but three Nobel Prizes, an additional one in chemistry and another in physics, only to be bitterly disappointed in each case when they were snatched away from her by rivals at the last minute.

Her first great disappointment came in 1932. With her husband she had been on a hunt for the identity of a mysterious type of powerful radiation originally observed in 1930 by Walther Bothe, Germany's foremost nuclear experimenter. In 1932 they were close to it. But somehow the prize, which turned out to be one of the greatest in modern science, eluded them.

In the Cavendish Laboratory at Cambridge University, then headed by the great Lord Rutherford, James Chadwick, one of Rutherford's pupils, was also searching for the mysterious ray. And the observations of the Joliot-Curies, ironically enough, provided him with just the clue he had needed to put him on the right track. A month later he made one of the most dramatic announcements in the history of science. He identified the mysterious ray as the neutron, one of the two fundamental building blocks of the universe, the particle that was to provide the key to the atomic age.

For this discovery Chadwick was awarded the Nobel Prize in physics in 1935, the coveted prize Irène Joliot-Curie just barely missed.

Chadwick won it because he had read a lecture delivered by Rutherford in 1920, in which the father of experimental nuclear physics predicted the existence of the neutron. Frédéric Joliot-Curie was reported to have said ruefully—after Chadwick had explained the true meaning of the Joliot-Curies' observations—that if he and his wife had read Rutherford's 1920 lecture, they would probably have identified the neutron themselves.

When the great Marie Curie died on July 4, 1934, Irène Joliot-Curie, then thirty-six, had just reached the pinnacle of her scientific career with the discovery (made jointly with her husband) of artificial radioactivity, thus greatly extending the vast domain of which her mother had been the reigning sovereign. It was the only example in the history of science in which eminence in one of the great fields of knowledge was passed on in a direct line of succession from mother to daughter.

But unlike her mother, Irène Joliot-Curie had a formidable rival. Lise Meitner, though less well known to the world at the time, had achieved great distinction for her pioneer contributions in the field of radioactivity. And, as frequently happens among scientists working in the same field, there were occasions at scientific congresses when Lise openly challenged the findings of her French rival.

Lise Meitner was born in Vienna, of Jewish parents, on November 7, 1878, and was thus nearly nineteen years older than Irène, who was born on September 12, 1897. At the age of twenty, when Irène was one year old, Lise, then a fledgling student of science at the University of Vienna, became fascinated with reports of the discovery of polonium and radium by Pierre and Marie Curie. It was this discovery, one of the great landmarks in history, that determined Lise to make the study of atomic physics, then a brand-new field of science, her life's work. And in this decision, which forty years later profoundly influenced the course of history, she was no doubt inspired by the fact that one of the outstanding pioneers in that fascinating new field was a woman.

In 1908, when Lise was thirty years old (she never married), her advanced studies brought her to the University of Berlin, then one of the world's greatest centers of atomic physics. There she studied theoretical physics with the great Max Planck, discoverer of the quantum theory, one of the most revolutionary concepts in history —for which Planck received the Nobel Prize in physics in 1918. At the same time she began her experimental work with Otto Hahn, who had studied under Rutherford. It was an association that was to continue for thirty years.

The team of Hahn and Meitner won world-wide recognition for

their contributions to knowledge in the field of radioactivity, which shed new light on the then baffling disintegration products of radium, actinium and thorium, and on the natural transmutations of these elements into a series of other elements by nature's own alchemy. In 1917 they discovered the rare element protactinium, element 91, which filled in the gap between thorium, element 90, and uranium, element 92. They named it protactinium because their studies revealed that it disintegrates into actinium, element 89.

The strange collection of radioactive elements created by Fermi in 1934 as the result of bombarding uranium with neutrons produced a sensation in the scientific world. In all the leading laboratories the most cunning devices of modern science were used in efforts to identify this bewildering variety of elements. As we know today, they were new radioactive varieties of elements about half the atomic mass of uranium, the fragments of split uranium atoms. But according to all the accepted concepts of the atom at the time, the splitting of an atom was impossible. So the scientists kept looking in the wrong direction for elements heavier than uranium, which simply were not there.

Among the most experienced and best known of the workers in this field were, of course, Otto Hahn and Lise Meitner, in Berlin, and Irène Joliot-Curie, in Paris, together with various collaborators. And in 1937 the team of Hahn and Meitner, assisted by another eminent radiochemist, Fritz Strassmann, described experiments that promised to open new paths in the scientific wilderness. They were in the midst of pursuing these new experiments in 1938 when the Nazi racial laws brought Lise Meitner's scientific career in Germany to an end.

Though she had lived and worked in Berlin for thirty years she had retained her Austrian citizenship, and she was allowed to continue working at the Kaiser Wilhelm Institute after the advent of Hitler in 1933, despite the fact that she was Jewish. But when the Germans invaded her homeland in March 1938 and made it part of Germany she became subject to the Nazi racial laws. She was dismissed from her post despite the intervention of Hahn and a personal appeal to Hitler by Planck. On being informed that the Nazis would not permit her to leave the country, her Dutch colleagues obtained permission for her to enter Holland without a passport. From there she went to Copenhagen, to visit for a time the famous Institute for Theoretical Physics, headed by Niels Bohr, where her nephew, Otto R. Frisch, like herself an exile from Germany, had become one of the leading lights. From there she went to Stockholm, where an honored position on the staff of the Physical Institute awaited her.

Lise Meitner's exile brought to an abrupt end thirty years of fruitful collaboration but not the close friendship between her and her "cockerel" (*Hahn* is the German word for rooster). So closely linked had the names of Hahn and Meitner become, both in Germany and abroad, that the mention of the one inevitably brought to mind the other. Hahn tells of the amusing episode when Lise Meitner, addressed by a colleague at a scientific congress, absent-mindedly replied, "I think you've mistaken me for Professor Hahn."

Just before she was exiled, the team of Hahn, Meitner and Strassmann had completed an elaborate set of experiments which made it appear as though order had at last been established among the elements. After Lise Meitner's departure Hahn carried on, with Strassmann, his investigations of what he believed to be the transuranium elements, but at the same time he was in frequent communication with Meitner in Stockholm, keeping her informed of his progress and welcoming her criticisms and suggestions. All the subsequent experiments seemed to confirm the results obtained before Lise's exile. All, the team believed, pointed to the fact that the bombardment of uranium with neutrons led to the creation of four new elements beyond uranium (element 92)—elements 93, 94, 95 and 96—as well as of several heavier forms (isotopes) of uranium itself.

But Irène Joliot-Curie completely upset the neat order they had created among the elements. Working in collaboration with Paul Savitch, a talented Yugoslav radiochemist, she reported having found a new element. It had chemical properties resembling actinium, element 89, which could, with difficulty, have been made to fit into the Hahn-Meitner-Strassmann scheme of things. But Irène Joliot-Curie, using a procedure first developed by her mother, presented evidence that radioelement X was definitely not actinium. Indeed, element X behaved in every way as if it were the rare-earth metal lanthanum, element 57, whose atomic mass is 100 units less than that of uranium. If that were true, it could only mean that the uranium atom had been split into two nearly equal halves. But Irène Joliot-Curie, using highly ingenious chemical detective techniques, was led to believe—erroneously, alas—that the substance was not lanthanum either. Instead she and Savitch decided that element X was a new transuranium element, different in every way from the ones in the neatly ordered scheme of Hahn and his colleagues.

Hahn's astonishment was great when the Curie-Savitch report reached him, in the summer of 1938. In the words of an eyewitness, the Canadian radiochemist L. G. Cook, who was in Berlin at the time, Hahn's reaction was "that it just could not be, and that Curie and Savitch were very muddled up."

The tragic fact was that Curie and Savitch were, indeed, "very muddled up," but for the very opposite reason Hahn had in mind. As Hahn himself was soon to discover, the mysterious element X discovered by Irène Joliot-Curie was, indeed, none other than lanthanum, the element half the atomic weight of uranium. She had discovered uranium fission but had failed to recognize it.

For the second time within the course of a short six years, Irène Joliot-Curie had missed making a discovery for which someone else—none other than Otto Hahn—was to win the Nobel Prize. With a little luck on both occasions she would have been the only scientist—man or woman—to win three Nobel Prizes, not only equaling but surpassing her mother's unique achievement.

Irène Joliot-Curie's second great disappointment came as the result of an unfortunate error. In her earlier experiments she had observed that when ordinary lanthanum was introduced into the solution containing element X, the lanthanum would carry the X element down with it as a precipitate. This meant that element X had chemical properties similar to those of lanthanum, but this, of course, did not mean that the two were identical.

To establish whether or not two elements thus carried down together are identical, chemical methods are used to determine whether or not they can be separated. Identical elements cannot, of course, be separated, since they would respond exactly alike to any chemical manipulation. Hence, when one has a mixture of two elements, one known and the other unknown, the failure to separate them by any chemical means is definite proof that the two elements are identical. On the other hand, if it is found that they can be separated that is positive proof that the two elements are not identical.

This is exactly what Irène Joliot-Curie tried to do in attempting to determine whether element X was or was not a radioactive form, or isotope, of lanthanum, but by a strange turn of fate she came up with the wrong answer. She believed, and so reported, that she had succeeded in separating radioelement X from the lanthanum, whereas, in fact, as Hahn was to prove a few months later, the two elements were identical and therefore could not be separated by any known means. Thus she had been "very muddled up" indeed, because she finally came to the conclusion that element X was not lanthanum.

Her misfortune was mainly due to the fact that there had been present in her solution an impurity that possessed chemical properties similar to those of lanthanum. It was this impurity that was actually separated from the element-X–lanthanum combination, whereas the lanthanum remained tightly bound to element X. But, alas, Irène Joliot-Curie mistook the impurity for the lanthanum. And thus it came about that her failure to have read a lecture by Rutherford cost her the Nobel Prize in physics for the discovery of the neutron, while her failure to detect, or to look for, an impurity cost her what would have been a third Nobel Prize for the discovery of uranium fission.

To add irony to the poignant tragedy, which greatly embittered Irène Joliot-Curie for the rest of her life (she died in 1956), the method she employed for separating the lanthanum from element X was one devised by her own mother.

That impurity in Irène Joliot-Curie's experimental vessel played a vital role in world history. Had it not been present, the discovery of uranium fission would have come in May 1938 instead of December. This would have meant that the atomic bomb would have been ready early in February 1945 instead of August, which would have meant an end of World War II some six months, and possibly even a year, sooner.

That little impurity thus changed the course of history.

CHAPTER FOUR

The Discovery of Fission

OTTO HAHN and Fritz Strassmann set out on a hunt to track down Irène Joliot-Curie's elusive element that appeared to disguise itself either as lanthanum or as the heavy element actinium, yet on closer examination turned out, as Irène Joliot-Curie concluded, to be neither lanthanum nor actinium, but still another element beyond uranium.

They never found Irène Joliot-Curie's lanthanum-like "transuranium" element. Instead they found three never-before-seen substances, which, their tests led them to believe, were three new varieties of radium. Never before had uranium, element 92, been transmuted into any form of radium, element 88, and the transmutation of element 92 into element 88 was in itself a very remarkable phenomenon. But astonishing as this was, it was nothing compared with the tremendous discovery that was to follow.

For a closer look at one of the three varieties of what they had at first believed to be a new isotope of radium revealed to their unbelieving eyes that it was, instead, a new, radioactive variant of barium, element 56, only a little more than half the atomic weight of uranium.

And as if having seen the impossible taking place before their incredulous eyes was not enough of a surprise, they saw a second impossibility materialize in their chemical "brewery." For the second of the three new varieties of their alleged radium turned out to be none other than a radioactive variant of lanthanum, element 57, barium's neighbor in the Periodic Table of Elements. Indeed, it was the very lanthanum that Irène Joliot-Curie had first looked at, only to be misled by an impurity into believing that it wasn't lanthanum.

"How can it be?" they asked each other. It was as though they had put an ostrich egg into an incubator and seen it hatch out into a chicken and a pigeon.

No wonder they did not at first believe what they had seen. They were certain that some mistake had been made, although their experiments had been the most meticulous of their kind. But as they set out to find the error that might have misled them, they could not find the slightest weak link in their chain of evidence. They devised not one, but a whole series of cunning and subtle tests, designed to reveal any possible error that might have been made, but each test, instead of weakening their evidence, gave more and more conclusive proof that the elements were indeed radioactive variants of barium and lanthanum. And to make the mystery even more profound, they found good reason for believing that the third of their three radium variants was a new radioactive variant of cerium, element 58.

There could no longer be any doubt about it: The chemical evidence was proof that the bombardment of uranium with neutrons of very low energy (of about one fortieth of an electron volt) resulted in the production of three radioactive varieties of the light elements barium, lanthanum and cerium, elements 56, 57 and 58, respectively.

Where could these three light elements have come from? Since nothing ever comes from nothing, the only possible source of these elements was the uranium atom; and that, of course, would mean that the neutron had accomplished the unheard-of feat of splitting the nucleus of the heavy uranium atom into two nearly equal halves, the barium, lanthanum and cerium each being one of the larger fragments—fifty-six, fifty-seven and fifty-eight positive atomic units split off from the ninety-two positive units of the uranium nucleus.

Indeed, this turned out to be the case, as an astonished scientific world was to learn a few weeks later. But Hahn and Strassmann were chemists and they knew only too well that according to all the universally accepted concepts of physics the splitting of the uranium atom was unthinkable. It would be highly presumptuous for them, as chemists, to challenge such illustrious names in physics as Einstein, Planck, Bohr and Fermi.

As Hahn told me several years later, "The physicists wouldn't allow it."

Yet as chemists they were certain that the radioactive variants of barium, lanthanum and cerium had definitely been produced by the bombardment of uranium with neutrons, though their true origin was still a mystery for the physicists to solve. Whatever the solution, they knew that they had made a great discovery which was bound to lead to new domains of knowledge. And they also realized that they were in a great race with their long-time rival, Irène Joliot-Curie, who, any day, might recognize her error and announce to the world that she had produced lanthanum out of uranium—and possibly also (being a physicist) that she had split the uranium atom.

So, even before all their tests had been fully completed, Hahn and Strassmann prepared a detailed scientific report on their epoch-making experiments, at the same time being very careful not to step on the toes of their colleagues the physicists. After describing what they had found, they concluded with one of the strangest passages in the annals of science, in which they presented their observations but refused to draw any conclusions from them.

As chemists, they said in substance, they could only report that the three elements believed at first to be radium were, in fact, barium, lanthanum and cerium.

However, they added, in what has since become a famous example of intellectual caution, "as nuclear chemists, closely allied to physics," they could not bring themselves "to make this jump, so contradictory to all the phenomena observed until now in nuclear physics."

After all, they concluded, "it is possible that a number of rare accidents may have fooled us into making erroneous observations."

Having thus protected themselves against any possible ridicule from the nuclear physicists, they decided not to lose any time in establishing their priority of discovery. So on December 22, 1938, they dispatched their historic report to the German scientific weekly *Die Naturwissenschaften* (*The Natural Sciences*).

To make sure that their report would be published at the earliest possible date, Hahn telephoned the director of the publishing house, Dr. Paul Rosbaud, a personal friend. It would appear in the January 6, 1939, issue, Dr. Rosbaud assured him. That was much sooner than normal in scientific publication, but Hahn could think only of the two long weeks that were still to pass. Two weeks, in which Irène Joliot-Curie might snatch the great prize out of his hands any day.

Before he told his astonishing discovery to anyone, Hahn dispatched a letter to his lifelong colleague and friend, Lise Meitner, in Stockholm, telling her in detail of his experiments and the unbelievable results he and Strassmann had been confronted with. Anxiously he awaited her reaction. She was one of the world's great physicists, a keen analyst and a sharp critic. Would she find his data ridiculous, as, indeed, they had appeared at first to him? Would she find basic flaws in his procedures that he had overlooked? Was his reputation as a chemist, built up over long years, about to suffer a severe blow?

Hahn's letter reached Lise Meitner at a hotel in the small town of Kungelv, near Göteborg, a seaside resort, nearly deserted during the winter season, where she had gone to visit friends for the Christmas holidays. Visiting with her was her nephew, Otto R. Frisch. He had come for a double purpose—to be with his aunt during her first holiday in exile and to talk shop with her about a research project he was planning at the time. But destiny decreed otherwise.

The startling news from Hahn produced the equivalent of an atomic explosion in Lise Meitner's mind. She read the letter over several times, and the more she read it the more fantastic it all seemed. Here was, indeed, an anomaly, two fields of science contradicting each other, chemistry discovering facts that physics said were forbidden by nature. Yet from long years of association she knew that Hahn was not the kind of chemist who would go off half cocked, and the chances were infinitesimal that all the meticulous tests he and Strassmann had carried out were wrong. If the chemical facts observed by Hahn and Strassmann were true, it could only mean that a revolutionary new phenomenon of nature had once again been discovered by serendipity.

The nature of the new phenomenon overwhelmed her. Barium, she knew, could have come only from the splitting of the uranium atom's nucleus of ninety-two positive atomic units (protons) into two lighter elements of fifty-six and thirty-six positive atomic units, which correspond to barium and the rare gas krypton. But all the known laws of physics decreed that such a cosmic cleavage was forbidden by a basic law of nature. If such a cleavage actually occurred, then that basic law of nature would have to be drastically modified.

She was happy that her nephew Otto, a young physicist with a fresh mind, was with her. Together, she felt, they would find an answer to the riddle. Hidden in the barium, she realized, was one of the greatest secrets of nature, a message from the inner sanctum of the cosmos. It was providential that her nephew happened to be with her to help her decipher this message.

But, to her dismay, when she told her nephew of what Hahn had found he refused to listen. "Incredible!" he exclaimed. It was a waste of time even to discuss anything that was impossible. He wanted to discuss his own project, which was one of the principal reasons for his visit.

When his aunt persisted he suggested that they take a walk in the snow. A little exercise and fresh air, he thought, was what she needed to bring her to her senses. So they went for a walk, she on foot, he on skis. It must have been a strange sight to see: the diminutive sixty-year-old lady trudging alongside the thirty-four-year-old man on skis on the long, flat stretches of snow around the town, she animated, gesticulating, obviously trying hard to drive home a point, and he indifferent and preoccupied, occasionally shaking his head in a gesture of disbelief. If she succeeded in making a dent in his intellectual armor there was no outward sign of it when they returned to their hotel.

But the formidable arguments presented by the agile mind of his aunt succeeded finally in piercing her nephew's resistance. On the days following their walk, animated discussions took place in the lounge of the provincial hotel, and out of the exchange of ideas a momentous new concept was born.

"It took her a little while to make me listen," he reminisced fifteen years later, "but eventually we got to arguing about the meaning of Hahn's result, and very gradually we realized that the break-up of the uranium nucleus into two almost equal parts was a process so different [from the disintegration of the radium nucleus] that it had to be pictured in quite a different way."

The picture, he continued, was not that of the disintegration of the radium nucleus by the emission of one helium nucleus at the time, over the course of two thousand years, "but rather the gradual deformation of the original uranium nucleus, its elongation, formation of a waist, and finally separation of the two halves . . . The most striking feature of this novel form of nuclear reaction was the large energy liberated."

The realization that the results of Hahn's experiment meant the fission of the uranium nucleus was an overwhelming experience to Otto Frisch. "I was excited and uncertain what to do," he wrote me, "because I felt that this was a much bigger thing than I knew how to handle." To his mother, Lise Meitner's sister, he wrote at the time: "I feel as if I had caught an elephant by its tail, without meaning to, while walking through a jungle, and now I don't know what to do with it."

The first thing to do, he and Dr. Meitner agreed, was to present Hahn's discovery and their interpretation of it to Niels Bohr, who was then preparing to leave for the United States. So on January 6, the day the Hahn-Strassmann report was published in Germany, Frisch went to Copenhagen. And when he told the story to Bohr, the great physicist slapped himself a resounding blow on the forehead.

"How could we have missed it all this time!" he exclaimed in utter astonishment. He was so excited that only with difficulty could he tear himself away to catch the boat for Sweden, where he boarded the ship for the United States with only minutes to spare.

CHAPTER FIVE

Fission Comes to America

BOHR SAILED for the United States from Göteborg, Sweden, the following day, January 7, 1939, on the Swedish-American liner *Drottningholm*. He planned to spend several months with Einstein at the Institute for Advanced Study at Princeton, New Jersey, where Einstein was elaborating his most ambitious theory of the cosmos. Neither Bohr nor Einstein could even remotely suspect that much more immediate problems involving this little earth of ours would soon require them to postpone their contemplations of the cosmos at large.

It was on Sunday, January 15, as Bohr was approaching New York Harbor, that Frisch performed in Bohr's laboratory the crucial experiment that proved beyond doubt that his and Lise Meitner's interpretation of Hahn's experiment—uranium fission—was correct beyond any shadow of doubt. With surprisingly simple apparatus, a bit of uranium in an ionization chamber, a tube of radium and beryllium as a source of neutrons, a pair of headphones and one valve for amplification, he soon demonstrated that the bombardment of uranium with neutrons led to the registration on a television screen of the most intense electrical pulses ever observed.

The height of these pulses served as an atomic thermometer, as it were, recording the amount of energy liberated inside the chamber. And, as he stood there watching with that sense of elation and awe that can be experienced only by one privileged to lift the veil

31

for the first time from one of nature's secrets, he saw the atomic thermometer indicate an energy 100 million times as great as the energy released in the burning of one hydrogen atom in oxygen.

That was exactly the amount of energy he and Lise Meitner had calculated would be liberated if the nucleus of a uranium atom were to split in two nearly equal parts. Uranium fission had thus been demonstrated for the first time as a fact on this earth, and it may therefore be said that January 15, 1939, was the day the atomic age was born.

Essentially, Frisch's experiment was the same one first performed by Fermi and his co-workers. But the experiment in Copenhagen in 1939 differed in one highly important respect from the one in Rome in 1934. This time there was no three-mil strip of aluminum foil to blot out from view the atomic volcano that was erupting within the chamber.

On the following day, Monday, January 16, 1939, two weeks to the day after Fermi's arrival in the United States, Meitner and Frisch sent a historic report to the British scientific journal, *Nature,* which bore the title "Disintegration of Uranium by Neutrons: A New Type of Nuclear Reaction." The report was laboriously composed by long-distance telephone between Meitner in Stockholm and Frisch in Copenhagen, and its publication marked a milestone in the history of science.

After outlining the basic scientific reasons for their conclusions, they wrote the lines that have since become famous:

It seems therefore possible that the uranium nucleus has only small stability of form, and may, after neutron capture, divide itself into two nuclei of roughly equal size. . . . These two nuclei will repel each other [because they both carry large positive charges] and should gain a total of kinetic energy of about 200,000,000 electron volts, as calculated from nuclear radius and charge.

That energy is three million times the heat energy content of coal and twenty million times the explosive energy of TNT, in terms of equal weights.

In this same report, which appeared in *Nature* on February 11, 1939, Meitner and Frisch also christened the "new type of nuclear reaction" as "nuclear fission," because, as Frisch explained later, "of the striking similarity of that picture with the process of fission by which bacteria multiply."

That same Monday, January 16, Frisch sent *Nature* a second report, describing his experiment of the day before demonstrating the reality of nuclear fission. That report, entitled "Physical Evidence for the Division of Heavy Nuclei under Neutron Bombardment," was published in a supplement to *Nature* of February 18, a week after the publication of the original Meitner-Frisch report.

It was on that historic Monday that Bohr landed in New York. But when he arrived in Princeton that afternoon he did not go to see Einstein to discuss abstract theories of the cosmos. Instead he called on his former pupil John Archibald Wheeler, then an assistant professor of physics at Princeton University, to tell him about the Hahn-Strassmann experiment and its interpretation by Meitner and Frisch. Together they talked about the potential significance of the discovery, and young Wheeler, who was then twenty-seven, laid plans for a special meeting to be called at Princeton to which a select number of American physicists would be invited to hear Bohr tell the story in detail. One of these was Willis Lamb, a twenty-five-year-old physics instructor at Columbia, who was to win the Nobel Prize in physics sixteen years later.

So it came to pass on the afternoon of Wednesday, January 25, 1939, that Willis Lamb dashed, breathless, into Fermi's laboratory at Pupin Hall, Columbia University.

"Bohr has leaked out great news," he said. Lamb was "very excited," Fermi reminisced fifteen years later.

Fermi himself was stunned at the news. It was nearly five years since he had performed the first experiment, and all that time he, and all the others who followed him, had been lost in a scientific dream world. There is no record that, like Bohr, he slapped himself on the forehead. But, as history records, he more than made up for his failure to recognize the great new domain of knowledge of which he had been the discoverer.

At the time, Fermi had been in the United States about three weeks. That day his course for the next seven years was set by destiny.

With Professors George B. Pegram and John R. Dunning he discussed an experiment that would demonstrate fission. But Fermi did not wait for the experiment to take place. He had an important date with Bohr in Washington for the following morning, Thursday, January 26, when a meeting on theoretical physics was scheduled to begin at George Washington University.

At about seven o'clock that Wednesday evening, Dunning went down to the cyclotron laboratory in the basement of Pupin Hall. There he found Dr. Francis G. Slack, then a visiting professor of physics from Vanderbilt University, and Dr. Eugene T. Booth. Together they began setting up the apparatus that was to make uranium fission a reality for the first time in the New World.

Inside a metal chamber Dunning arranged two metal plates parallel to each other with a gap between. One plate was coated with uranium oxide and the second was to catch any particles shooting off the uranium-coated plate. This plate was connected to the grid of the first vacuum tube in a multistage amplifier and the output of the amplifier led to a television tube.

Inside the chamber was also a tiny glass vessel containing beryllium powder and radium, the combination used as the standard source of neutrons. It was the same type of neutron gun used by Fermi.

Then Dunning moved the neutron gun close to the plate coated with the uranium and watched the dancing line on the television tube. In the darkness of the basement they watched a strange, ominous green line, shooting upward to unprecedented heights. And the closer to the uranium he moved his neutron gun the greater was the height of the green line.

The dancing green line was telltale evidence of the fission of the uranium on the metal plate. It was, in fact, the explosion of a miniature atomic bomb, though they did not think of it at that time in terms of a bomb.

Dunning, Booth and Slack were elated, but Dunning wanted to make sure. Again and again he moved the neutron gun close to the uranium plate. Again and again the dancing green line on the television screen rose sharply.

It was eleven o'clock when the three Columbia scientists, tired but elated, called it a day. At that time they did not know that Frisch had preceded them by ten days.

Early the next morning Fermi and Bohr entered a George Washington University classroom where a meeting on the properties of helium at very low temperature had just started. Oblivious to their surroundings, they sat in one of the back rows talking, gesticulating, now the one, now the other, and scribbling symbols on the backs of envelopes. Word was passed around that the two Nobel laureates were about to report a new discovery. Soon the entire room was in a state of excitement. The speaker on the platform continued talking about the strange behavior of helium at a temperature near absolute zero, but no one paid any attention. All present waited impatiently for the ringing of the bell signaling the end of the speaker's time.

And when the bell did ring at last, and the chairman politely asked for the customary discussion of the subject just presented, all eyes turned to the great Bohr as he walked to the platform. And the tale he told them made them sit up in amazement, every one of them figuratively slapping himself resoundingly on the forehead.

They had all been like Molière's M. Jourdain, who discovered that he had been speaking prose all his life without knowing it. Ever since Fermi's first experiment in 1934 they had been splitting uranium atoms without realizing what they had been doing.

Fermi grinned when his turn came, and his audience grinned with him. Though he had learned of nuclear fission only the day before, he now recognized the true meaning of the elusive, puzzling phenomena he had seen during his five years of wandering in the atomic wilderness. In a flash of recognition, the pieces of the jig-saw puzzle all fell into their proper places and the true picture stood revealed at last.

In the course of his talk, Fermi mentioned the possibility that neutrons might be emitted in the process of nuclear fission. At the time it was only a guess, but its implication of the possibility of a chain reaction was obvious, though the term "chain reaction" was not mentioned that Thursday morning.

One by one the youthful physicists were seen hurriedly leaving the room, some doing so even before Bohr had finished speaking. Those from the Carnegie Institution of Washington and Johns Hopkins University rushed off directly to their laboratories, hoping to be first to perform the fission experiment. Those from farther away rushed to the nearest telephone to tell the great news to their co-workers in hopes that they would be the first to split uranium atoms. For Bohr had not yet been informed that Frisch had already performed his classic experiment, nor did anyone yet know about the experiment at Columbia the night before.

It was not until about a week later that Bohr was informed in a letter from one of his sons in Copenhagen that Frisch had found the large electrical pulses on January 15, ten days ahead of Columbia. "I had not written to him [Bohr] myself," Frisch related some years later, "wanting to make sure and to follow up various questions, but I had told his son."

The news brought by Bohr was the biggest bombshell ever exploded at a scientific meeting. It was the intellectual forerunner of the atomic bomb, in the development of which Fermi and Bohr were to play leading roles.

CHAPTER SIX

The "Story of Creation"

ON THE THIRD of March, 1939, Leo Szilard and Walter Zinn performed a simple experiment on the seventh floor of Pupin Hall at Columbia University.

After two days of preparation [Szilard wrote several years later], everything was ready and all we had to do was to turn a switch, lean back and watch the screen of a television tube.

If flashes of light appeared on the screen, that would mean that neutrons were emitted in the fission process of uranium, and this, in turn, would mean that the large-scale liberation of atomic energy was just around the corner.

We turned the switch and we saw the flashes.

We watched them for a little while and then we switched everything off and went home.

That night there was little doubt in my mind the world was headed for grief.

Those flashes of light Szilard and Zinn saw that night suggested that a chain reaction was definitely possible. They provided the first experimental evidence that the vast energy released in the fission of uranium could be utilized either in an atomic power plant or in an atomic bomb equal in destructiveness to thousands of conventional bombs of the same size.

37

The same crucial discovery—that each uranium atom split liberates extra neutrons that may serve to split more uranium atoms, thus making the fission process self-perpetuating—was made independently at about the same time, by different methods, by two other scientific teams: H. von Halban, Jr., Frédéric Joliot-Curie and Lew Kowarski in Paris, and Fermi and Herbert L. Anderson at Columbia. These epoch-making discoveries provided strong support to the speculations of Fermi and Bohr about the possibility of a chain reaction. Yet a number of formidable obstacles still had to be surmounted before the small-scale laboratory experiments could be translated into atomic power plants or atomic bombs.

One of the major difficulties stemmed from the fact that, as Bohr had concluded on the basis of sound reasoning, only the light uranium, U 235, was the fissionable element, whereas the heavy form of uranium, U 238, absorbed an appreciable number of the neutrons necessary to carry on the chain reaction. Since uranium as found in nature is a mixture of 140 parts of heavy uranium to one part of the light uranium, it was evident that 140 atoms of the nonfissionable heavy uranium would be competing with each atom of the light uranium for every single available neutron needed by the light uranium to keep the chain reaction going.

This made it obvious at the very beginning that to make an atomic bomb it would be necessary to separate the 0.7 per cent of the light uranium, U 235, from the 99.3 per cent of the heavy variety, U 238. But there was no way of doing it on any practical scale.

One does not have to be an expert to know why it is impossible to separate the light uranium from the much more abundant heavy variety by chemical means. To separate one element, such as silver, for example, from another element, say copper, advantage is taken of the fact that the two elements have different chemical properties, each one responding differently to any given set of conditions. Conditions therefore can be created that precipitate silver, for example, but not copper, thus bringing about the separation of the one from the other.

But in the case of the two isotopes of uranium such methods are wholly inapplicable. Though one is lighter than the other by three atomic units, both are nevertheless the same element, possessing exactly the same chemical properties. No chemical methods could therefore be devised to separate them.

38

There was an apparatus, known as the mass spectrometer, which could separate variants of the same element, including the light and heavy uranium, by electromagnetic means. But the rate of separation by the spectrometer was so infinitely slow that it would have taken 27,000 years for one of these to produce just one gram of the light uranium and 27 million years to produce one kilogram. Or, if you will, it would have required 27 million spectrometers to produce one kilogram a year. Obviously, as far as the mass spectrometer was concerned, uranium 235, the key element for atomic power and the atomic bomb, might as well have been on the moon.

Yet no one, neither a Fermi nor an Einstein, could guarantee that a discovery might not be made that would open the way to a simple and rapid process for isolating U 235 in quantities large enough to make atomic bombs. And since such a bomb in the hands of the Germans would enable them to take the world by force, it was imperative for the scientists of the free world to devote all their energies to the question of building a nuclear weapon. If such efforts proved futile, we would at least have a certain measure of assurance that the German scientists might be equally frustrated.

At that very time the British scientists, who took the matter much more seriously than our scientists did, were already considering such an effort. They hoped to employ an adaptation of the gaseous-diffusion method, based on the principle known as Graham's law.

According to Graham's law, if two gases, one lighter than the other, are made to pass through a porous medium, a little more of the lighter gas than of the heavier will diffuse through the medium, in a definite ratio according to the molecular weight of the two gases. In the case of two gases in which the difference in molecular weight is very small, as is the case of U 235 and U 238, they must be made to pass through the porous medium in thousands of successive stages, the concentration of the lighter gas being increased at each stage by a definite small amount, until 100 per cent concentration is achieved in the final stage. Since uranium is a solid, it must first be converted into a gas, known as uranium hexafluoride, a compound of uranium and fluorine.

This, in fact, was the method utilized later at Oak Ridge, Tennessee, where in 1944 a gigantic $500-million gaseous-diffusion plant was built; from it came the major part of the U 235 for the Hiroshima bomb. Since the end of the war we have built many more such huge multimillion-dollar gaseous-diffusion plants for the separation of U 235, in Oak Ridge, in Paducah, Kentucky, and in Portsmouth, Ohio. Gaseous-diffusion plants also produce the U 235 for Britain and for the Soviet Union.

But in 1939 the British scientists were almost alone in seriously considering the gaseous-diffusion method as the most promising and, indeed, the only possible method for isolating U 235 in large quantities. It was not until late in 1942 that any consideration was given to it by scientists in the United States. Only one scientist, Dunning of Columbia, an engineer as well as a physicist, fully recognized the great potentiality of the method, but for a long time he was completely ignored.

Graham's law of gaseous diffusion was first promulgated by the great Scottish chemist Thomas Graham in 1829. It was further elaborated in 1896 by Lord Rayleigh, Nobel Prize-winning British physicist. It is therefore one of the mysteries of the workings of the human mind that, with the single exception of Columbia's Dunning, our scientists took such a long time to realize what it could mean to the future of the free world.

That the German scientists were equally blind to the great prize within their reach was simply providential. One cannot help wondering what the world of today might have been like had the decision to build the gaseous-diffusion plant been arrived at in 1939, or 1940, instead of 1942.

As far as I know, neither Fermi nor Bohr, nor anyone else among the pioneers in uranium fission, was even aware of the possible application of Graham's law to the separation of U 235. A gaseous-diffusion plant was a major chemical-engineering project, and chemical engineering is a subject wholly alien to nuclear physicists. It was this division of science into compartments, each compartment hermetically sealed from the others, that was largely responsible for the nuclear physicists' failure to recognize the possible application of chemical-engineering principles to the solution of their problems. What made the difference in Dunning's case was that he was an engineer as well as an experimental nuclear physicist.

I was just as unaware of Graham's law as the nuclear physicists, and Dunning, if he had thought about it at the time, did not take me into his confidence.

Since none of the scientists admitted that they shared my forebodings on the danger of the Germans' developing an atomic bomb, I did not consider the time ripe to discuss the subject in a newspaper article. I decided to wait until I could build a more solid foundation to anything I might report, so that it would carry more weight in influencing public opinion and in alerting our military and civilian leaders to the great potential danger the free world might be facing in the immediate future. I read all the latest reports on fission in the scientific journals, both American and foreign, and made it a point to interview any scientist from abroad, particularly from Germany, who arrived in this country either as an exile or as a visitor.

One of the questions I would ask these visitors was on the whereabouts of the well-known German scientists and what they were working on. "What is Heisenberg doing these days?" I would ask casually. "Where is Hahn? Is he doing any further work on fission?"

Bit by bit I pieced together a picture of the leading German physicists and chemists moving from their laboratories in various parts of Germany to one location—the Kaiser Wilhelm Institute in Berlin.

The picture came into sharp focus on April 28, 1940, with the arrival in this country from Germany of Dr. Peter J. W. Debye, Dutch-born Nobel Prize-winning chemist. My interview with him at a meeting of the American Chemical Society soon after his arrival yielded positive confirmation of what until then I had merely suspected.

Professor Debye had been working at the Kaiser Wilhelm Institute in Berlin. Abruptly he was informed by the authorities, he told me, that his laboratory was needed "for other purposes." He had made a few discreet inquiries and learned that a large part of the Institute was being turned over to research on uranium.

This intelligence was all the more disturbing when I recalled that the rape of what was left of democratic Czechoslovakia, in March 1939, had given the Germans the richest uranium mine in Europe, while the violation of Norway earlier that April of 1940 had given them the world's only refinery of heavy water, the substance that would serve as the most efficient regulator in an atomic power plant.

And another event of vital importance took place in the Columbia physics laboratories. Two minute samples of concentrated U 235 had been produced by the mass spectrometer at the University of Minnesota and the research laboratories of the General Electric Company in Schenectady, New York. Both samples were rushed to Columbia for checking on the Bohr-Wheeler theory that only the U 235 would be fissioned with neutrons slowed down to speeds of one mile per second, whereas the heavier U 238 would remain untouched. The experiments, directed by Dr. Dunning, proved conclusively that the theory was absolutely correct.

That experiment was of vital importance in more than one respect. Its proof that only the light variant of uranium would fission with slow neutrons set the pattern for the later-day atomic power plants. Equally important, the fact that one half of the theory was proved to be correct gave strong support to the belief that the second half, that of chain reaction, was also true in every respect.

I decided that the time had come for me to write the Big Story.

I knew that I would require many columns to tell it in its full perspective, more space than a city editor was likely to grant. Furthermore, I wanted to make sure that the story, as I wrote it, would not be cut in later editions to make room for additional news.

So I went to my managing editor, the late Edwin L. (Jimmie) James, a great newspaperman and grand gentleman of Virginia. To save time, I came prepared with a detailed memorandum in which I outlined the scientific background of the story, the evidence of what the Germans were doing, and the scientific and military implications for the world we lived in.

Jimmie James knew a good story when he saw it, but this time I could see that his credulity was being taxed.

"Where and how did you get it?" he asked.

"From leading physicists, such as Enrico Fermi and Niels Bohr," I told him. "From Columbia University and from leading scientists coming from Germany. It has taken me more than a year of patient gathering of bits of information from a great many sources to put the story together."

He was obviously impressed. "Go ahead and write it," he said.

"I'll need a good deal of space to tell it properly," I said.

"You may have a column and a half," he said.

"I'll need more than that," I told him.

"Then make it two columns. There's a war on, you know."

"This may turn out to be the greatest story of the war," I argued. "It's worth at least five columns, and I may need as much as seven." I could see him getting ready to say something sarcastic and I cut him short.

"Now don't hand me that old chestnut about the Story of Creation being told in ten lines. It was the work of God, and you can't expect me to be *that* good. If you were managing editor of the Cosmic Gazette and a reporter handed you the Story of Creation in a measly ten lines you would fire him on the spot."

Jimmie guffawed. "Get out of here," he chortled. "Write what you want and we'll cut it to size."

"You'd better not," I shot back. "Maybe it was the managing editor of the Cosmic Gazette who cut the Story of Creation down to ten lines!"

The story, nearly seven columns long, appeared on page one of *The New York Times* on Sunday, May 5, 1940. Its headline read as follows:

VAST POWER SOURCE
IN ATOMIC ENERGY
OPENED BY SCIENCE

RELATIVE OF URANIUM FOUND TO
YIELD FORCE 5 MILLION TIMES
AS POTENT AS COAL

GERMANY IS SEEKING IT

SCIENTISTS ORDERED TO DEVOTE
ALL TIME TO RESEARCH—TESTS
MADE AT COLUMBIA

Nothing happened for two months. I was thoroughly discouraged and had already decided to try again with an article for publication in *The Saturday Evening Post* when something totally unexpected and bizarre took place. There was in those days a United States Senator from California, Sheridan Downey, who had one simple cure-all for the problem of unemployment—guaranteed universal employment. On reading my *Times* article he concluded that atomic energy would soon put the coal and oil industries out of business and thus greatly increase the number of unemployed. This, he reasoned, gave him a powerful new argument for his thesis of guaranteed universal employment as an effective "economic vaccine" against the coming industrial revolution to be brought about by atomic energy.

On August 5, 1940, three months to the day after the publication of my *Times* article, Senator Downey made a long speech in the Senate. He began by quoting the introductory paragraphs in my report, which, at his request, was published in full as Exhibit A in the *Congressional Record* issue of August 15 that year. That speech makes interesting reading for its strange mixture of fact and fancy. It began as follows:

Mr. President, in 1929 we saw the primary economic crisis develop that now engulfs the Nation. About a year ago we were thrown into a secondary crisis by this war. Before we had ever even begun to understand the depression of 1929, the war threat now frightens and confuses us.

Mr. President, I should like to present the possibility of a third crisis that may soon confront us in the hope that American leaders will awaken to the desperate conditions which may engulf us in the next three or four years. I shall read from *The New York Times,* quoting one of our greatest chemists. I wish to say that while this article was printed two months ago, I understand subsequent discoveries show that the development indicated in this article is more rapidly taking place than suggested in the article.

I shall read only a short portion of the article but I ask the article in full be printed in the *Record* at the conclusion of my speech. [This was done.]

"A natural substance found abundantly in many parts of the earth, now separated for the first time in pure form, has been found in pioneer experiments at the physics department of Columbia University to be capable of yielding such energy that one pound of it is equal in power output to 5,000,000 pounds of coal or 3,000,000 pounds of gasoline, it became known yesterday.

"Prof. John R. Dunning, Columbia physicist, who headed the scientific team whose research led to the experimental proof of the vast power in the newly isolated substance, told a colleague, it was learned,

44

that the improvement in the methods of extraction of the substance was the only step that remained to be solved for its introduction as a new source of power. Other leading physicists agreed with him.

"A chunk of 5 to 10 pounds of the new substance, a close relative of uranium and known as U 235, would drive an ocean liner or an ocean-going submarine for an indefinite period around the oceans of the world without refueling, it was said, for such a chunk would possess the power output of 25,000,000 to 50,000,000 pounds of coal or of 15,000,000 to 30,000,000 pounds of gasoline."

Mr. President, many of the greatest chemists in the world now anticipate that within less than five years the secret of atomic energy will be ours. Chemists in Germany have probably gone further than ours in this development. Many of their greatest chemists are developing this new form of energy.

For the past 50 years scientists have foreseen the possibilities of the endless and cheap power which might flow from atomic energy. Within the past year the final discovery has been made, and if its commercial use becomes an accomplished fact—as conservative scientists of the world now say it will—we shall see the end of our petroleum industry, the coal industry, the utility industry, and many others. We shall again see the face of the earth changed, just as radio, airplanes, and fast transportation have changed it in the past 25 years.

American businessmen have suggested that any form of energy which could be produced so cheaply, and which would destroy great segments of our present businesses, should be suppressed by the Government. But alas, Mr. President, the chemists of the totalitarian States are working night and day to perfect this new form of energy, and if we lag behind them in the development of that great new source of energy the results to American civilization may be calamitous indeed.

So I say, Mr. President, that the governmental leaders in America had better lift their vision beyond the immediate emergency of airplanes, navies, and conscription—important as they are—to an understanding of what may happen in this Nation two or three or five years from now.

Perhaps some Senators are wondering what the possibility of atomic energy has to do with the discussion of the pending measure. I answer that question by saying that we had better speedily initiate the right of universal and total employment before it is too late. In other words, if atomic energy should destroy certain industries and bring cheap and unlimited power and greater wealth to us, society as a whole would have nothing to be distressed about so long as we provide the opportunity for work for all our citizens. But if we are to continue to operate our industries and farms at about 60 per cent of capacity, when we tremendously increase the present capacity disaster will indeed lie ahead of us.

Since the Senator was interested only in the effect that atomic energy would have on employment, he completely ignored what to me at the time was much more alarming—the fact that Germany was engaged in a major effort to harness the atom to its military machine. He therefore failed to mention the vast military implications of atomic energy, which, in fact, was the principal reason that impelled me to write the article.

Under the subhead "Nazis Push Research," I had written as follows:

The main reason why scientists are reluctant to talk about this development, regarded as ushering in the long dreamed of age of atomic power and, therefore, as one of the greatest, if not the greatest, discovery in modern science, is the tremendous implication this discovery bears on the possible outcome of the European war.

The news has leaked out, through highly reliable channels, that the Nazi government . . . had ordered its greatest scientists to concentrate their energies on the solution of this problem. Every German scientist in this field, physicists, chemists, and engineers, it was learned, have been ordered to drop all other researches and devote themselves to this work alone. All these research workers, it was learned, are carrying out their tasks feverishly at the laboratories of the Kaiser Wilhelm Institute at Berlin.

The American scientists are in the dark as to what their German colleagues are doing and what progress, if any, they have made. . . . New plans are being made to isolate the substance [U 235] on a practical scale, but the plans and designs for these will be kept a secret to be given only to the United States Government to do with as it sees fit.

Under the subhead "Terrific Explosive Power" I had written:

46

It was figured out that one pound of the U-235 contains as much energy as 15,000 tons (30,000,000 pounds) of TNT, or 300 carloads of 50 tons each. If this one pound of U-235 exploded within one ten-thousandth of a second, as does ordinary TNT, the pressure produced would be of the order of 100,000,000,000 [100 billion] atmospheres (10 to the seventeenth power dynes to a square centimeter), about 1,000,000 times the pressure produced by TNT or by nitroglycerin.

Later it was established that one pound of U 235 was equivalent in explosive energy to ten thousand tons of TNT, but that it would explode in one ten-millionth of a second, a thousand times faster than TNT, which would make its destructive force about a thousand times greater than the earlier figure had indicated.

The fact that my *Times* article did not in any way create the impression I had hoped it would was a frustrating experience. I had expected that my story, painstakingly gathered in the course of more than a year, would produce an effect in high places somewhat similar to that of the now historic Einstein letter to President Roosevelt. I decided to try again, hoping that an article in an influential mass-circulation magazine such as *The Saturday Evening Post,* telling the story in all its dramatic details, together with their implications, would arouse public opinion to an extent that would lead to action on the part of our leaders in Washington.

I submitted the article, titled "The Atom Gives Up," to the *Post* early in June 1940. The fact that fourteen years later it was selected by the *Post* editors for inclusion in *The Saturday Evening Post Treasury,* a collection described by them as "the brilliant best of more than two centuries of inspired writing and editing," would seem to indicate that they thought the article made good reading. Yet apparently it presented them with a dilemma. Though the conservative and highly trustworthy *New York Times* had published it on its front page, the *Post* editors were still dubious; so dubious, in fact, that before accepting my article for publication, they insisted that it be endorsed by not one but three leading physicists, none of whom was mentioned in the article.

I was outraged at such apparent lack of confidence in my reliability as a reporter. But I was a man with a mission and I accepted the terms, humiliating to me though they were at the time. I was anxious to get the matter before the public as quickly as possible, so I sent the article to Professor Arthur H. Compton, Nobel Prize winner in physics, then at the University of Chicago; Professor Edwin M. McMillan of the University of California, who was to share the Nobel Prize in chemistry in 1951 for his pioneering work that led to the discovery of plutonium, and Professor Philip M. Morse of the Massachusetts Institute of Technology.

Drs. Compton, McMillan and Morse fully endorsed the article, after I had made some minor changes suggested by them. With their permission I submitted the slightly revised text to the *Post* together with their letters, and the article was accepted for publication. It appeared in the September 7, 1940, issue.

In an introduction to that article in *The Saturday Evening Post Treasury* the current editors of the *Post* wrote as follows:

Five years before the big explosion at Hiroshima the *Post* printed this dramatic account of the discoveries that made it possible. This article also told how the Nazi scientists were frantically trying to make use of atomic power for war. Further than that the author did not go, although he knew as much as anyone about the possibilities of an atomic bomb.

The least I expected as the result of the publication of the article was to be called to Washington by one or more agencies of government for further details about such an important subject. But nothing happened. Congress was still in recess, an exciting Presidential election was under way, and no one seemed to be interested in the atom.

But, as I learned five years later, the article had an interesting history.

In 1942, after it had been decided to go all out on the production of an atomic bomb, the editors of the *Post* were requested to take the September 7, 1940, issue out of circulation. So were the libraries throughout the country. Anyone who asked for the issue had his name taken under some pretext and was investigated by the F.B.I.

Early in the spring of 1945, after I had been invited to join the inner circle of the atomic-bomb project, I learned, to my amazement, that the article had been classified as secret and that I would not be permitted to carry it around with me. A copy in my briefcase was stamped "Secret" and solemnly locked in a large safe.

A few days after the bombing of Hiroshima, *The Saturday Evening Post* published many thousands of reprints of my article, with the headline "Story Behind Atomic Bomb Appeared in *The Saturday Evening Post,* Sept. 7, 1940."

Under this headline the *Post* editors proclaimed the following to the world at large:

The discovery and early developments that led to the atomic bomb, the terrifying new weapon called the greatest achievement of organized science, are fully described in this article reprinted from *The Saturday Evening Post,* September 7, 1940.

"One pound of pure U-235 would have the explosive power of 15,000 tons of TNT," was then predicted by William L. Laurence, author of this *Post* article—the same man who was recently asked by the War Department to prepare the official release of August 6, 1945.

Here is the story of the refugee scientists who helped develop the atomic bomb, of the beginnings of our race to beat Germany to the mastery of it, and of the gigantic initial efforts involved before secrecy was clamped down.

The *Post* brought this news to its readers, with all its implications, a full five years ago and sends you this reprint believing you will be interested in having the background story of the scientific developments that led to smashing and harnessing the atom.

I shall always remember an episode that occurred a few days before my departure for Tinian, the tiny island in the Marianas, about 100 miles from Guam, that served as the top-secret atomic-bomb base for the B-29s that carried the bombs to Hiroshima and Nagasaki.

One day late in July 1945, as I was busily engaged preparing final copy for release after the bomb was used, I was summoned to the office of a colonel in military intelligence whom I had never met before. The scene was the office of the Manhattan Engineer District (code name of the wartime atomic-bomb project) on the fifth floor of the building now occupied by the State Department.

The colonel looked very solemn. "We have bad news about

you," he said, in tones that sounded severe. After a pause, he added, "We have just obtained evidence that you have been helping the Germans."

"What kind of silly joke is this?" I exploded.

"I have the evidence right here," he replied, still solemn.

He then went to a large safe and out of it pulled a scrapbook. There on the first pages, meticulously covered with cellophane, was my September 7, 1940, article in the original English, and on every page facing it was a complete translation in German. The colonel laughed.

"We have just captured this item in one of the German laboratories," he said.

The article was the last in any American publication, scientific or popular, in which atomic energy was ever mentioned during the war. From then on until August 6, 1945, when President Truman announced the dropping of the atom bomb on Hiroshima, the subject vanished behind an impenetrable atomic curtain.

CHAPTER SEVEN

Hitler Could Have Had
the Atom Bomb in 1943

Ever since 1945, when our successful development of the atomic bomb was revealed to the world, we have been led to believe that, from the time the discovery of uranium fission was announced, in January 1939, until the very end of the war in Europe in May 1945, we had been engaged in a life-and-death Battle of the Laboratories, in which our scientists were in a nip-and-tuck race against the scientists of Germany to stop the Nazis from being first with the ultimate weapon that would give them world domination.

And when Germany collapsed, it is still widely believed, her scientists were just on the verge of producing the weapon that would have enabled Hitler to turn defeat into a last-minute victory.

Unfortunately all this is a legend. The truth is that for three full years we stood practically still, despite ominous reports that kept coming out of Germany that her top scientists and engineers had been ordered by Hitler to put the vast energy of fission at the service of the Wehrmacht.

During those years of destiny, when the very fate of civilization was at stake, there was no race of any kind. And we can only thank our lucky stars that Hitler failed to recognize the need for such a race, which might well have given him his "Thousand-Year Reich."

It was just sheer luck that the leaders of German science were even less alert to the potentialities of fission than the influential leaders in American science. Had they realized in 1939, or even in

1940, that it was possible to produce a fission bomb within reasonable time, they would have had the atomic bomb by the spring of 1944, months before the Normandy landing.

Professor Leo Szilard, one of the pioneers in our atomic-bomb project, testified before a Senate committee in 1945 that if the Germans had known in 1940 certain facts that were known to our scientists "they might very well have started an atomic project [in 1940]; and, with their eyes on the ball, they might very well have brought it to a successful conclusion by the spring of 1944. They might have won before we had a chance to invade Europe."

It was "the compartmentalization of information, which was practiced in the atomic-energy project from November 1940 on," Dr. Szilard testified, "that was the cause of our failure to recognize that light uranium [uranium 235] might be produced in quantities sufficient to make atomic bombs. We should have known that in the fall of 1940.

"We might have failed to realize this altogether, just as the Germans failed to realize it," Professor Szilard continued, "if we hadn't had the good fortune that the British scientists were not compartmentalized. They were able to put two and two together and communicated their conclusions to the United States Government in the middle of 1941. Had we in the United States reached these conclusions in the fall of 1940, we most likely would have had bombs ready before the invasion of Europe."

At this point Senator Millard E. Tydings of Maryland posed the following question to Dr. Szilard:

SENATOR TYDINGS: Suppose Hitler had assumed that this thing might reasonably be invented. Suppose that assumption had first come to him in 1939 [when uranium fission was discovered] and that he had then assembled all his available scientists and engineers that he had and said: "I want you to do everything possible to develop an atomic bomb, or an instrument of death more deadly than any you have with atomic energy. We will put at your facility every asset of this Government, every resource of this Government."

If that had happened in 1939, with the engineers, the scientists, and the materials and the industrial plants then available in Germany, would it have been possible under reasonably human conceptions for Hitler to have had the bomb preceding our own having it?

DR. SZILARD: I am quite convinced he would have had it about eighteen months before we had it.

SENATOR TYDINGS: He would have had it eighteen months before us?

DR. SZILARD: We could have had it eighteen months earlier, and with their chemical industry they could have moved equally fast.

SENATOR TYDINGS: Why do you suppose that the scientists of Germany who were then loyal to the Hitler concept failed to impress this fact on Hitler's mind, that it was a possibility and that its devastating effect might decide the war?

DR. SZILARD: They slipped up on one point, on which we slipped up also. They did not put two and two together. We did not put two and two together because the two twos were in different compartments; they were not together. That is, the men working on that property of uranium from which they could deduce how much was needed for the bomb had no idea that you could extract light uranium [U 235] in appreciable quantities.

SENATOR TYDINGS: How do you account for that breakdown of putting two and two together?

DR. SZILARD: In Germany I cannot account for it. It is true that they were split up in small groups, but they were not compartmentalized.

SENATOR TYDINGS: Do you think the very Nazi system itself might have destroyed the free interchange of ideas?

DR. SZILARD: It might have been, but I have no really good explanation for it. I think it was largely a matter of chance.

SENATOR TYDINGS: Just luck?

DR. SZILARD: It was luck.

[Senator Tydings then asked Dr. Szilard what, in his opinion, would have happened if the scientists exiled from Germany had stayed behind.]

DR. SZILARD: I do not know. It is difficult to know what would have happened.

SENATOR TYDINGS: It might have conceivably, as a matter of deduction, changed the whole atomic-bomb development in Germany from what it was to what it might have been.

DR. SZILARD: I might say that the three men in England who were instrumental in reaching the conclusion that atomic bombs could be made came out of Germany in 1933. At that time in England, in 1941, most English physicists were engaged in radar work, and other types of work, and these refugees, who were not taken into that work, which was considered of very great importance to the war, had more leisure than their English colleagues to think of such remote possibilities as atomic bombs.

The three refugees from Germany who "had more leisure than their English colleagues to think of such remote possibilities as atomic bombs" were Dr. Francis E. Simon (knighted in 1954), Dr. Rudolf Peierls, and Otto R. ("Fission") Frisch. Their studies were not so leisurely when they came to Los Alamos with the British scientific mission to help us build the atomic bomb at a time when we believed we really were in a race with Germany.

It was not until December 6, 1941, the day before Pearl Harbor, after the British scientists had shown us that an atom bomb was a definite possibility, and when it appeared that we had handed the Germans a head start of three full years, that we at last decided to go start work on the project. And even then, most of the year 1942 was spent in organizational work, and it was not until the spring of 1943 that the actual building of our gigantic atomic-bomb plants got under way.

With all due respect to such an authority as Dr. Szilard, it was not compartmentalization alone that was responsible for the agonizing delay that might have cost the free world its very existence. There was a much more profound reason and it was stated succinctly by Professor Henry De Wolf Smyth in his official report on the development of the atomic bomb.

American-born nuclear physicists [Professor Smyth wrote] were so unaccustomed to the idea of using their science for military purposes that they hardly realized what needed to be done. Consequently the early efforts both at restricting publication (of atomic developments) and at getting government support were stimulated largely by a small group of foreign-born physicists, centering on Leo Szilard and including Eugene Wigner, Edward Teller, Victor F. Weisskopf and Enrico Fermi.

Of these five, all of whom later made major contributions to the development of the atomic bomb, Fermi was the best known. But he had been in the United States only a few weeks, and by temperament and disposition he was not the type who would feel at home among politicians and military men. Yet it wasn't long before he found himself in the strange role of trying to explain the intricacies of nuclear physics to men in Washington who had never heard of a neutron and cared less.

The Fermi Five, later to be joined by Albert Einstein, fought a heartbreaking battle that appeared to be hopeless. As the news came trickling out of Germany about work on the atomic bomb, the five found themselves more and more in the position of the prisoner in Poe's horror tale, "The Pit and the Pendulum." The uranium pendulum kept slowly swinging down and down, over a world that was fast asleep and refused to be awakened.

On March 16, 1939, the day Germany occupied what was left of the Republic of Czechoslovakia, Fermi went to Washington. With him he carried a letter of introduction from the late Professor George B. Pegram, then dean of the graduate faculties of Columbia University, to Admiral S. C. Hooper, in the Office of the Chief of Naval Operations. Dean Pegram, a noted physicist of high standing, informed the admiral of experiments at Columbia that "might mean the possibility that uranium might be used as an explosive that would liberate a million times as much energy per pound as any known explosive."

"My own feeling is," Dean Pegram added, "that the probabilities are against this, but my colleagues and I think that the bare possibility should not be disregarded. . . . There is no man more competent in the field of nuclear physics than Enrico Fermi. . . ."

Armed with this introduction, Fermi presented himself early the next morning at the Navy Department. As far as is known he never saw the Admiral himself. Soon he found himself in the presence of two younger officers of the rank of lieutenant commander.

Before these rather puzzled young men, Professor Fermi outlined in his still halting English the possible military importance of uranium fission. Even at that early date, he suggested the possibility of achieving a controllable chain reaction with slow neutrons, which would mean atomic power plants for submarines and other

Navy vessels, or a chain reaction with fast neutrons that would make possible atomic bombs millions of times more powerful than any known explosive.

The Navy men listened patiently and politely and asked to be kept informed of any further developments. But according to legend current in scientific circles, no sooner had Fermi left when one said to the other, "That wop is crazy!"

There the matter rested for several months, months in which the Fermi Five grew more and more concerned about what the Germans might be doing.

Finally, at the suggestion of Szilard, the most worldly of the five, they came to a decision. To get action they must reach the President himself. And the only one among them who would be permitted even to see the President, and to whom the President would listen with respect, was Albert Einstein.

So a delegation of the five headed by Szilard went to call on Einstein with their idea. Einstein shook his head.

"I don't know the President and the President doesn't know me!"

"He knows you and respects you. You are the only one he'll listen to. It is vital to the country and to the world that something be done. There is no time to be lost."

As Einstein still refused to go personally, they compromised on a personal letter from Einstein to the President. By the time the letter was ready for his signature, Einstein had left for a vacation at Nassau Point, on Long Island.

So on August 2, 1939, Dr. Teller, who had an automobile, drove to Long Island with a document that has since become part of history, the original of which is now at the Franklin D. Roosevelt Library at Hyde Park. In it the man who risked his life in Germany during World War I for his outspoken pacifist beliefs urged "quick action, if necessary," in the building of the most destructive weapon ever conceived by science. And to add to the irony, it was this gentle scholar's own formula that provided the key to the weapon.

Einstein read the document over as Teller, the man who was to make the atomic bomb obsolete some twelve years later, sat and watched in silence. Einstein signed it and went back to his sailboat. Teller returned to Princeton.

Here is the text of the Einstein letter:

Albert Einstein
Old Grove Road
Nassau Point
Peconic, Long Island
August 2nd, 1939

F. D. Roosevelt
President of the United States
White House
Washington, D. C.

SIR:

Some recent work by E. Fermi and L. Szilard, which has been communicated to me in manuscript, leads me to expect that the element uranium may be turned into a new and important source of energy in the immediate future. Certain aspects of the situation which has arisen seem to call for watchfulness and, if necessary, quick action on the part of the Administration. I believe therefore that it is my duty to bring to your attention the following facts and recommendations.

In the course of the last four months it has been made probable through the work of Joliot in France as well as Fermi and Szilard in America—that it may become possible to set up a nuclear chain reaction in a large mass of uranium, by which vast amounts of power and large quantities of new radium-like elements would be generated. Now it appears almost certain that this could be achieved in the immediate future.

This new phenomenon would also lead to the construction of bombs, and it is conceivable—though much less certain—that extremely powerful bombs of a new type may thus be constructed. A single bomb of this type, carried by boat and exploded in a port, might very well destroy the whole port together with some of the surrounding territory. However, such bombs might very well prove to be too heavy for transportation by air.

The United States has only very poor ores of uranium in moderate quantities. There is some good ore in Canada and the former Czechoslovakia, while the most important source of uranium is the Belgian Congo.

In view of this situation you may think it desirable to have some permanent contact maintained between the Administration and the group of physicists working on chain reactions in America. One possible way of achieving this might be for you to entrust with this task a person who has your confidence and who could perhaps serve in an unofficial capacity. His task might comprise the following:

a) to approach Government Departments, keep them informed of the further development, and put forward recommendations for Government action, giving particular attention to the problem of securing a supply of uranium ore for the United States;

b) to speed up the experimental work, which is at present being carried on within the limits of the budgets of University laboratories, by providing funds, if such funds be required, through his contacts with private persons who are willing to make contributions for this cause, and perhaps also by obtaining the cooperation of industrial laboratories which have the necessary equipment.

I understand that Germany has actually stopped the sale of uranium from the Czechoslovakian mines which she has taken over. That she should have taken such early action might perhaps be understood on the ground that the son of the German Under-Secretary of State, von Weizsäcker, is attached to the Kaiser-Wilhelm Institute in Berlin where some of the American work on uranium is now being repeated.

> Yours very truly,
> (signed) *A. Einstein*
> (ALBERT EINSTEIN)

To write the letter was one thing, but to make sure that it was delivered to the proper person when that person happened to be the President of the United States was another. It wouldn't do, they all agreed, to send it through the mails. It must be delivered to the President personally by someone who could explain the subject to him in greater detail and point out the urgent need for immediate action.

But as the weeks passed they could find in the scientific community no person of the stature to command respect at the White House who was willing to carry the Einstein message to Roosevelt. So they compromised on Alexander Sachs, a Russian-born economist, whom Szilard tutored intensively in the intricacies of fission. More than two months had passed from the time the letter had been signed.

It was not until October 11, 1939, that Sachs, who had served the President on occasion as an informal adviser, managed to obtain an appointment at the White House. He read the contents of the letter to the President and also read from a memorandum prepared by Dr. Szilard explaining the meaning and potential significance of uranium fission in popular terms.

The President listened attentively and carefully examined the Einstein letter.

"What you are after is to see that the Nazis don't blow us up," Mr. Roosevelt said.

"Precisely," Sachs replied.

The President called in Brigadier General Edwin M. Watson, his military secretary, known as "Pa."

"Pa," the President said, "this requires action."

The impression is widespread that the Einstein letter served as the spark that immediately set in motion the two-billion-dollar atomic-bomb project. Unfortunately, this too is a fine bit of folklore that has no factual basis. The tragic truth is that the Einstein letter produced hardly any action worth mentioning; it played no part whatever in the later decision to go all out on the building of an atom bomb. For all the good it did, it might as well never have been written.

More than two agonizing years, years in which Hitler might have won the world, or destroyed it, passed with practically no action whatsoever. Einstein's letter lay gathering dust in some White House pigeonhole. And it wasn't until the end of 1941, two years and two months after the letter had been presented to the President, that the decision to build the bomb was finally taken.

That decision came following a visit to the United States of Dr. M. L. E. Oliphant from England. He brought news that could no longer be ignored. The British scientists, at that time miles ahead of ours, largely because they had recognized the danger from the beginning, had performed experiments and carried out other far-reaching studies that made it nearly certain that an atomic bomb could definitely be built and that it could be made in time to be of use in the war against Germany.

And what is more, Britain stood ready to invest millions on the project, and her scientists invited us to join them, offering to share all they knew with us, despite the fact that at the time we had very little, if anything, to offer them in return in that particular field.

"If Congress knew the true history of the atomic-energy project," Dr. Szilard commented in 1945, "I have no doubt but that it would create a special medal to be given to meddling foreigners for distinguished services, and Dr. Oliphant would be the first to receive one."

It was this very same Dr. Oliphant whose application in 1951 for a visa to enter this country to attend a scientific meeting was held up for months.

The only action that came as the result of the Einstein letter was the formation of a committee "to look into the matter," which became known as the Advisory Committee on Uranium. This committee, composed of an Army lieutenant colonel and a Navy commander, and headed by Dr. Lyman J. Briggs, then director of the National Bureau of Standards, held its first meeting ten days later.

A number of scientists were invited to the meeting. Whoever these were, many among them were singularly lacking in vision. Many of them expressed themselves, Sachs testified later, as opposed to the support of such a project by the government.

It was Sachs's task in those early days, he told the Senate, to try to convince "these gentlemen of science and government officials, including the Army and the Navy, to indulge . . . in a 'willful suspension of disbelief.' "

On November 1, 1939 a report was submitted to the President which contained the following:

The energy released by the splitting of a mass of uranium atoms would develop a great amount of heat. If the chain reaction could be controlled so as to proceed gradually, it might conceivably be used as a continuous source of power in submarines, thus avoiding the use of large storage batteries for underwater power.

If the reaction turned out to be explosive in character it would provide a possible source of bombs with a destructiveness vastly greater than anything now known.

The military and naval applications . . . must at present be regarded as only possibilities because it has not yet been demonstrated that a chain reaction in a mass of uranium is possible. Nevertheless, in view of the fundamental importance of these uranium reactions and their potential military value, we believe that adequate support for a thorough investigation of the subject should be provided.

We believe that this investigation is worthy of direct financial support by the Government.

Despite this recommendation, no funds came forth. The military and naval men kept saying, "Well, this is still so remote. What is this thing? Let's wait and see."

Hardly any progress was made in six months following the delivery of the Einstein letter. Mr. Sachs talked the matter over with Dr. Einstein, and on March 7, 1940, the scientist addressed a letter to Sachs for presentation to President Roosevelt. In it Einstein wrote:

Since the outbreak of the war, interest in uranium has intensified in Germany. I have now learned that research there is being carried out in great secrecy and that it has been extended to another of the Kaiser Wilhelm Institutes, the Institute of Physics. The latter has been taken over by the Government and a group of physicists, under the leadership of C. F. von Weizsäcker, who is now working there on uranium in collaboration with the Institute of Chemistry. The former director was sent away on a leave of absence apparently for the duration of the war.

It was at about that time that the first transfer of funds from the Army and the Navy was made. It was the munificent sum of $6,000. And within the next two years the grand total of funds made available to a project that was to cost $2 billion from 1943 to 1945 reached $300,000, which was divided among sixteen institutions. As Professor Smyth said:

Scale of expenditures is at least a rough index of activity. It is therefore interesting to compare this figure of $300,000 in 1940 and 1941 with those in other branches of war research. By November, 1941, the total budget approved by the NDRC [National Defense Research Committee] for the Radiation Laboratory at the Massachusetts Institute of Technology was several million dollars. Even a relatively small project like that of Section S of Division A of the NDRC had spent or been authorized to spend $136,000 on work that proved valuable but was obviously not potentially of comparable importance to the uranium work.

In the light of what we know today, one wonders what the history of the world might have been had we decided to go all out on the atomic bomb in the summer or fall of 1939, at the time of Einstein's letter to the President. There can be no question that had we done so we would have had the bomb ready by the end of 1943, instead of the middle of 1945, at a time when Germany was still deep in Russian territory and Japan was still in control of much of the Pacific.

It is not unreasonable to speculate that many of our postwar troubles with the Soviet Union and China would never have come about. It is certain that the Yalta agreement of February 1945, in which Stalin obtained important concessions in China in return for his promise to join us in the war against Japan, would never have been made.

CHAPTER EIGHT

Atomic David with a Slingshot

THE YEAR 1940 dragged along at an agonizingly slow pace for Fermi and the small group of fellow exiles, who kept receiving disturbing reports from their colleagues abroad about increasing numbers of eminent German scientists and engineers joining the uranium fission project at the Kaiser Wilhelm Institute in Berlin. The more they studied the available evidence, meager and sketchy though it was, the more convinced they became that the odds were greatly in favor of the possibility that the fission of uranium could be used to produce the world's most destructive weapon.

They fully realized that the very heart of the atomic problem was to obtain definite experimental proof that a chain reaction which would light an atomic fire, or explode an atomic bomb, would definitely take place, provided a sufficient quantity of the fissionable element, U 235, could be concentrated. But here was the grim joke nature had played. She had mixed up its only fissionable element with an atomic-fire extinguisher, U 238, that would not permit an atomic fire (chain reaction) ever to get started, while at the same time she made it impossible to separate the fissionable element (U 235) from the atomic-fire extinguisher.

A self-sustaining chain reaction, their theories strongly indicated, would, when properly controlled, yield tremendous amounts of atomic power for industry, while a chain reaction allowed to go uncontrolled would yield an explosive force millions of times greater

63

than TNT. A controlled chain reaction would be like the controlled burning of gasoline in an automobile engine. An uncontrolled chain reaction would be like the dropping of a lighted match in the gasoline tank.

Definite proof that a chain reaction was possible would mean, they knew, that we would have to go all out to develop an atomic bomb, since the chances would then be great that the Germans already had a head start on us and might be on the verge of producing the weapon.

On the other hand, should experiment reveal some unknown factor that would make a chain reaction impossible, we would then have definite proof that it would be impossible for the Germans to produce an atomic bomb.

Furthermore, news had come from the University of California that the inert, nonfissionable heavy uranium (U 238) could be transmuted by neutrons into an entirely new element that did not exist in nature, an element two rungs above uranium (element 92) on the atomic ladder—element 94.

What made this discovery of transcendent importance was the fact that element 94, later named plutonium, would be just as efficient a fissionable element as the unattainable U 235. Even more important was the fact that plutonium was an element chemically different from uranium, which meant that it could be isolated from its parent substance, U 238, in kilogram quantities by chemical methods. In other words, the obstacle that made it impossible to isolate U 235 from U 238 would be completely removed by doing away with the need for U 235 altogether.

But no sooner was a way found to remove one of nature's formidable obstacles than the scientists were faced with another equally formidable. For, to make plutonium out of uranium 238, large quantities of neutrons were needed, and the only way to get these neutrons was through the fission of U 235 in a chain reaction, which the very presence of the U 238 would prevent from taking place.

"The sheer cussedness of nature," Fermi sighed.

Nature, indeed, was playing a sardonic game with man. She had first showed him an element that held the key to the powerhouse of the cosmos but had mixed it inextricably with large amounts of another element that prevented an atomic fire from being lighted.

She then dangled before him another element, equally good, that could be created out of the very substance of the fire extinguisher; but she made the creation of the new element contingent on the lighting of an atomic fire that the presence of the extinguisher would make impossible.

Yet from the very beginning the brilliant deductions of Bohr and Wheeler had strongly suggested that the neutron-stealing fire-extinguishing element had a pronounced weak point that, if fully exploited, would prevent it from carrying out its obstructive role. These deductions indicated that the troublemaking U 238 could accomplish its neutron-stealing act—the very act that would prevent the chain reaction—only under certain specific conditions. A change in these conditions would deprive it of its strength.

Bohr and Wheeler's deductions had provided strong grounds for believing that the U 235 could be fissioned by high-energy neutrons, traveling with speeds of more than ten thousand miles per second, as well as by very slow neutrons, slowed down by a moderator to speeds of only one mile per second. At the same time, the theoretical evidence of Bohr and Wheeler showed, the "neutron thief" in U 238 could steal only neutrons of a specific range of intermediate speeds, whereas the U 235 had a very strong affinity for low-speed, slow neutrons, attracting them to its nucleus before the "neutron thief" in the U-238 nucleus could steal them. In other words, this meant that the U 238 would be completely powerless to prevent a chain-reacting atomic fire from being started and maintained in U 235 by neutrons slowed down to very low speeds of no more than one mile per second.

The scene of this new scientific triumph was to be a structure built of bricks of natural mixed uranium and large bricks of graphite, the form of carbon used in lead pencils, an element Fermi had determined to be the most economical moderator then available for slowing down neutrons.

In such a structure, Fermi, Szilard and their colleagues had calculated that the neutrons from the U 235 would be slowed down to the desired speed of one mile per second after being made to pass through some sixteen inches of graphite. The slow neutrons, thus placed beyond the reach of the "neutron thief" in the U 238 in the natural uranium bricks, would then be free to start and maintain a self-perpetuating chain reaction in the U 235.

The slow, one-mile-per-second neutrons would therefore behave like powerful little magnets attracting a small quantity of iron filings scattered in a huge pile of sand.

Control of such an atomic fire could be achieved by regulating the number of neutrons present in the structure at any given time. This would be done by the use of rods made of certain elements, such as boron and cadmium, that have a strong affinity for neutrons. If the number of neutrons threatened to become too large, a condition that might lead to a runaway atomic fire, rods of boron and cadmium would automatically be inserted into the structure. On the other hand, if the neutron population appeared too low, the rods would be automatically pulled out.

The rods were to be graduated in inches, each inch representing an absorption capacity of a definite number of neutrons.

That lattice work of graphite bricks honeycombed at definite intervals with cubes of natural uranium and interspersed with rods of cadmium and boron must rank as one of the greatest technological breakthroughs in the history of civilization. From the moment it was conceived the road was open to the Atomic Age.

CHAPTER NINE

The First Atomic Fire

WITH THE $6,000 given to Columbia by the Army and the Navy in 1940, Fermi bought what at the time seemed huge amounts of graphite. And since pure uranium metal did not exist at the time, he had to be satisfied with a uranium compound—uranium oxide.

As a result of handling these large quantities of the two black substances, Fermi and his team of "bricklayers" on the seventh floor of Pupin Hall started to resemble coal miners, and their wives wondered what was happening, since the scientists had already decided upon secrecy.

"We all know there is smoke in the air," Fermi reminisced a few months before his death in November 1955, "but after all . . ."

They were building columns of graphite about four feet on the side and ten feet high. It was the first time Fermi had used an apparatus so big that he had to climb on top of it. "I am not a tall man," he said.

The time came when the column of graphite had reached the ceiling and was found to be still much too low. So Fermi went to Dean Pegram, who was then the man "who could carry out magic around the university," and explained to him that they needed a bigger room, "a really big room."

"Pegram said something about a church not being the most suitable place for a physics laboratory, but I think a church would have been just precisely what we wanted," Fermi related. "So Pegram scouted around the Columbia campus, and we went with him to dark corridors and under various heating pipes to visit possible sites for this experiment, and eventually a big room, not a church, but something that might have been compared in size with a church was discovered in Schermerhorn Hall.

"Well," Fermi continued, "there we started to construct this structure that at that time looked again in the order of magnitude larger than anything we had seen before. Actually, if anybody would look at that structure now he would probably extract his magnifying glass and go close to it. But for the ideas of the time it looked real big. It was a structure of graphite bricks, and spread through these graphite bricks in some sort of pattern were big cans, cubic cans, containing uranium oxide.

"Now, as you know, graphite is a black substance. So is uranium oxide. And to handle many tons of both makes people very black. In fact, it requires even strong people. Well, we were reasonably strong, but we were, after all, thinkers.

"So Dean Pegram again looked around and said, 'Well, that seems to be a job a little bit beyond your feeble strength; but there is a football team at Columbia that contains a dozen or so of very husky boys who take jobs by the hour just to carry them through college. Why don't you hire them?'

"And it was a marvelous idea. It was really a pleasure for once to direct the work of these husky boys, canning uranium—just shoving it in—handling packs of fifty or a hundred pounds with the same ease another person would have handled three or four pounds. And as they were passing these cans, fumes of all sorts of colors, mostly black, would go in the air."

Early in 1942 the entire graphite-uranium contraption, together with Fermi and his team, was moved to Chicago, which had been chosen as the center for studies on the chain reaction. The project, which was directed by Professor Arthur H. Compton, was given the code name "Metallurgical Laboratory."

The crucial experiment that made the atomic bomb possible, and marks the official beginning of the atomic age was performed on December 2, 1942, in the gloomy, cold squash court underneath the stands of Stagg Field on the University of Chicago campus. On that day the scientists learned, after many months of anxious labors in great secrecy, that just one atom of uranium split will release the energy to split two other atoms, the two atoms splitting four, and so on in a geometrical progression. This meant that an atomic explosion would take place in a self-perpetuating chain reaction, in the manner of a chain of firecrackers.

On that historic day in December they had completed the first atomic furnace (also known as a "pile," or a nuclear reactor), fashioned of bricks of uranium and graphite, in which they ignited the first atomic fire on earth. It was, in fact, the first fire on earth that did not have its origin in sunlight. In effect, that first fire was also the first atomic explosion, except that it was on a small scale that could be kept under control. Or so they had hoped.

For actually the scientists did not know that the fire, once it was started, could be kept under control, and they had visions of starting a Chicago fire even more disastrous than the one attributed to Mrs. O'Leary's cow. They had used, of course, all the devices known to science to dampen the fire, but since no one had ever before built an atomic fire they could not guarantee with certainty that the controls—until then tested only on a small laboratory scale—would work.

The scene that day was a mixture of the sublime and the ridiculous. The entire uranium-graphite structure was encased in a ridiculous square rubber "balloon," which they believed at the beginning to be vital for success but which turned out to be not necessary at all.

Knowing that the elements cadmium and boron are to an atomic fire what water is to an ordinary fire, they inserted many rods of these two elements into strategic spots in the atomic furnace. As extra-special precautions, two young scientists stood tense and silent on a platform overlooking the furnace, holding buckets filled with solutions of cadmium. They were known among their colleagues as the "suicide brigade." They stood there for two hours waiting for the signal to go into action.

The great moment came when Fermi ordered his assistant, George Weil, to pull out the last control rod "another foot." All the other control rods had been pulled out previously.

"This is going to do it," Fermi told Dr. Compton, who was standing beside him on the balcony overlooking the furnace.

Four tense minutes passed. The neutron counters began to click louder and louder, faster and faster. Fermi, who was doing fast calculations on a slide rule as his eyes darted from one dial on the instruments to another, suddenly closed the rule with a click that could not be heard amidst the racket of the neutrons in the instruments. He looked calm, detached, a captain bringing his ship into port.

It was three-twenty-five in the afternoon in Chicago. The moving pencil that recorded what was going on inside the atomic furnace moved upward and up, upward and up, in a straight vertical line that did not level off as it had done before. This meant that a chain reaction was taking place inside the structure. The first atomic fire had been lighted.

"The reaction is self-sustaining," Fermi said amidst the violent clicking of the neutron counters. His face, tense and tired, broke into a broad smile.

For twenty-eight minutes the atomic fire was allowed to burn. Then Fermi gave the signal and it was stopped abruptly. Man had released the energy of the atom's nucleus and had also proved that he could control it at will.

As the experiment was going on, a conference was being held three blocks away, in Room 209 of Eckhart Hall, to decide whether to begin the construction of gigantic plutonium plants.

At that time such plants, calculated to cost about $400 million, were still dreams, for the success of the operation depended on a chain reaction and no one knew whether or not a chain reaction could actually be sustained. Nevertheless, the Du Pont Company was invited to proceed with the design and construction of the plants as a calculated risk, on the assumption that a chain reaction was feasible. Time was of the essence.

None of the conferees, who included a number of Du Pont's top engineers, had the slightest inkling of what was going on in the squash court. They had been arguing back and forth for two days without arriving at any conclusion. As the experiment on Stagg Field was about to reach its climax, Dr. Compton invited Dr. Crawford H. Greenewalt, then a member of the Du Pont board of directors, who has since become president of that company, to come over. Dr. Compton had just enough time to explain to Dr. Greenewalt what the doings were all about when the chain reaction got under way.

Dr. Greenewalt rushed back to Eckhart Hall. "Gentlemen," he said, "there is no need for further discussion."

"Though he had been sworn to absolute secrecy," Dr. Compton told me, "all you had to do was to look at him. Greeney's eyes popped."

A few minutes later there took place the unrehearsed, historic conversation in code over the long-distance telephone between Dr. Compton in Chicago and Harvard president Dr. James Bryant Conant in Cambridge:

COMPTON: Jim, this is Arthur. I thought you'd want to know that the Italian navigator has just landed in the New World.

CONANT: What? Already?

COMPTON: Yes, the earth was smaller than estimated and he arrived several days earlier than he had expected.

CONANT: Were the natives friendly?

COMPTON: They were indeed. Everyone landed safe and happy.

CONANT: Fine news. I'll be eager to learn what you find on the new continent.

When the fire was extinguished, Dr. Wigner, with the flourish of a magician, pulled a bottle of Chianti out of an imaginary hat. All drank a silent toast out of paper cups.

And as they all filed out of the heavily guarded gate much earlier than usual, a puzzled guard asked, "Say, Doc, anything happen in there?"

"Oh, yes, indeed!" they might have answered if they could. "We have just proved that we can make an atom bomb as well as an atomic power plant. And we have found a way to transmute the useless, most abundant variety of uranium—U 238—into a most useful fissionable element, good as a super-explosive for atom bombs and as a super-fuel for the production of vast quantities of industrial power.

"Yes, indeed, we have just now created a neutron-machine, a machine for the transmutation of the elements. We have, in fact, found the Philosopher's Stone."

By coincidence, Enrico and Laura Fermi had invited a number of the "metallurgists" and their wives to their home that night. To

Laura's puzzlement, each male guest, as he arrived, shook Fermi warmly by the hand murmuring, "Congratulations."

"What is all this about?" Laura would ask. "What is Enrico being congratulated for?"

As she could get no satisfactory answer from the male guests, Laura turned to Leona Woods, the only woman among the "metallurgists." Leona, who later married Dr. John Marshall, one of the "mets," bent down and whispered, "Sh-sh, he has sunk a Japanese admiral."

"You are making fun of me," said Laura. But Leona assured her she was in earnest and she was soon fully supported by her male colleagues, who chided poor Laura for thinking that anything was beyond her husband.

Laura was beset with doubts. Maybe there was something to it, after all. Maybe Enrico had discovered some "power ray" that would sink a ship in the Pacific from as far away as Chicago.

In the days that followed she made futile efforts to clear up her doubts.

"Enrico, did you really sink a Japanese admiral?"

"Did I?" Enrico would ask, poker-face.

"Then you didn't sink a Japanese admiral!"

"Didn't I?" Enrico would ask with the same poker-face, puckish expression.

It was not until after Hiroshima that Laura found out.

CHAPTER TEN

The Vikings March Again

W HEN NORWAY WAS INVADED by the Germans in April 1940, British scientists at once called to the attention of the authorities the need to keep a watchful eye on the Norsk Hydro hydrogen electrolysis plant in Vemork, in the Norwegian province of Telemark. That plant was at the time the largest producer of heavy water, that is, water in which the hydrogen atoms consist of deuterium, the hydrogen variant (isotope) that has an atomic weight twice the weight of ordinary hydrogen, its atomic mass being 2 instead of 1. Heavy water exists in nature mixed with ordinary water in the ratio of one part to 6,400; that is, 6,400 gallons of water contain just one gallon of the heavy water. Its production is accomplished by electrolysis (separation by passage of an electrical current), and in 1940 large-scale concentration was a singularly slow business.

Since heavy water is the most efficient moderator for neutrons, and therefore the most efficient substance for the construction of a chain reaction pile, and since even at that early date the possibility of producing plutonium for atomic bombs in such a pile had already become a strong possibility, it was evident that the possession of the only large heavy-water plant in the world would give the Germans a tremendous advantage.

As early as September 1939, German scientists had publicly stated that the manufacture of heavy water might become vitally important to their war effort. In May 1940, after the invasion of

73

Norway, the British Ministry of Economic Warfare received the disturbing intelligence that the Germans had ordered Norsk Hydro to increase heavy-water production to 3,000 pounds a year. In 1942 it was learned that Germany had demanded a further increase to 10,000 pounds.

That demand for such an enormous amount called for immediate action, for by that time British scientists were practically certain that, given sufficient heavy water and uranium, a chain-reacting pile could be made to operate. Since the Germans had already placed an embargo on the export of uranium from Czechoslovakia, it became evident that they were planning to build atomic reactors, which could be used for producing plutonium for atomic bombs or as power plants for the German submarines.

The matter was referred by the Ministry of Economic Warfare to Special Forces, the Allied organization entrusted at that time with the responsibility of co-ordinating resistance in the enemy-occupied countries, which, it was hoped, would have contacts in the area.

It so happened that one of a party of Special Force Norwegians who, on March 17, 1942, had captured a Norwegian coastal steamer (the *Galtsund*) and sailed her from Norway to Aberdeen had considerable knowledge of the neighborhood of Vemork and had been in touch with some of the Norsk Hydro engineers. His name was Captain Einar Skinnarland.

Captain Skinnarland, to whom we shall henceforth refer as Einar, the only name he was known by at that time, was given hurried training and precise instructions and was dropped by parachute on Telemark on March 28. He remained a permanent feature of the heavy-water operations.

A small follow-up party was formed to be dropped on Telemark the following month, but weather conditions prevented the carrying out of the operation for some time, and diminishing hours of darkness put an end to all night flights for that season.

In July 1942, after further disturbing intelligence, the War Cabinet Offices approached Combined Operations with a request that Vemork should be attacked. They urged that the very highest priority be given to the project.

Combined Operations then asked Special Forces to provide a small advance party to act as local guides and collectors of intelligence for a sabotage attack against the heavy-water plant—the attack to be carried out later by Combined Operations personnel, whom it was proposed to land by glider.

"From the outset it was realized," the official British report states, "that the operation was exceptionally dangerous. Of all countries, Norway is the least suitable for glider operations. Its landing-grounds are few; its mountains thickly clustered, precipitous and angry. The broken countryside throws up air-pockets and atmospheric currents. Weather conditions in the autumn of 1942 were vile."

To add to the difficulties, the Norsk Hydro plant is located on top of a high cliff overlooking the beautiful valley of the Moon River, and was inaccessible from the front, which was heavily guarded by a German garrison, and from the sides. The only possible approach was from the rear.

This required a landing on a high plateau, a precipitous descent down the valley and then a steep climb up the cliff. The landing, of course, had to be made many miles from the valley, in an isolated section in the snow-covered mountains.

Special Forces provided an advance party of two officers and two noncommissioned officers of the Norwegian Army's British-trained Linge Company, named after Captain Martin Linge, D.S.C., a Norwegian soldier killed in action after landing at Maaloy on December 27, 1941.

The party's leader was Jens Anton Poulsson. The others were Arne Kjelstrup, Claus Helberg, and Knut Haugland (who later became world-famous as a member of the celebrated *Kon-Tiki* raft expedition across the Pacific). Einar joined the party shortly after it landed and became its radio operator.

Knut Haugland, whom I had the pleasure of meeting in Oslo after the war, participated in no less than four major missions. Yet when I tried to express my admiration for his exploits he said with the utmost sincerity, "Your kind words about me overstate my importance quite a bit. I just tried to do my job as thousands of others did in the war."

The advance party was given the code name Swallow. They were to be followed at the proper time by a demolition party, specially trained for the job.

Two attempts to drop the group in September failed because of heavy clouds. Swallow finally made a parachute landing on a mountainside east of Fjarefit in the Songadal, with equipment in containers and packages, at eleven-thirty on the night of October 15, 1942.

It took the party two days to collect the equipment and put it in order. Half the food supply, together with equipment not immediately needed, was hidden at a "base depot" to which it was planned that Swallow should retreat when the operation had been completed.

The weather was fine during these days, with patches of snow scattered lightly over the mountain. But on October 21 a tremendous snowstorm swept over the countryside, and within a matter of hours Swallow saw the arrival of full winter and fair skiing weather. Swallow advanced to the operational area.

Swallow's leader and Claus skied with full packs into Haugedal, where they knew there was a hut. They failed to find it before nightfall and heard later that it had been moved. It was a heavy march back, in the dark and mist.

The other two tried in vain to make radio contact with London. They had no fuel for their stoves and therefore had to avoid mountain routes where there was no wood to be found; so they decided to advance through the Songadal, where there were birch woods and huts in which they could spend the night.

They set out on their heavy march the next day, October 22, hoping that their food, with the strictest rationing, would be sufficient for thirty days. They had been ordered not to make outside contacts except in the gravest emergency.

At high altitudes no man, Jens wrote in his diary, "can be expected to carry a load weighing more than sixty-five pounds." Their equipment consisted of eight such loads. This meant that, in the party of four, each man had to make three journeys every day over the same stretch.

The terrain was rugged, the snow deep. Men who left the ski tracks sank up to their knees. It was mild weather, and clumps of snow stuck to the bottom of their skis. The little bit of skiway that they had wished to keep for the retreat had been snowed under. The lakes, marshes and rivers were not properly covered with ice and could be crossed only here and there. There was surface water on the ice, and their feet were soaked all the time.

So the day's marches were "sorrowfully short," the leader wrote in his report. They often advanced only a few miles a day. On the very first day the leader broke a ski pole. It was a month before he got a new one.

After a march of two days they reached a deserted farmhouse at Barunuten, where they found meat and flour and ate their fill for the first time since their arrival. They also found a ski toboggan.

Six days later they reached Reinar. Now they were getting near inhabited places. They were very tired. Jens had a throbbing boil on his left hand and had to keep his arm in a sling. They had kept themselves in good shape during the waiting period in England, but the hard toil on short rations had soon sapped their strength. A day's ration consisted of a quarter-slab of pemmican, one handful of grits, one handful of flour, four biscuits and a little butter, cheese, sugar and chocolate.

Claus was sent back to the empty farmhouse at Barunuten to steal all the food he could carry. Arne and the leader went forward to reconnoiter the line of advance. Einar, the radio operator, stayed to make a further attempt at contacting London. A rendezvous was arranged for November 3.

Claus traveled to Barunuten and back—a distance of fifty miles —under terrible conditions. As Jens remarked later, "He proved the old saying, 'A man who is a man goes on till he can do no more and then goes twice as far.' "

Jens and Arne did not do many miles. Jens fell through the ice while crossing a river. This was the second time it had happened to him. Next day they tried to cross another river but found no ice, and they returned, tired out, to Reinar, where the radio operator informed them that his storage battery had run out at the moment he succeeded in making contact with London. Their plans had to be changed, as the accomplishment of their mission now depended on their finding a new battery.

On November 6 they reached their operational base at Sandvatn, completely exhausted. The march had taken fifteen days. Claus had procured a battery from the keeper of a local dam at Mösvann.

The first thing they had to do was to get into contact with England. Antenna masts of a good size were put up. But they failed again, this time because the radio set was damp.

Three full days passed before they made contact with England.

After that the set worked. They prepared for the reception of the gliders.

Officers at Special Force headquarters, London, breathed a sigh of relief when Swallow came on the air—even though the intelligence received was rather disturbing. The Germans, who had a strong garrison in the area, had set wire barricades around the factory and alongside the penstock lines which carried water down the mountainside to the factory's dynamos.

The glider parties in England stood by. Mock-ups, models of the machinery to be attacked, based on Swallow's intelligence, were built at a training school. Selected airborne troops were trained for the specific demolitions required. Swallow, working in constant difficulty at an altitude of four thousand feet, in a temperature continually below zero Centigrade, daily transmitted weather reports and further intelligence with accuracy and punctuality.

On November 19 two aircraft, each towing airborne troops in a glider, took off from Scotland. It was a doomed mission. One aircraft and both gliders crashed on the southwest coast of Norway about a hundred miles from the target.

London's radio message about the glider disaster was a hard blow to Swallow. It was sad and bitter, especially as the weather in Swallow's part of the country improved during the following days. But they were glad to hear that another attempt was to be made in the next moon period.

This second attempt was mounted and manned by Special Force personnel only. Six volunteers from the Linge Company were selected to form the assault party and given intensive special training.

The difficulties of attack had been multiplied. German interrogation of the survivors of the November 19 disaster had enabled them to guess its operational objective. The Rjukan garrison was again increased, the area combed for saboteurs, and many innocent Norwegians were arrested. The German Reichskommissar, Josef Terboven, and General von Falkenhorst both personally inspected the Vemork defenses.

Special Forces was fortunate in having the services of the late Major Leif Tronstad, formerly professor of industrial chemistry at Trondheim University. His knowledge of heavy water and of the Vemork plant was unique. Swallow waited patiently, continued its watch and sent its signals, working in snow and ice, short of food and with failing power in its radio set.

To make matters worse, everybody except the leader developed fever and stomach pains. They were short of food and were obliged to begin eating reindeer moss. Einar found a Krag rifle and some cartridges. Jens went out every day after reindeer, but the weather was bad and he could find none. The supply of dry wood came to an end.

On December 19 Einar went to Langsj to steal food from a hut. He came back the next day with fish preserved in earth. On December 23 the weather cleared and Jens at last shot a reindeer. They celebrated a happy Christmas, feasting all day.

The same patience had to be exercised, and even greater nervous strain suffered, by the party mobilized in England. Although their training had been completed and they were ready to leave, the weather prevented their departure. On the night of January 23, 1943, they actually flew over Norway, but, after circling over Telemark for two hours, they were forced to turn back, as fog obscured the landing point as well as the lights that Swallow had laid out for their landing.

On February 10, 1943, Swallow signaled the exact position of all sentries and guards at Vemork. At midnight on February 16 the six Norwegian soldiers from Special Forces were dropped by parachute on the frozen surface of Lake Skruken, thirty miles northwest of Swallow. A radio message from London informed Swallow of the party's arrival. But contact had still to be made; and a journey of thirty miles in the Norwegian winter can take as long as three hundred miles in warmer, flatter lands.

This second party was given the code name Gunnerside. The dramatis personae of this modern saga, whose names have not been previously recorded, were Joachim Rönneberg (the leader), Kasper Idland, Fredrik Kayser, Hans Storhaug, Birger Strömsheim and Gunnar Syverstad.

When the Gunnerside six finally landed, a full four months after Swallow had dropped out of the Norway skies, it was joined by one of the Swallow five, Knut Haugland.

Gunnerside's jump was made from a thousand feet. One package (containing four rucksacks) landed and was dragged by a wind-filled parachute for more than a mile. It came to rest in an open ice crack, from which it was salvaged. One sleeping bag and two rucksacks were damaged. Otherwise all gear landed safely.

The equipment was unpacked the next day. Items required for the advance were repacked and the remainder hidden to form a depot. The necessary stakes were placed as landmarks in the snow and their bearings taken. The job was finished at four in the morning, by which time driving snow had already hidden every trace of the landing and the digging. They slept at an uninhabited hunting lodge.

By five in the afternoon of the same day all was prepared for the first leg of the advance. There was strong wind-driven snow and a moon. The packs weighed sixty-five pounds and the two toboggans weighed 110 pounds each. After an hour's heavy going, the drifting snow became so thick that it was impossible to find the way. Joachim (the leader) gave the order for a return to the hunting lodge, which was reached at 8 P.M. It was then very cold with a full westerly snowstorm.

The following day a snowstorm of great violence broke out. It was impossible to go out of doors. All hands felt ill owing to the change of climate. Two had bad colds.

The driving snow continued for two days. The party made an attempt to reach the depot to fetch more food but had to give up for fear of losing its way. During the night the chimney pot blew off the hunting lodge.

Another day brought clear skies and less wind, but the snow continued. The group made another attempt to fetch food, but the snowstorm had so changed the landscape that even their stakes were hidden. After three hours the attempt was abandoned. They made a final try the same afternoon and at length found one container. The position of the depot was remarked.

The next day, February 21, the snowstorm raged with renewed power. Visibility was zero. All hands were filled with great weariness and lassitude, and the two men who had been suffering from colds were now seriously ill.

On February 22 the storm finally blew itself out. The weather turned fine and the leader gave the order to prepare for departure at noon.

The next day, nearing Kallung, they were alarmed to see two bearded civilian skiers, apparently in first-class physical condition. Joachim ordered one of his men to put on his camouflage ski smock and a civilian ski cap and to set out to make contact with the strangers. If questioned, he was to say that he was a reindeer warden on his rounds. The rest of the party went under cover.

For a while there was silence among the Gunnerside party as its members waited and wondered. Each man's hand was near his holster. Then, suddenly, above the noise of the wind sounded what Joachim described as "three wild yells of joy." Gunnerside had at last met Swallow.

The great hour they had been waiting for had come at last. Together that night, in a remote mountain cabin, the eleven members of Swallow and Gunnerside laid out their plan of attack. Without knowing the full significance of their mission, each of them was aware that they were about to engage in a major battle of the war. And so they laid their plans in minute detail, each man to play his part with a precision demanding split-second timing.

During the months of waiting for Gunnerside's arrival, Swallow had gathered all the vital information they needed to outwit the enemy. They knew the exact number of German and Norwegian guards at each post, inside and outside the plant, and the exact time at which they were changed. They knew every entrance and exit, the exact position of every door and every window, the underground tunnels and pipes through which one could gain entrance or escape.

Up to a certain moment the eleven were to act as a co-ordinated team. After that everyone was to be on his own. The password was "Piccadilly? Leicester Square!"

And all solemnly agreed that "if any man is about to be taken prisoner, he undertakes to end his own life."

The weather was overcast, mild with much wind. They left their advance base, a hut in Fjösbudalen, at about eight on the night of February 27. They started on skis but were later forced to continue on foot down to the Mösvann road. Along the telephone line it was very difficult, steep terrain, and they sank in it up to their waists. At Vaaer Bridge they had to take cover, as two buses were coming up the road with the night shift from Rjukan. They followed the road to the power-line cutting. It was thawing hard and the road was covered with ice.

Skis and sacks were hidden close to the power-line cutting, from which they began a steep and slippery descent to the river at 10 P.M. On the river, the ice was about to break up. There was only one practicable snow bridge, with three inches of water over it.

From the river they clambered up sheer rock face for about 500 feet to the Vemork railroad line. They advanced to within about 1,600 feet of the factory's railroad gate. Carried on a strong westerly wind came the faint humming note of the factory's machinery. They had a fine view of the road and of the factory itself.

Here they waited till 12:30 A.M. and watched the relief guard coming up from the bridge. They ate some of the food they had in their pockets, and once more the leader checked up to make sure that every man was certain about his part in the operation and understood his orders.

Cautiously they advanced to some storesheds about 300 feet from the gates. Here, one man was sent forward with a pair of armorer's shears to open the gates, with the rest of the covering party of seven in support. The four-man demolition party stood by to follow up immediately.

The factory gates, secured with padlock and chain, were easily opened. Once inside, the covering party took up temporary positions while the demolition party opened a second gate thirty feet below the first with another pair of shears.

Joachim stopped and listened. Everything was still quiet. Visibility was good; the blackout of the factory was poor and there was a good light from the moon.

At a given sign the covering party advanced toward the German guard hut. At the same moment the demolition party moved toward the door of the factory cellar, through which it was hoped to gain entry. The cellar door was locked. They were unable to force it, nor did they have any success with the door of the floor above. Through a window of the high-concentration plant, where the target lay, a guard could be seen.

During their search for the cable tunnel, which was the only remaining method of entry, they became separated from one another. Finally Joachim found the opening and, followed by only one of his men, crept in over a maze of tangled pipes and leads. Through an opening in the tunnel's ceiling the two could see the plant.

Every minute was precious. As there was no sign of the other two demolition party members, the two decided to carry out the demolition alone. They entered a room adjacent to the target, found the door into the high-concentration plant open, went in and took the Norwegian guard completely by surprise. They locked the double doors between the heavy-water storage tanks and the adjacent room, so that they could work undisturbed. One of the party kept watch over the guard, who seemed frightened but was otherwise quiet and obedient.

Joachim began to place the charges. This went quickly and easily. The models on which they had practiced in England were exact duplicates of the real plant.

Joachim had placed half the charges in position, when there was a crash of broken glass behind him. He looked up. Someone had smashed the window opening onto the back yard. A man's head stood framed in the broken glass. It was the third man of the demolition party, who, having failed to find the cable tunnel, had decided to act on his own initiative. He and the fourth missing member climbed through the window, helped Joachim place the remaining charges and checked them twice while the leader coupled the fuses. They then checked the entire charge once more, before ignition. There was still no sign of alarm from the yard.

They lighted both fuses. Joachim ordered the captive Norwegian guard to run for safety to the floor above. Then they left the room.

Twenty yards outside the cellar door, they heard the explosion. The sentry at the main entrance was recalled from his post. They passed through the gate and climbed up to the railroad track.

For a moment Joachim looked back down the line and listened. Except for the faint hum of machinery that they had heard when they arrived, everything in the factory was quiet.

About three thousand pounds of heavy water, many times the supply in the rest of the world, were destroyed, together with the most important parts of the high concentration plant.

Five of the Gunnerside party crossed the Swedish border into safety after a 250-mile journey on skis and in uniform, under conditions of almost unendurable hardship and in the vilest weather. They were flown back to England shortly afterward.

The sixth of their number, Knut, remained behind in Norway for a third job. The Swallow party also remained to report results, and then it gradually dispersed, leaving only the original Einar, now an exceptionally efficient wireless operator, and Claus.

From them London learned that General von Falkenhorst, German Supreme Military Commander in Norway, visited Vemork immediately after the disaster. He described the operation as "the best *coup* I have ever seen."

Across the Special Forces report on the activities of Gunnerside and Swallow Prime Minister Winston Churchill wrote: "What is being done for these brave men in the way of decorations?" Eight British and nine Norwegian military decorations were awarded.

Von Falkenhorst reacted energetically. The German guards were removed and punished. Once again the Gestapo combed Rjukan and arrested many innocent Norwegians. Mountain troops patrolled the area; some of them fired nervously at each other. German reconnaissance aircraft hovered in the neighborhood, and one crashed. Mountain huts were broken into and burned.

Claus was the only one who came into contact with the enemy. On the high Hardangervidda Plateau he was suddenly confronted, on March 25, 1943, by three Germans who appeared around a hill three hundred feet ahead and started firing. He turned and went off on his skis, but after two hours he found that one of the enemy would inevitably outdistance him. The story is best told, in a shortened form, in his own words:

I therefore turned around, drew my pistol, and fired one shot from my Colt .32. I saw to my joy that the German only had a Lüger, and I realized that the man who emptied his magazine first would lose, so I did not fire any more, but stood there as a target at 150 feet range. The German emptied his magazine at me, turned and started back. I sent a bullet after him, he began to stagger and finally stopped, hanging over his ski sticks. I turned back to get clear away, as the other two might come at any time. Half an hour later it was completely dark. After another two hours I went over a cliff, falling 120 feet, damaging my right shoulder and breaking my right arm.

The following day Claus encountered another large German patrol, but he told a plausible story which deceived them, and they detailed an escort to take him to a German doctor. The doctor attended to him and dispatched him in an ambulance to the Barkedli Tourist Hotel, where he was given a room. But as night fell, Terboven, the *Reichskommissar* of Norway, and his staff arrived and

84

demanded accommodations. Claus was left undisturbed, and Ter-boven occupied the room next to his.

Next morning all the guests at the hotel, including Claus, were bundled into a bus and sent off to the Grini concentration camp, as one of the lady guests had refused to entertain Terboven during the night. Using a certain amount of guile, and aided by the lady, Claus distracted the attention of the armed guard and managed to change his seat from the back of the bus to one alongside the driver and the door. Toward dusk he seized his opportunity, flung open the door and jumped out. Picking himself up, he staggered across a field toward a wood, followed by the explosions of two grenades thrown by the guard and several pistol shots fired by the motorcycle orderly who had preceded the bus. He escaped, and after further adventures he succeeded in returning to Great Britain.

The directors of Norsk Hydro tried to persuade the Germans to halve the manufacture of heavy water but were overruled. In Eng-land the Combined Chiefs of Staff recommended a more powerful type of persuasion. Accordingly, on November 16, 1943, strong formations of the Eighth U.S. Bomber Command attacked the Vemork power station and electrolysis plant. A further 120 pounds of heavy-water stock were lost.

The directors of Norsk Hydro repeated their plea and this time the Germans, a shade abjectly, granted it. On November 30, 1943, Swallow (the constant Einar) reported that all heavy-water instal-lations at Vemork were to be dismantled and sent to Germany. On February 7, 1944, he added that the transport of existing stocks to Germany would take place in about a week's time.

This information was passed on to the War Cabinet Offices in London, which issued top-priority instructions the same day to do everything possible to destroy the stocks in transit. By evening, ap-proval had been obtained from the Norwegian Defense Minister in London to attack the stocks despite danger of local reprisals on innocent Norwegians.

Immediate information to this effect was sent to Einar and to Knut Haugland, the one remaining member of Gunnerside, who was then fifty miles to the west. Knut was instructed to join Einar, and to make sure that the remaining stocks of heavy water did not reach Germany. At the same time a message was sent to another of the Special Forces parties in Vestfold to proceed to Skien and prevent any special cargo from Rjukan from being loaded at the port.

On February 10 Knut was given permission to carry out a plan he proposed for sinking the Lake Tinnsjö ferryboat *Hydro* on which the remaining heavy-water containers were to be loaded for the second stage of their long journey to Hamburg. A jubilant reply from Swallow contained a complete list of heavy-water stocks ready for shipment.

The enemy was on his toes. Special S.S. troops were sent into the Rjukan valley. Two aircraft patrolled the mountains each day and new guards were stationed on the railroad line from Vemork to the ferry quay; but, by some freak of folly, not a single German guard had been posted on the *Hydro* herself.

Knut, the demolition party leader, tells the story:

At 1 A.M. on the morning of Sunday, February 20, I and three colleagues left Rjukan in a car procured for the purpose. I went on board the *Hydro* with two men, while the third (Einar) stood by the car on shore.

Almost the entire ship's crew was gathered together below, around a long table, playing cards rather noisily. Only the engineer and stoker were working in the engine room, so there was no question of going in there. We therefore went down to a passenger cabin, but were discovered by a Norwegian guard. Thank God he was a good Norwegian. We told him that we were on the run from the Gestapo and he let us stay.

Leaving one in the cabin to cover us, the other and I wriggled through a hatch and crept along the keel up to the bow. I laid my charges in the bilges, hoping that the hole in the bow would lift the stern of the ferry and render it immediately unnavigable. I coupled the charges to two separate time-delay mechanisms tied to the stringers on each side. These time delays I had had specially constructed out of alarm clocks. I reckoned that the charge was big enough to sink the ferry in about four or five minutes.

I set the time delay for 10:45 the same morning. This was the time which (as I discovered on a previous reconnaissance trip aboard the *Hydro*) would bring the ship to the best place for sinking.

By 4 A.M. the job was finished, so we left. The car took us to Jondal and we were in Oslo the same Sunday evening.

A copy of the Quisling newspaper *Fritt Folk* was in Einar's hands early on Monday morning. Banner headlines announced the mysterious sinking of the ferry steamer *Hydro* at approximately 11 A.M. on February 20. An explosion had been heard. The ship's forepeak had filled with water. Propeller and rudder were lifted clear, and certain freight cars had trundled forward the full length of the deck to fall, irretrievably lost, into the deep waters of Lake Tinnsjö.

Swallow came on the air later with a report to close the story. This said that 3,600 pounds of heavy-water stock had been sunk with the ship.

Later the party at Skien complained bitterly that they were waiting, had marked down the ship which was to take the special cargo by sea to Hamburg, had made their plans to destroy her and had all their preparations ready, but no special cargo had come.

Two of the figures in this saga later gave their lives to make sure that the Nazis did not succeed in rebuilding the heavy-water plant at Vemork. One of these was Professor Leif Tronstad, whose intimate knowledge of the plant, which he had designed and directed, made it possible for Swallow and Gunnerside to know every nook and corner of the place. The other was Gunnar Syverstad, his laboratory assistant, who had served as one of the Gunnerside six.

They were safely in England, but Professor Tronstad had heard some very disturbing news from intelligence sources—that the Nazis were readying a V-3 with an atomic warhead, with which they hoped to end the war. He had also heard that the heavy-water plant was once again in production.

"I must return to Norway and destroy the plant myself," he told Combined Operations. And so one day in the autumn of 1944, Professor Tronstad, after some lessons in parachute jumping, leaped with engineer Syverstad from a British plane over the mountains of Telemark.

They were betrayed by a half-witted quisling farm hand and were captured by a Gestapo patrol after a fierce battle. Less than two months before Norway's liberation, the Germans took the professor and his laboratory assistant into the mountains and killed them. They burned their bodies and scattered their ashes over the snows over Norway.

CHAPTER ELEVEN

We Got the Atom Bomb by Mistake

WHILE THE EXPLOITS of Swallow and Gunnerside put a major obstacle in the path of Germany's atomic-energy program, it was nevertheless generally believed that the German scientists were far ahead of us. For we had realized by that time that we had frittered away several precious years, from the beginning of 1939, when fission was first announced in Germany, to the day before Pearl Harbor, when we finally decided to go all out on the development of an atomic bomb. All our intelligence reports had led us to believe that the Germans had been working energetically to harness atomic energy to their military machine as a weapon and as an atomic engine for submarines, aircraft and industrial power.

The fact is, and it turned out to have been a very fortunate fact indeed, that our information about what the Germans were doing was very far from true. Had we known how far they were from making an atomic bomb we most certainly would not have spent $2 billion to catch up with them.

Until near the end of 1944 all our information about how far the German atomic-bomb project had progressed was based on rumor and guesswork. Only then did we obtain any real firsthand knowledge.

The true facts were so startling as to be at first unbelievable. But as one by one we captured and questioned the leading German atomic scientists, confiscated their laboratory equipment and their scientific records, and closely examined all their atomic installations, there could no longer be the slightest doubt that, far from being ahead of us, the Germans were hopelessly behind us.

It was in the middle of 1944, following the liberation of France, that a War Department mission, bearing the code name Alsos, was sent overseas to find out what the German progress had been on the development of the atomic bomb. Alsos, the Greek word for grove, was named after Major General (now Lieutenant General, retired) Leslie R. Groves, head of the atomic-bomb project.

Alsos was a joint military-scientific mission. Its Army leader was Colonel Boris T. Pash and its scientific leader was the Dutch-born and -educated American physicist Dr. Samuel A. Goudsmit, who knew all the principal scientists in Germany and where to look for them. The mission was described as "one of the finest examples of co-operation of the scientists and the armed forces."

Sam Goudsmit, as he is affectionately known among his wide circle of friends, scientists and laymen alike, of whom I am proud to be one, is one of the most brilliant physicists in the world. With his fellow physicist Professor George E. Uhlenbeck, who was also Dutch-born and who is now at the University of Michigan, he discovered in 1925, at the age of twenty-three, one of the most fundamental phenomena in the atomic world—the spin of the electron. That he did not receive the Nobel Prize in physics for this outstanding discovery, when many a lesser contribution has been given this recognition, is a major mystery that only the Nobel Award Committee in Sweden could try to explain. If they can't, and no physicist believes that they ever could, then it is still time to correct this rank injustice.

The first real breakthrough for Alsos came after the occupation of Strasbourg in November 1944. There they found papers that "suddenly raised the curtain of secrecy." There, "in apparently harmless communications, was a wealth of secret information available to anyone who understood it," and Sam Goudsmit was just that man.

They had found the names and addresses of all the leading German scientists and the locations of their laboratories. From then on a relentless pursuit began. Often small groups of Alsos military personnel would filter through the German lines ahead of the advancing American armies to capture a much-bewildered German scientist with all his equipment and scientific data and take him back as prisoner.

One by one the leading German scientists were taken prisoner in this unorthodox, and often not strictly legal, manner, and thoroughly questioned. Bit by bit the story was pieced together. By the end of 1944 the picture was complete and the whole truth of Germany's truly miserable atomic-bomb project was revealed to us.

When the first atomic bomb was dropped on Hiroshima, ten of the topflight German atomic scientists, nuclear physicists and chemists, were interned at Farm Hall, a pleasant eighteenth-century English country house, in a setting of green meadows and tall trees, at Godmanchester, near Cambridge. They included Werner Heisenberg and Max von Laue, two of the world's outstanding physicists, both Nobel Prize winners, and Otto Hahn, discoverer of fission, for which he had won the Nobel Prize in chemistry. The others were Carl Friedrich von Weizsäcker, distinguished physicist; Walther Gerlach, supreme head of German nuclear-physics research; Kurt Diebner, Erich Bagge and Paul Harteck, experts on isotope separation; Karl Wirtz and Horst Korsching. Von Laue had always been an outspoken opponent of the Nazi regime. Hahn, though less outspoken, was also known to be entirely out of sympathy with the Nazis. The others were above all German nationalists who secretly hoped that the Nazi evils were but a passing phase in Germany's evolution.

All their lengthy scientific discussions as well as their private conversations and table talk were recorded by means of concealed microphones. For reasons unknown, these recordings are still being kept top secret in the archives of the British and American intelligence services, but Sam Goudsmit heard most of them before they were impounded. He was particularly interested in the recordings describing the reactions of these German scientists, all of whom had worked on the German atomic project, when they first heard the news over the British radio of the dropping of the atomic bomb on Hiroshima. He tells about it vividly in his official report, *Alsos* (New York: Henry Schuman, Inc., 1947):

It was on August 6, at dinner time, that the interned German scientists first heard the news of Hiroshima. Their initial reaction was one of utter incredulity. Impossible, they said. After all, they themselves had been working on the uranium problem for several years and had proved that an atomic bomb was too difficult to achieve in such short order. Then how could the Americans do it? It was preposterous.

"It can't be an atomic bomb," one of them said. "It's probably propaganda, just as it was in Germany. They have some new explosive, or an extra large bomb they call atomic, but it's certainly not what we would have called an atomic bomb. It has nothing whatever to do with the uranium problem."

That being settled, the German scientists were able to finish their dinner in peace. But at 9 o'clock came the detailed news broadcast . . . The impact on the ten scientists was shattering. Their whole world collapsed. At one stroke, all their self-confidence was gone and the belief in their own scientific superiority gave way to an intense feeling of despair and futility.

After getting over their state of shock, the German scientists spent considerable time trying to guess at the bomb's mechanism. But it was not until more than a full day had passed that Heisenberg realized the full significance of the Allied achievement.

He called his colleagues together and gave them a lecture about how the Americans had made an atomic bomb. As they listened they became more and more crestfallen. How could they have failed where the Americans had succeeded? How could they ever live down the blow to the prestige of German science?

They were still interned when the legend of their apology to the world and to history began to take shape. This legend, which has gained widespread circulation in Germany and abroad, runs as follows: It was for moral and humanitarian reasons that the German scientists did not work on an atomic bomb. Not only did they not recommend the construction of such a bomb, they actually succeeded in diverting the minds of the Nazi leaders from the idea of "so inhuman a weapon."

That this is an entirely false picture, developed as an afterthought, is revealed in the tape recordings of their conversations immediately after they learned about the bomb, as heard by Sam Goudsmit. All these show that, with the exception of Otto Hahn and Von Laue, the German scientists did not push for the construction of an atom bomb because they did not believe that one could be made, not because they were opposed to it on moral and humanitarian grounds. The records further show that the German scientists, in the arrogant belief of their superiority, were confident that if they could not make an atom bomb then no other nation could. Hence their shock when they learned that American, British and exiled scientists, mostly from Germany, had accomplished what they themselves regarded as impossible.

All this is amply corroborated by the diary of Professor Bagge, one of the internees, published (in Germany) in the volume *From Uranium Fission to Calder Hall* (*Rohwohlt's German Encyclopedia*, No. 41, Hamburg). In an entry dated August 7, 1945, the day following the announcement of the bomb, Professor Bagge wrote:

Tuesday, August 7, 1945

That was an exciting evening yesterday. The British radio announces that an atomic bomb was dropped on a locality in Japan. We were at dinner when the sensational news amazed our group. Immediately an extremely lively discussion develops whether this was really possible or whether perhaps we misunderstood. Heisenberg strongly holds the view that "perhaps they have a new explosive with atomic hydrogen or oxygen or something like it." . . . Hahn is quite shaken and he hopes, therefore, that Heisenberg is right, as he dreads the thought that his own discovery could have been used for war-making purposes. Harteck calculates that even under the best conditions an explosive of atomic hydrogen or oxygen could produce an explosive force no more than tenfold that of any known explosive, whereas it had been announced that the one bomb by itself had the explosive power of 20,000 tons TNT. That could only be a uranium bomb. Von Laue and Gerlach are very much shaken. Gerlach holds the thing very difficult to believe, but suggests waiting until the next broadcast at 9 o'clock. Von Weizsäcker asks Heisenberg to state his view once again in greater detail and Heisenberg affirms once again that from a practical point of view he still did not believe it, although after hearing the calculations of Harteck, which were also supported by Hahn, he has become somewhat uncertain and therefore thought it would be best to wait for the 9 o'clock broadcast. Diebner, on the other hand, holds it as possible that it actually is an atomic bomb, and Korsching supports him on the conjecture that the Americans produced the explosive atomic material by separating the uranium isotopes with the diffusion method.

In any case, it was naturally clear that the explosive material could have been produced only by isotope separation, although it is also conceivable that a separation method of the mass spectrometer (i.e., electromagnetic) type was the one employed.

The Germans had decided that the construction of a bomb would be a superhuman effort that could not be realized in a lifetime, Professor Goudsmit told me, but their principal error, he added, was a misguided belief in their own scientific superiority. This attitude was exemplified in a secret official letter written on July 8, 1943, by the chief of German research on the project to Goering's headquarters. The letter, which was later confiscated by Alsos, states:

As you can see from the report, the work [on uranium] has progressed rather considerably in a few months. Though the work will not lead in a short time toward the production of practically useful engines or explosives, it gives on the other hand the certainty that in this field the enemy powers cannot have any surprise in store for us.

This was written more than seven months after Enrico Fermi and his team had lighted the first atomic fire at Chicago University's squash court, and two months after the Manhattan Project got under way.

Even in their attempts to build a "uranium machine," the Germans' term for a nuclear reactor, which did not involve any moral scruples, the German scientists were hopelessly behind. Whereas Fermi and his team had produced their first chain reaction on December 2, 1942, the Germans were still far from that stage at the war's end. "The German design of an atomic reactor," Professor Goudsmit told me, "could only be called primitive. They completely overlooked the need for controls, control rods being mentioned very casually only once in all their numerous secret reports. According to Diebner and Bagge the Allied destruction of the Norwegian heavy-water plant was the main reason why their primitive reactor couldn't work."

The story of Alsos had its tragic interlude, when Sam Goudsmit went to The Hague to visit the house where he was born and where he spent his childhood and formative years.

Climbing into the little room where he had spent so many hours of his life, he found a few scattered papers, among them his high-school report cards that his parents had saved so carefully through all the years. Here was the glassed-in porch, his mother's favorite breakfast nook. There was the corner where the piano always stood. The little garden in the back of the house looked sadly neglected. Only the lilac tree was still standing.

As I stood there in that wreck that had once been my home [Dr. Goudsmit writes in *Alsos*], I was gripped by that shattering emotion all of us have felt who have lost family and relatives and friends at the hands of the murderous Nazis—a terrible feeling of guilt. Maybe I could have saved them. After all, my parents already had their American visas. Everything had been prepared: all was in readiness. It was just four days before the invasion of the Netherlands that they had received their final papers to come to the United States.

It was too late. If I had hurried a little more, if I had not put off one visit to the Immigration Office for one week, if I had written those necessary letters a little faster, surely I could have rescued them from the Nazis in time. Now I wept for the heavy feeling of guilt in me. I have learned since that mine was an emotion shared by many who lost their nearest and dearest to the Nazis. Alas! My parents were only two among the six million victims taken in filthy, jampacked cattle trains to the concentration camps from which it was never intended they were to return.

The world has always admired the Germans so much for their orderliness. They are so systematic; they have such a sense of correctness. That is why they kept such precise records of their evil deeds, which we later found in their proper files in Germany. And that is why I know the precise date my father and my blind mother were put to death in the gas chamber. It was my father's seventieth birthday.

I know exactly how Sam Goudsmit felt. For the Germans did the same thing to my invalid seventy-seven-year-old mother, my sister and my half-blind brother when they entered my native village of Salantai in Lithuania and murdered all its inhabitants.

94

CHAPTER TWELVE

My Life in Atomland

ONE BY ONE the leading physicists disappeared, shortly after Pearl Harbor, to parts unknown. So did the subject of uranium fission and everything pertaining to atomic energy disappear from the scientific journals. A heavy curtain of secrecy, so thick that one could feel it in the air, hid everything pertaining to the atom. I sensed something was up, but it was not until 1943 that I pieced together enough stray bits of information to suspect that something truly big was going on somewhere in Tennessee, in the state of Washington and in New Mexico.

But while I felt that we were doing something really big, I was still greatly worried about what the Germans were doing. We had given them a head start, I was sure. Would we be able to catch up with them and overtake them? No one would talk. In fact, there was no one to talk to, as every physicist in the country appeared to have vanished.

I kept writing stories speculating on the secret weapons that Hitler and Goebbels were boasting would soon win the war for them. But ever since Pearl Harbor we had established an office of voluntary press censorship, of which Byron Price was the director, and any story dealing with such things as uranium, atomic energy, atomic weapons or any related subject was withheld.

Story after story I submitted to Byron Price's office was returned with the request not to publish. Even speculation on what the enemy might be doing was out of bounds, since, as was explained to me, we did not want the enemy to know what we knew about him. Any speculation, I was told, might hamper our intelligence efforts to find out what the enemy was doing.

This state of affairs lasted until early in the spring of 1945, when one day Jimmie James came out of his office with a letter in his hand.

"I have a letter here from a General Leslie R. Groves. He wants to see you."

"What do you suppose he wants of me?"

"Don't know. Better be here. He's coming here tomorrow."

When I saw the General, all he would tell me was that he wanted me to work for him on a top-secret war project. Could it be the atomic-bomb project?

I decided to take a shot in the dark.

"If you want me to do any writing," I said, "I must be given access to firsthand sources. I hope you'll permit me to go to Tennessee, Washington and New Mexico."

At this General Groves winced. But Mr. James, who had talked with him before I was called in, burst out with a hearty chuckle.

"You'll go farther than that!" he said. General Groves must have told him that he wanted me to cover the dropping of the atomic bomb over Japan. But he gave me no inkling of it until weeks later.

And thus it came about that I became the official historian of the atomic-bomb project.

I found that in two years' time, beginning in May 1943, we had built a secret empire spread throughout the United States and Canada, and as far away as the Belgian Congo. It was named the Manhattan Engineer District. We had built three secret cities of which the one in Tennessee, named Oak Ridge, had reached a population of about eighty thousand, making it the fifth largest city in the state. It was known as "Dogpatch," or just "the Patch," but to me, as I visited it for the first time, it was "the Shangri-La of the South."

There were two other secret cities, one, in the state of Washington, named Richland, and another, hidden away among the canyons of New Mexico, named Los Alamos.

But it wasn't the fact that secret cities had been built and popu-

lated within two years that made it impossible for me at first to convince myself that I was not suffering from some kind of hallucina-
tion. It was the contents of these cities and the strange atmosphere
of unreality that surrounded them. In Oak Ridge I met the "impossible" everywhere I went. Apparatus that before the war I could
pick up with one hand had been expanded to cover an area the size
of city blocks. I saw oval buildings enclosing magnets the size of a
small race track—and, indeed, they were known as "race tracks."
I saw for the first time the prototype of a nuclear reactor operating
at an energy level five thousand times the level of the reactor in
which Fermi had started the first atomic fire on December 2, 1942.
When I stood in front of it in a state of unbelief, I was informed
that it was only a small model. "Wait until you see the real nuclear
reactors in Hanford, Washington," I was told. It was in these giant
reactors, built in a semidesert area covering six hundred square
miles, that man for the first time was producing an artificial element, plutonium—in quantities large enough to make atomic
bombs. Richland, several miles away, was the administrative center
for these plants.

While Los Alamos was the smallest of the three in population,
it was in many ways the most remarkable. It was the brain center
of the atomic-bomb project. There, under the direction of Dr.
J. Robert Oppenheimer, the elite of science worked as a composite
giant brain, devoting millions of man-hours to develop a "gadget,"
as they called it, that would yield up its tremendous explosive force
in less than a millionth of a second.

I shall never forget the feeling of awe I experienced when I
first saw in the semidesert of Washington State the gigantic plants
known as the Hanford Engineering Works, where the plutonium
for atomic bombs was being created by modern alchemy. That
night, while the memory of that overwhelming experience was
still fresh, I tried to express my impression in words. Here is what
I wrote:

To behold these atomic power plants standing in their primeval
majesty is one of the most terrifying and awe-inspiring spectacles on
earth today. There is not a sign, not the slightest hint, that within these
huge man-made blocks titanic cosmic fires are raging such as had never
raged on earth in its present form. One stands before them as though

beholding the realization of a vision such as Michelangelo might have had of a world yet to be, as indescribable as the Grand Canyon of Arizona, Beethoven's Ninth Symphony, or the presence "whose dwelling is the light of setting suns."

In these Promethean structures, which may well stand as eternal monuments to the spirit of man challenging nature, mighty cosmic forces are at work such as had never been let loose on this planet in the million years of man's existence on its surface, and probably never in the 3,000 million years of the earth's being. Here, for the first time in history, man stands in the presence of the very act of elemental creation of matter. Here in the great silences—for the plants operate in a stillness where even the beating of one's heart can be heard—new elements are being born, a phenomenon that, as far as man knows, has not happened since Genesis.

This development no doubt will rank in the future story of mankind as a definite landmark, signalizing a new cultural age, the Age of Atomics, or of Nucleonics, as some scientists prefer to designate it. For this there is no parallel. All the great ages—the Iron Age, the Bronze Age, the ages of steam and electricity, each of which revolutionized conditions of living—arrived imperceptibly, and man did not become aware of them until their effects were fully felt. This marks the first time in the history of man's struggle to bend the forces of nature to his will that he is actually present at the birth of a new era on this planet, with full awareness of its titanic potentialities for good or evil.

One is reassured on seeing the most remarkable system of automatic controls, and controls of controls, devised to keep this man-made Titan from breaking his bonds. Left without control for even a split second, the giant would run wild. Enormous as the mass is, its mechanisms and controls are adjusted with the fineness of the most delicate jeweled watch, and they respond with the sensitivity of a fine Stradivarius. The slightest deviation from normal behavior and the automatic controls go into operation. They can stop the Titan in his tracks almost instantly.

Life in the secret cities was a study in contrasts. As R. L. Duffus stated in *The New York Times*, "the centuries jostle each other." Only a few years back the people at Oak Ridge, and at nearby Happy Valley, most of whom come from stock that has lived long in these Tennessee hills, were existing on their worn-out land under conditions not very different from those of centuries gone by. "Now, by a stupendous leap," to quote Mr. Duffus, "they have been projected into the twenty-first century. On one side of a certain highway there are tall stacks to dissipate the radioactive fumes from atom-splitting. On the other side is a plain log cabin, chinked with clay and whitewashed—and lived in less than three years ago."

During my sojourn in Atomland my identity was supposed to be kept secret. One reason was that my presence might create the impression that the whole atom-bomb secret was about to be published in the newspapers, which might lead to a relaxation of security. Hence only a few key scientists in each plant were informed about my presence.

But a very embarrassing situation arose on my first visit to Los Alamos.

I had arrived early one Saturday morning in May 1945 and had spent most of the day with Dr. Oppenheimer and the security officer, both of whom naturally knew about my mission. On the evening of that day, as I was sitting in my room in the Blue Lodge going over in my mind the marvels I had seen and heard earlier, there came a knock on my door. Dr. Oppenheimer and his assistant director, Dr. Samuel K. Allison of Chicago University, had come to invite me to a social gathering that evening.

The first person I met that night was Fermi, who was playing some kind of indoor game on the large porch. It was the first time I had seen him for a number of years and I was delighted to find out where he had been hiding. I tapped him lightly on the shoulder and as he turned around and saw me standing there he burst out laughing. It was the laughter of a child playing hide-and-seek who finds himself finally discovered.

Inside the main room there was much gaiety. An orchestra composed of physicists, many of them of world renown, was playing Viennese waltzes. Gaily waltzing around the room were most of the top scientists who had disappeared soon after Pearl Harbor. I had discovered a lost world on a mesa in New Mexico.

But I had no sooner entered the room than the music and the dancing all came to a sudden stop. Transfixed, as if seeing a ghost, the orchestra and the dancers stood looking at me, with a mixture of amazement and incredulity. I could almost read their thoughts:

How the devil did he get in here? Has the secret at last leaked out? Where is Colonel Tyler? We must tell him at once. Something must be done in a hurry. They should arrest him and keep him confined for the duration. . . . No one showed the slightest sign of knowing me.

Colonel Gerald R. Tyler was the officer in charge of the military contingent that was guarding Los Alamos against unwanted visitors. Naturally he knew all about my arrival, and in fact he was the first man I had called upon.

Colonel Tyler was seated in the balcony enjoying the dancing and the music when a couple of young scientists came rushing up to him, breathless.

"Colonel," one of them blurted out, "you see that fellow down there? His name is Laurence and he is a reporter for *The New York Times!*"

Colonel Tyler assured them that he knew all about it and that I was being carefully watched. He advised them to go on with their dancing and playing as though nothing had happened.

The music and the dancing resumed, and it was soon decided that there were simply too many people who knew me at Los Alamos, and that under the circumstances they might just as well be told about my mission.

CHAPTER THIRTEEN

Of Men and Atoms

ON FRIDAY MORNING of January 27, 1939, a young physicist named Luis Alvarez, tall, blond and twenty-seven, was having his hair cut at the Stevens Union on the University of California campus in Berkeley. He was quietly perusing the morning newspaper when his eye fell on the following headline: "Uranium Atom Split in Two Halves; 200,000,000 Electron Volts of Energy Liberated."

Out of the barber's chair bounded Dr. Alvarez. The startled barber and the customers waiting their turn watched in amazement as he rushed out of the shop, his hair only partly cut, a long white sheet still tightly wound around his neck. Up the hill he went, the newspaper clutched in his hand, the sheet waving in the morning breeze, as he ran as fast as his long legs would carry him. Ignoring the startled gaze of passers-by, he arrived, breathless and panting, at California's famed Radiation Laboratory. His colleagues of the crew of atomic physicists soon forgot their amazement over the ghostlike apparition in their midst when they heard the news he had brought—news of the discovery that led to the atomic bomb.

This is one of the favorite true stories atomic scientists like to tell in moments of relaxation as they reminisce about those historic years, 1939–1945. There are many of these anecdotes, for there was a human side to the atom, light moments in the grim business of harnessing atomic energy in the greatest weapon of destruction ever conceived.

Among the anecdotes atomic scientists enjoy telling are those about Professor Bohr, who fully lived up to the reputation of the proverbial absent-minded professor.

Professor Bohr was caught in Copenhagen when the Nazis invaded Denmark in the spring of 1940. The German scientists, who respected him highly, interceded for him with the Nazi authorities, and he was allowed to continue working in his laboratory unmolested. His most highly treasured possession was about a pint of heavy water. To prevent its falling into the hands of the Germans, he put it in a large green Danish beer bottle and kept it in a refrigerator.

In the fall of 1943, when our atom-bomb project was getting into full swing, it was recognized that the vast knowledge and counsel of Professor Bohr would be of inestimable value, and so, in due time, he was smuggled out one dark night disguised as a fisherman and taken by fishing boat, protected by British submarines, to Sweden, whence he was flown to England in a British fighter plane. He left all his belongings behind, carefully taking with him only one possession—his precious green bottle of heavy water.

Professor Bohr, a heavy-set individual, has a remarkably large head size, so large that when he got into the plane, which had to fly at very high altitude, none of the standard-size oxygen masks would fit him. As a result, when the plane finally landed in England the great physicist was found unconscious from lack of oxygen.

When he was revived, his first act was to reach for the green bottle of heavy water. Much to his dismay, however, he discovered that in his haste he had taken with him the wrong bottle, which contained nothing but good Danish beer.

Members of the Danish underground were sent posthaste to rescue Professor Bohr's precious beer bottle before the Germans discovered it. Its rescue was one of the heroic feats of the war, as the bottle had to be removed from under the noses of the guards, who took over Dr. Bohr's laboratory as soon as his escape was discovered.

The Danish beer was drunk as a toast to the Danish underground after they had delivered the beer bottle containing the priceless heavy water.

There was another bottle in Professor Bohr's laboratory—a chemical flask filled with pungent nitric acid. The Germans who occupied the laboratory paid no attention to it. Dissolved in the acid was Dr. Bohr's large gold medal, the Nobel Prize medal he had won in 1922, and there it remained, safe from German greed, until after the war. On Dr. Bohr's return, the gold was precipitated out from the nitric acid and the original medal was reconstituted in its full splendor.

As soon as the first small batch of uranium 235 was produced in the giant plants at Oak Ridge, Tennessee, it was rushed by a special courier to Los Alamos, New Mexico, where the atomic bomb was being designed. The courier, driving a limousine, was not told, of course, what the precious small box contained, but he had heard lurid tales about what was being produced at Oak Ridge, including the speculation that they were producing a "death ray," and the farther he drove the more uneasy he became. He made up his mind that at the slightest sign of queer behavior on the part of the box behind him he would run for his life.

He was crossing a long bridge when suddenly from behind him came a loud boom. Like one possessed he dashed out of the car, running faster than he had ever run in his life. Then, exhausted, he stopped to examine himself to make sure that he was still in one piece. Meanwhile a long line of exasperated motorists was loudly honking behind him.

When he made his way cautiously back to his abandoned car, he found to his amazement that his vehicle, as well as the box, were intact. But as he took his place at the wheel and was about to resume his journey, once again there came a loud boom, and once again the instinct of self-preservation started him on a second mad dash for his life. On being overtaken by a very irate motorcycle policeman, he learned, after showing his official government credentials, that the booms he had heard came from a nearby Army proving ground, where new artillery shells were being tested.

At Oak Ridge men and women lived in an atmosphere of unreality. They were working in huge plants, consuming vast quantities of materials, out of which nothing ever seemed to come except the long processions of empty trucks following the delivery of their loads.

When I asked a worker at one of the plants what he thought he was making, he answered, "I'm making a dollar thirty-five an hour," considered a high wage for unskilled labor in that part of the country during the war. Others believed that the whole thing was a gigantic boondoggle.

"I'll bet," one of the latter remarked, "that whatever they're making here, they could get it much cheaper if they went out and bought it."

The stock jest was that they were making "front ends of horses to be shipped to Washington for assembly." Many believed the whole project was a scheme of Mrs. Roosevelt's to turn Negroes white. This outraged some of them to the point where they refused to continue on the job.

In my office at Oak Ridge, where I was doing most of my writing, there was a large metal wastebasket, painted red, with the word "BURN" inscribed in large white letters. In it I threw all my discarded copy, after I had torn it into little bits. Every day at five, two guards, armed to the teeth, came into my office with a wheelbarrow and carted the wastebasket to the incinerator, where the contents were carefully burned in the presence of both. I learned after a while that these particular guards had been carefully chosen after it had been determined that both were illiterate.

The project naturally brought great prosperity to many of the neighboring communities, and the Chamber of Commerce in one of these decided to tender a testimonial dinner to a high-ranking Army officer who was in charge of one of the plants in Hanford, Washington. After many speeches, and even more highballs, the guest of honor rose to make an announcement that electrified his audience.

"You are all such fine citizens," he said, "that I asked and received special permission to tell you, in absolute confidence, what we are making in those plants."

There was a pause as everyone leaned forward to listen.

"We are making," he said, and his voice dropped to a whisper, "wheels—for miscarriages."

The need for absolute secrecy created many a dilemma. One of the strangest concerned a Navy ensign on the project who suffered a complete mental breakdown and began ranting about the terrible weapon that would soon bring about the end of the world. It was considered too risky to confine him to a regular Navy mental institution, as, unfortunately, the fellow's ravings made a good deal of sense, even to one with only an elementary knowledge of physics. The only solution was to build a special wing at the hospital in Oak Ridge, and to staff it with a select group of psychiatrists, physicians, nurses, orderlies and guards, all specially picked for their trustworthiness after a thorough security check-up. To keep the patient from talking, the physicians agreed to maintain him under prolonged sedation. As soon as he began talking a nurse was always there with a hypodermic.

The ensign's family was told that he was away on a long secret mission at sea. His Navy superiors, however, had to be told the truth, that the unfortunate young officer had "gone off his rocker." Soon a high-ranking Navy officer arrived on the scene to investigate. The officer, a member of the Navy Medical Corps, was dismayed to discover that the special psychiatric wing had been organized according to Army specification, apparently an unheard-of breach of protocol. This made it necessary to rebuild and restaff the special wing according to Navy specification.

All the prominent scientists, whose presence might arouse suspicion, were ordered to go under assumed names. The most prominent went under several aliases. Dr. Bohr, for example, was known in Los Alamos as Mr. Nicholas Baker, or, more familiarly, as "Uncle Nick." Dr. Fermi was known as Mr. Henry Farmer. Dr. Wigner was known as Mr. Eugene Wagner.

One afternoon "Mr. Farmer" and "Mr. Wagner" were challenged by a guard as they were coming out of one of the guarded areas of the gigantic plutonium plants at Hanford, Washington. "Mr. Farmer" produced his identification card with his photo and his driver's license, but "Mr. Wagner" had somehow mislaid his credentials.

The guard had a list of those authorized to enter or leave the plant. "What's your name?" he asked.

The absent-minded professor mumbled, "Mr. Wigner," then quickly corrected himself. "Mr. Wagner," he said.

But by that time the guard, ever on the alert, had become suspicious. "Mr. Wagner" was on his list, but definitely no "Mr. Wigner." He turned to "Mr. Farmer," whom he had seen several times on previous occasions. "Is this man's name Wagner?" he asked.

"His name is Wagner just as sure as my name is Farmer," Dr. Fermi solemnly assured him. The guard waved them on.

Dr. Compton, who, as one of the high command of the atomic project, had to travel back and forth to all the principal installations throughout the country, East and West, had several aliases, a different alias for each part of the country. Thus he was known as "Mr. Comas" in Hanford and as "Mr. Comstock" in the East.

Once when he traveled with his wife from Oak Ridge to Gatlinburg, Tennessee, he was instructed to register in the hotel as "Mr. and Mrs. A. Holly." Their son, Arthur, a captain in the Army, who had a few days' leave, came to join them, and this created a rather awkward situation, as the son did not think it was proper for an Army officer to go under an assumed name.

Dr. Compton's wife, Betty, ever resourceful, was equal to the situation. Usually, in introducing her son, she would just mumble his name. On one occasion, however, when the young officer's true identity could no longer be held back, Betty Compton introduced him as "Captain Compton, my son by my first marriage." It was, of course, as Dr. Compton said later, "a literally correct subterfuge."

Once Dr. Compton, boarding a plane for Hanford, was handed tickets under the name of Black. Late at night the plane made a stop at Cheyenne, Wyoming, and Dr. Compton, who had been sleeping during the long flight, got off for a bit of exercise. As he was returning on board he was stopped by the stewardess who, as was customary in wartime, was making a careful check of the passengers.

Dr. Compton was stumped. He remembered that he had been given the name of some dark color, but he was not sure whether it was black or brown. He took a gamble on black and he was allowed aboard.

On another occasion he was on a flight from California to New York when he was awakened from his nap by the hostess asking for his name. Semiawake, and by that time conditioned to the fact that he had different names in the East and the West, his first reaction was to look out the window to find out, if possible, what part of the country he was in. It being dark, he turned to the hostess for help.

"Where are we?" he asked. This time he was in a more serious predicament than he had been in Cheyenne, as he had neglected to look at his ticket to see in what name it had been made out.

Luckily, at that moment Dr. Compton's armed bodyguard, who was traveling with him, came to the rescue. As was customary, the guard was seated directly behind, and he had dozed off when the hostess came around. Coming to with a start, he produced both his own ticket and the one for "Mr. Comas."

Ostensibly for their protection, but more likely to guard them against their own absent-mindedness, General Groves assigned special guards from Army Intelligence to the brass among the scientists. The guards' duty was to stay with them, travel with them, carry their important top-secret documents in briefcases chained to their wrists, and help them in every way possible, including such items as helping them remember their names.

These guards were chosen for their mental as well as their physical endowments. Dr. Compton's guard, Julian Bernacchi, was a law graduate and member of the Chicago police force. He was useful to Dr. Compton in many ways, particularly in keeping him from inadvertently violating some of the many stringent security regulations.

As might be expected, Fermi also was assigned an armed bodyguard, an Illinois-born son of immigrants from northern Italy, named John Baudino. Like Dr. Compton's guard, Baudino was a man of athletic build and by profession a lawyer. In addition, he was ever eager to learn and he made good use of his opportunity while acting as Fermi's chaperon to learn all he could about physics. Fermi, a superb teacher, was delighted. Soon Baudino learned how to operate the original Stagg Field reactor, which had been moved to the Argonne Laboratory some twenty miles from Chicago, and to assist Fermi and others in their experiments.

Which led Fermi to remark one day, "Soon Baudino will need a bodyguard. He knows too much!"

The late Judge Robert P. Patterson, then Under Secretary of War, acted as the paymaster for the project. He was greatly perturbed one day in September 1944 when he discovered that he had paid out nearly two billion dollars on the operation without really knowing much about it. Suppose it later turned out to be a fizzle. Suppose a Congressional investigating committee later pointed an accusing finger at him and he had to confess that he had paid out two billions without even taking the trouble to find out what it was actually all about!

So he sent a New York construction engineer, Michael Madigan by name, who served as his special assistant, to look into the matter. Madigan went and saw things no engineer ever dreamed of—huge buildings covering thousands of acres; new cities that did not exist on any map; thousands of new gadgets that performed the impossible; magnets of staggering dimensions. He, too, saw thousands of tons of raw materials entering the plants in a constant stream, day and night, but he never saw anything come out of them. The more he saw the more fantastic the whole project appeared.

In due time Madigan went back and reported to Judge Patterson. "Judge," he said, "I have been all over the place and have seen everything, and I'm here to tell you that you have nothing at all to worry about, nothing at all!"

After a pause, he continued. "Listen, Judge! If this thing works, they won't investigate anything! And if it doesn't work—if it doesn't work—" he repeated, "they won't investigate anything else!"

Here he paused again to allow his words to sink in, then went on. "We have done a lot of crazy things in the Army that might well be investigated. But alongside this screwball thing everything crazy we have done will look sensible by comparison!"

One of the most bizarre episodes happened shortly after the Hanford plutonium plants were completed. Suddenly they were plunged into total darkness and everything came to a standstill. Investigation revealed that a Japanese balloon had drifted all the way across the Pacific and landed on, of all places, the power line feeding the plants, causing a short circuit that cut off the power. The Japanese never learned that one of their balloons had stopped production of atomic-bomb materials for an hour or so.

It was these plants that produced the plutonium for the bomb that destroyed Nagasaki.

CHAPTER FOURTEEN

Letter to the Editor

SHORTLY AFTER I had joined the Manhattan Project, General Groves asked me to prepare a list of the subjects I intended to write about. Item 26 on that list read: "Eyewitness account of the July 15 test at New Mexico," to which I added in parentheses, "in case eyewitness survives." Item 27 was to be an eyewitness account of the atomic bombing of Japan, again with the parenthetical "in case eyewitness survives." On July 15, when I protested to General Groves that my observation spot was too far away ("How do you expect me to give an eyewitness account twenty miles from the scene?") he curtly reminded me that he had a considerable interest in having the eyewitness survive.

Sometime in the middle of May of 1945, General Groves had summoned me to his office in Washington and had shown me a map of New Mexico with a large red ring around a spot near Alamogordo. In measured words he had informed me that at the spot within the circle the atomic bomb was to be tested about July 15, two months hence.

"Why waste an atomic bomb on American soil?" I protested.

"Supposing it's a dud," the General answered quietly. "We would then be handing it to the Japs on a platter. If it doesn't work we want to know why. And if it isn't as good as expected, we also want to know why."

He then explained what he wanted me to do. He outlined four possibilities, in case the bomb was not a dud. I was to prepare in advance four individual reports, to be given out as official statements, in explanation of any of the four possible events, without, of course, giving away the secret.

The first two were easy: a loud explosion heard for many miles accompanied by a great burst of light, but without any damage to property or any loss of life; and a similar but somewhat larger explosion, heard and seen over a larger area, with some damage to property.

The third possibility that I was asked to explain in advance was considerably more difficult, as it involved an even larger explosion than the first two, with considerable damage to property and loss of life.

But the fourth was the most difficult of all. In this case the property damage was much more extensive, while those who lost their lives numbered among them many of the country's top scientists. What, in heaven's name, were they doing in the desert at that hour of the morning? And since I had been told by General Groves that I was to be among those privileged to witness the test, it was obvious that the fourth explanation, if it were to be used, would also include my own obituary.

I told a lurid story of several large dumps of an extremely powerful new explosive, without telling what it was, that had blown up accidentally. As for the scientists' being there, I explained it as one of those strange coincidences that sometimes take place by unfathomable quirks of fate. It happens that Dr. Oppenheimer owns a dude ranch in that part of New Mexico, and I blamed it all on the fact that he had invited his colleagues to spend a weekend with him in the salubrious New Mexico climate. Their being there, of course, had nothing to do with the explosion.

It was my special job to prepare in advance a series of articles on the development of the atomic bomb, to be held for release on the day when the bomb was first used in Japan, and to be given to the newspapers following a radio announcement by President Truman of the dropping of the bomb. This plan had to be changed, since the President was in Potsdam at the time. One of the articles I prepared as far back as May 1945 was a draft for a half-hour radio address by President Truman, which formed the basis of his as well as Secretary of War Henry L. Stimson's statement on the day following Hiroshima.

By Thursday, July 12, I had prepared all the advance articles on the material I had gathered and was ready to start out for Alamogordo and beyond. Having accounted (plausibly, I hoped) for the untimely and unfortunate end of Dr. Vannevar Bush, director of the Office of Scientific Research and Development, Dr. Conant, Fermi, Sir James Chadwick, Ernest O. Lawrence, Dr. Oppenheimer, and many other eminent scientists, and having otherwise attended to several last-minute details (including the preparation of my last will and testament), I felt the urge to warn *The New York Times* that zero hour for the revelation of the Big Secret was approaching.

One of my worries had been that the story of the atom bomb would break around deadline time, with all bedlam breaking loose around the heads of the poor editors. So, without violating security, I typed a letter to Mr. James—the only letter I sent to the outside world, except, of course, the letters to my wife. I had kept no copy of it and I had forgotten all about it, when one day some years later Mr. James returned it to me. Here it is:

CONFIDENTIAL

Thursday, July 12, 1945

DEAR MR. JAMES:

Forgive me for not writing sooner. I have been busier than the proverbial one-armed paperhanger ever since I left. I have covered lots of ground and seen things that made me dizzy. In fact, I have been in a constant state of bewilderment now for some two months and the biggest surprises are still ahead.

The story is much bigger than I could imagine, fantastic, bizarre, fascinating and terrifying. When it breaks it will be an eighth-day wonder, a sort of Second Coming of Christ yarn. It will be one of the big stories of our generation and it will run for some time. It will need about twenty columns on the day it breaks. This may sound overenthusiastic, but I am willing to wager you right now that when the time comes you will agree that my estimate is on the conservative side.

I am going to do my best to arrange to give you sufficient notice in advance (through the proper channels) so that you may have the time to prepare for it. We hope we can control the timing, but that is in the lap of the gods.

This is not just one big story. There are at least twenty-five individual page-one stories to be given out following the break of the Big News. When it does break you will undoubtedly think of many other angles, national, international, political, diplomatic, industrial and what not. The world will not be the same after the day of the big event. A new era in our civilization will have started, with enormous implications for the postwar period, from both a military and an industrial standpoint.

I am expected to stay on the job until the Big Day. As you already know, I am going places some distance away. Nobody as yet knows the exact date. Under the circumstances I am figuring on being back on the job sometime between September 15 and October 1. I hope it will be earlier than that, but I will not be told until the last minute and then probably I will not be in position to let you know until the "break."

In addition to the privilege of writing one of the big stories of our day it is also a great privilege to be of some service to the nation. The proper handling of the story will be of considerable importance as to what happens in the future. I hope I can live up to the responsibility.

I know that when the proper time comes the *Times* will be the only one to do the story justice, despite the fact that my services are not to be exclusive. I wish they could be.

I will advise the authorities to call you in consultation sometime before the release date. I hope you will be in town at the time.

At present I am one of the few men in the world who knows the complete story, with the exception of dates. The security regulations are so stringent that I am afraid even to talk to myself. Even my identity is kept a deep secret and I find myself slinking around corners for fear someone may recognize me.

While the job is naturally exhilarating and thrilling, it has been a tremendous weight on one's shoulders. It goes against one's grain to write a big story and mark it "Top Secret" and lock it up in a safe. I am looking forward to the day when I can dig up a good story and dash to the nearest Western Union office.

There is another consolation for my prolonged absence from the staff. After the story breaks I will be the only one with firsthand knowledge of it, which should give the *Times* a considerable edge. Much of it, however, will be kept on ice for some time.

My wife knows nothing about my future movements and it may come as a great shock to her when she finds out. I deeply appreciate your kindness to her and if she ever calls on you for help I hope it won't be too much of an imposition. People have been badgering her day and night about my whereabouts and have impinged on her nervous system, already somewhat on edge because of the uncertainty of my movements.

The time is soon coming when she won't hear from me for a considerable "blackout" period, though I will give her warning in advance not to expect letters from me for a while because of "censorship regulations." I know you won't mind if she calls on you for some reassurance and I want to offer my heartfelt thanks to you in advance.

I am looking forward to the time when I can see you again. My desk probably looks much too clean at present and that must look unnatural to you. As usual I am in need of a haircut.

With my best wishes to you, I am, as always,

Faithfully yours,
BILL LAURENCE

P. S. My permanent address now is
P.O. Box 2610
Washington, D. C.

CHAPTER FIFTEEN

The Atomic Age Begins

I WATCHED THE BIRTH of the atomic age from the slope of a hill in the desert land of New Mexico, on the northwestern corner of the Alamogordo Air Base, about 125 miles southeast of Albuquerque. The hill, named Compania Hill for the occasion, was twenty miles to the northwest of Zero, the code name given to the spot chosen for the atomic-bomb test. The area embracing Zero and Compania Hill, twenty-four miles long and eighteen miles wide, bore the code name Trinity.

The bomb was set on a structural steel tower one hundred feet high. Ten miles away to the southwest was the base camp. This was G.H.Q. for the scientific high command, of which Professor Kenneth T. Bainbridge of Harvard University was field commander. Here were erected barracks to serve as living quarters for the scientists, a mess hall, a commissary, a post exchange, and other buildings. The vanguard of the scientists, headed by Dr. Oppenheimer, lived like soldiers at the front, supervising the enormously complicated details of the test.

Here early that Sunday afternoon had gathered General Groves; Brigadier-General Thomas F. Farrell, hero of World War I, General Groves's deputy; Dr. Fermi; Dr. Conant; Dr. Bush; Professor Robert F. Bacher of Cornell; Colonel Stafford L. Warren, University of Rochester radiologist; and about 150 other leaders in the atomic-bomb project.

At the base camp was a dry, abandoned reservoir, about five

hundred feet square, surrounded by a mound of earth about eight feet high. Within this mound bulldozers dug a series of slit trenches, each about three feet deep, seven feet wide and twenty-five feet long. At a command over the radio at zero minus one minute all observers at base camp were to lie down in their assigned trenches, "face and eyes directed toward the ground and with the head away from Zero." But most of us on Compania Hill remained on our feet.

At our observation post on Compania Hill the atmosphere had grown tenser as the zero hour approached. We had spent the first part of our stay eating an early-morning picnic breakfast. It had grown cold in the desert, and many of us, lightly clad, shivered. Occasionally a drizzle came down, and the intermittent flashes of lightning made us glance apprehensively toward Zero. We had received some disturbing reports that the test might be called off because of the weather. The radio we had brought with us for communication with base camp kept going out of order, and when we finally repaired it some noisy band would drown out the news we wanted to hear. We knew there were two specially equipped B-29 Superfortresses high overhead to make observations and recordings in the upper atmosphere, but we could neither see nor hear them. We kept gazing through the blackness.

Suddenly, at 5:29:50, as we stood huddled around our radio, we heard a voice ringing through the darkness, sounding as though it had come from above the clouds: "Zero minus ten seconds!" A green flare flashed out through the clouds, descended slowly, opened, grew dim, and vanished into the darkness.

The voice from the clouds boomed out again: "Zero minus three seconds!" Another green flare came down. Silence reigned over the desert. We kept moving in small groups in the direction of Zero. From the east came the first faint signs of dawn.

And just at that instant there rose as if from the bowels of the earth a light not of this world, the light of many suns in one. It was a sunrise such as the world had never seen, a great green supersun climbing in a fraction of a second to a height of more than eight thousand feet, rising ever higher until it touched the clouds, lighting up earth and sky all around with a dazzling luminosity.

Up it went, a great ball of fire about a mile in diameter, changing colors as it kept shooting upward, from deep purple to orange, expanding, growing bigger, rising as it expanded, an elemental force freed from its bonds after being chained for billions of years. For a fleeting instant the color was unearthly green, such as one sees only in the corona of the sun during a total eclipse. It was as though the earth had opened and the skies had split.

A huge cloud rose from the ground and followed the trail of the great sun. At first it was a giant column, which soon took the shape of a supramundane mushroom. Up it went, higher and higher, quivering convulsively, a giant mountain born in a few seconds instead of millions of years. It touched the multicolored clouds, pushed its summit through them, and kept rising until it reached a height of 41,000 feet, 12,000 feet higher than the earth's highest mountain.

All through the very short but long-seeming time interval not a sound was heard. I could see the silhouettes of human forms motionless in little groups, like desert plants in the dark. The newborn mountain in the distance, a giant among the pygmies of the Sierra Oscuro range, stood leaning at an angle against the clouds, like a vibrant volcano spouting fire to the sky.

Then out of the great silence came a mighty thunder. For a brief interval the phenomena we had seen as light repeated themselves in terms of sound. It was the blast from thousands of blockbusters going off simultaneously at one spot. The thunder reverberated all through the desert, bounced back and forth from the Sierra Oscuro, echo upon echo. The ground trembled under our feet as in an earthquake. A wave of hot wind was felt by many of us just before the blast and warned us of its coming.

The big boom came about a hundred seconds after the great flash—the first cry of a newborn world.

It brought the silent, motionless silhouettes to life, gave them a voice. A loud cry filled the air. The little groups that had hitherto stood rooted to the earth like desert plants broke into a dance—the rhythm of primitive man dancing at one of his fire festivals at the coming of spring.

They clapped their hands as they leaped from the ground— earthbound man symbolizing the birth of a new force that gives him means to free himself from the gravitational bonds that hold him down.

The dance of the primitive man lasted but a few seconds, during which an evolutionary period of 10,000 years had been telescoped.

Primitive man was metamorphosed in those few seconds into mod ern man.

The sun was just rising above the horizon as our caravan started on its way back to Albuquerque and Los Alamos. We looked at it through our dark lenses to compare it with what we had seen.

"The sun can't hold a candle to it!" one of us remarked.

On arriving at Los Alamos I called on Dr. Oppenheimer. He looked tired and preoccupied. I asked him how he felt at the moment of the flash.

"At that moment," I heard him say, "there flashed into my mind a passage from the Bhagavad-Gita, the sacred book of the Hindus: 'I am become Death, the Shatterer of Worlds!' "

I shall never forget the shattering impact of those words, spoken by a poet and a dreamer, one of the most civilized of men, called upon by destiny to direct the harnessing of one of the supreme achievements of man's intellect onto the chariot of Death.

Later that Monday morning, at the breakfast table in the pleasant dining room of the Los Alamos Lodge, the silence was broken by Dr. George B. Kistiakowsky of Harvard. Though he was seated next to me, his voice seemed to come from a great distance. And what I heard has been haunting me ever since.

"This was the nearest to doomsday one can possibly imagine," he said. "I am sure," he added after a pause, as though speaking to no one in particular, "that at the end of the world—in the last milli-second of the earth's existence—the last man will see something very similar to what we have seen."

And out of the silence that ensued I heard another voice—my own—which also sounded as though it came from a distance.

"Possibly so," I said, "but it is also possible that if the first man could have been present at the moment of Creation when God said, 'Let there be light,' he might have seen something very similar to what we have seen."

As I sat there waiting for an answer that did not come, there flashed into my conscious thought an entry from the journal of the brothers Goncourt, recording a conversation at a dinner in Paris on April 7, 1869. I have since learned to quote it verbatim:

They were saying that Berthelot had predicted that a hundred years from now, thanks to physical and chemical science, man would know of what the atom is constituted and would be able, at will, to moderate, extinguish and light up the sun as if it were a gas lamp. Claude Bernard, for his part, had apparently declared that in a hundred years of physiological science man would be so completely the master of organic law that he would create life in competition with God.

To all this we raised no objection, but we have the feeling that when this time comes in science, God with His white beard will come down to earth, swinging a bunch of keys, and will say to humanity, the way they say at five o'clock at the Salon, "Closing time, gentlemen!"

I came out of my reverie with a start. We still had twenty-four years to go before "closing time." Meanwhile there was work to be done. I had been greatly worried before the event whether, when the time came, I would find words to tell a story which no words could possibly describe. To my great relief, the words came as though an inner voice were dictating them.

Without full awareness, I took out my notebook and pencil and began writing feverishly, like one waking from a dream, in a frantic effort to record it before the return of full consciousness blotted it from my memory.

The atomic age began at exactly 5:30 mountain war time on the morning of July 16, 1945, on a stretch of semidesert land about fifty airline miles from Alamogordo, New Mexico, just a few minutes before the dawn of a new day on that part of the earth.

At that great moment in history, ranking with the moment when man first put fire to work for him, the vast energy locked within the heart of the atoms of matter was released for the first time in a burst of flame such as had never before been seen on this planet, illuminating earth and sky, for a brief span that seemed eternal, with the light of many super-suns.

The elemental flame, first fire ever made on earth that did not have its origin in the sun, came from the explosion of the first atomic bomb. It marked the climax of one of the greatest dramas in our history and the history of civilized man—a drama in which scientists in America were working against time to create an atomic bomb ahead of the Germans.

The atomic flash in New Mexico came as a great affirmation to the prodigious labors of scientists during the past four years. It came as the affirmative answer to the until then unanswered question: "Will it work?"

With the flash came a delayed roll of mighty thunder, heard, just as the flash was seen, for hundreds of miles. The roar echoed and reverberated from the distant hills and the Sierra Oscuro range near by, sounding as though it came from some supramundane source as well as from the bowels of the earth.

The hills said yes and the mountains chimed in yes. It was as if the earth had spoken and the suddenly iridescent clouds and sky had joined in one affirmative answer. Atomic energy—yes.

It was like the grand finale of a mighty symphony of the elements, fascinating and terrifying, uplifting and crushing, ominous, devastating, full of great promise and great forebodings.

That afternoon I encountered the late Dr. Lawrence, one of my neighbors on the hill in the desert.

"What a day in history!" he exclaimed.

"It was like being witness to the Second Coming of Christ!" I heard myself say.

It then came to me that both "Oppie" and I, and likely many others in our group, had shared in a profound religious experience, having been witness to an event akin to supernatural.

An embarrassing episode occurred a few days after I had witnessed the test at Alamogordo. I had just returned to my headquarters at Oak Ridge and was getting ready to leave for Tinian Island in the Marianas for the climax of my mission, and of my entire career—to fly with the atomic bomb over Japan.

There was no one at Oak Ridge with whom I could share my thoughts and forebodings, for I was not permitted to talk of my mission to anyone. But I had a number of good friends among the scientists, who had been told that I was preparing a technical report on some aspects of the work at the Oak Ridge plants. One of these was Dr. James R. Coe, Jr., inevitably called "Jerry Coe," who invited me on occasion to spend a few pleasant hours at his home.

I called on the Coes one afternoon following my return from Alamogordo. It was really to say goodbye, though of course I could tell them neither where I had come from nor where I was going.

We were sitting there drinking coffee, silently watching the sunset over the Tennessee hills. I must have been rather preoccupied, for I hardly noticed a young man entering the room, followed shortly by his attractive wife and another young couple. I did not get the mumbled names of the young man and his companions, but their unexpected arrival had apparently caused my hosts considerable embarrassment, as my presence at Oak Ridge, as well as my name, were supposed to be kept secret from all except a few.

"Jerry" soon called me outside on some pretext and informed me that the young man was Richard Gehman, who has since made a mark for himself as a novelist. At that time he was a soldier out of uniform, assigned to special duty on the staff of the Oak Ridge *Journal.* The reporter of the local newspaper, always on the lookout for a story, was the last person the Coes wanted around when they were playing host; as for me, I shuddered at the very thought of being discovered.

As the situation obviously became more embarrassing by the minute, the visitors soon left. It was not until more than a year had passed that I heard from Gehman again, when I read the delightful essay, headed "My Three Minutes with William L. Laurence," in which he reminisced about the episode that afternoon at the home of the Coes at Oak Ridge.

After the bomb had dropped on Hiroshima, and the restrictions were relaxed a little at Oak Ridge [Mr. Gehman wrote], one was at least able to say "atom" and "uranium" without feeling that the enemy, or one of the security agents, was listening. I was able, then, to compare notes with the Coes on that uncomfortable visit.

Laurence, they told me, had returned that day from witnessing the first test explosion in the New Mexico desert. Like all witnesses of that epochal event, he was moved beyond words, and for some days afterward was able to think of nothing else.*

As the Coes told me this, I began to remember Laurence as he looked that Sunday afternoon, and I think that I now understand something of the look that was on his face as he sat gazing into the sunset.

* AUTHOR'S NOTE: The Coes, of course, did not know it at the time, for I was not allowed to mention the test to anyone. But there were widespread rumors among the scientists, who put two and two together, that a test had taken place in New Mexico.

It was not the look of William L. Laurence, the science writer. It was the look of a man, privileged to peek through a crack in the wall that hides the mystery of the universe, confounded by what he had seen, awed in contemplation of his own insignificance, wondering where it will all lead. It was a look I will never forget.

CHAPTER SIXTEEN

Mountain of Fire

OVER THE ROAD from Santa Fe to Los Alamos many of the world's great scientists traveled incognito. On it were carried the finished products for Alamogordo, Hiroshima and Nagasaki. It was only a little road, but during the summer of 1945 it became one of the world's great highways. On it traveled the substance that changed the course of history.

Except for this road Los Alamos was inaccessible to the outside world. The Jémez Mountains flank it on the west and the Sangre de Cristo range, with Truchas Peak rising to a height of 13,800 feet, on the east. Deep canyons bar the approaches from north and south. All about are monuments of the great past, Indian, Spanish, Mexican, American. To the north are prehistoric ruins. The cliff dwelling ruins of the Bandelier National Monument are to the south. From Frijoles Canyon westward through the Jémez Mountains is the Valle Grande, the largest extinct volcano ever found, its crater fifteen miles in diameter. Past Cochiti and Santo Domingo Indian pueblos to the southwest is the old ghost town of Bland. To the east across the Rio Grande is the northern end of Jornada del Muerto, the Journey of Death.

As one progresses from Santa Fe to Española one somehow crosses the line from today to yesterday. Somewhere between Española and Los Alamos one floats across the gap between yesterday and tomorrow. One suddenly finds oneself transported into the twenty-first century.

By the summer of 1945 the vast majority of the scientists had lived with their families at Los Alamos for about two and a half years. As far as the world knew, they had vanished completely, lost without a trace. Arriving at the place and finding them all there gave one the sensation of discovering a lost world. The mountains and the canyons and the mesas provided the perfect setting for such a world.

One would descend a steep canyon and find a large structure half buried in the ground. Inside the building were men working with the most explosive material on earth.

I shall never forget my visit to the building where the Harvard cyclotron was installed. There in front of the apparatus was a huge pile of little cubes. I casually picked one up.

"What's this?" I asked Professor Robert R. Wilson, who was in charge of the work.

"U 235," he answered.

I looked at the pile. There was enough there to wipe out a city, but the fact that it was cut up into little cubes, separated here and there by neutron absorbers, kept the mass from becoming critical.

In their cubicles the *élite* among the scientists worked for hours with colored chalk on a blackboard or with pencil on pads of paper. At frequent intervals one heard the boom of mighty explosions on the distant canyons. These were in the true sense explosions of ideas in the minds of men. The mathematical symbols on the blackboards and pads of paper were exploding in the canyons below. Thousands of such ideas exploded simultaneously over Alamogordo, and over Japan.

The test at Alamogordo climaxed a series of other tests the world has not yet heard about, which in their way were equally spectacular and considerably more daring. As soon as sufficient quantities of the active material to form what the calculations had indicated would constitute a critical mass became available, tests were begun to check the accuracy of these calculations. In one of these a strange contraption known as the "guillotine" was rigged up. It consisted of a large wooden frame divided by two parallel vertical steel rods. To each of these rods was attached a large block of the active material. On top between the rods was suspended a smaller block of the substance.

The three blocks together formed a critical mass. At a given signal the "executioner" allowed the smaller block to drop through the space between the two larger ones, the three blocks coming together, thus forming a critical mass for a fraction of a second. The guillotine was hooked up to a series of neutron counters that registered the neutron flux at the time of criticality.

In another series of experiments a pile containing uranium and a moderator was built. The moderator, of course, made it a slow-neutron chain-reacting pile. Then bit by bit the moderator was removed, thus gradually changing the slow-neutron reaction to a reaction with fast neutrons, approaching more and more closely the conditions prevailing in the bomb.

This model of the atomic bomb was located in one of the semi-underground structures in one of the canyons. The scientists devised a series of extremely sensitive automatic controls that were to stop the reaction if it showed any sign of getting too close to critical. Outside, in the moonlit canyon, six cars with their engines running, their drivers tense at the wheel, were ready for a quick getaway. In charge of these tests was Dr. O. R. Frisch, the same Otto Frisch who, with Dr. Lise Meitner, was the first to grasp the full significance of uranium fission.

The controls worked. Dr. Frisch and his small band returned to their homes on the mesa at dawn. They were ready for Alamogordo.

The great cloud of fire that rose more than eight miles to the stratosphere over the New Mexico desert symbolized a funeral pyre for the Japanese Empire. The select few who witnessed the explosion knew at the instant of the explosion that the new weapon would prove decisive in a relatively short time. No power on earth could stand up against the elemental force liberated in those bombs.

Ten minutes after the explosion the following dialogue took place between General Farrell and General Groves:

General Farrell: "The war is over!"

General Groves: "Yes, it is over as soon as we drop one or two on Japan!"

A providential warning that came a few days before the test led to hasty last-minute changes designed to prevent a possible catastrophe that had not been foreseen. A bomb containing ordinary explosives, but otherwise an exact duplicate of the atomic weapon, had been set up on the tower as a practice model. A thunderstorm came along

and touched it off. This led to protective measures against the possibility that a bolt of lightning might set off the first atomic explosion
on earth, possibly at a time when the scientists were still in its vicinity.

The northwestern section of the 2,000-square-mile Alamogordo
Air Base was chosen as the test site because of its remoteness, its
isolation, its inaccessibility and its desirable meteorological charac-
teristics.

Everything relating to the bomb test—the spot where it stood on
its tower, the time scheduled for its detonation, as well as the bomb
itself—was referred to as Zero, the code name for the experiment.
For everyone concerned, Zero became the center of the universe.
Time and space began and ended at Zero. All life centered on Zero.
Everyone thought only of Zero and the zero hour, or rather the zero
microsecond.

The transfer of the bomb over a distance of more than 200 miles
from Los Alamos to Zero presented a major problem, involving
both security and safety. Several units of the complicated assembly
left Los Alamos on Thursday morning, July 12, 1945, in a convoy
accompanied by armed guards and several scientists, and arrived at
Zero that same afternoon. Another convoy left Los Alamos at 12:01
Friday morning, July 13, arriving at Zero nine hours later. Professors Bacher and Kistiakowsky were in charge of the assembly of the
principal units.

Tests by the score were carried out to make certain that every
part functioned properly. A week earlier a group of leading radiol-
ogists under the direction of Colonel Warren had begun setting up
a network of radiological stations at various distances to measure
the radiation effects of the explosion.

Final assembly of the bomb began on the night of July 12, in an
old ranch house. Special teams took over their different roles in the
assembly process. As various component assemblies arrived from
distant points, tension rose among the scientists. They knew failure
was an ever present possibility. They also knew that one false move
would blast them and their entire effort into eternity. And a few
were also haunted by the specter of too great a success.

Dr. Bacher was the man charged with the assembly of the vital
core. A bad few minutes developed when an important section became tightly wedged and would go no farther. Dr. Bacher, how-

ever, was undismayed, and he reassured the group that time would solve the problem. After three minutes, which seemed an eternity, the entire unit, which had been machine-tooled to the finest measurement, gradually slid down to its place and the basic assembly was completed without further incident.

On Saturday, July 14, the unit was elevated to the top of the steel tower. All that day and the next the job of preparation went on, amid lightning flashes and peals of thunder. In addition to the apparatus necessary to cause the detonation, complete instrumentation to determine the "pulse beat" and all the reactions of the bomb was rigged on the tower.

The last men to inspect the tower with its cosmic bomb were Dr. Bainbridge, Dr. Kistiakowsky and Lieutenant Howard C. Bush, of Brooklyn, New York, who was in charge of the military-police detachment. These three stood watch on top of the tower from one o'clock until half an hour before zero, their silhouettes outlined at intervals by a flash of lightning. If they thought of the dummy bomb that had been touched off by lightning on the same tower a few days before, they showed no sign of it. As we left them, they looked very lonely up there, so small, yet so big, men against the gods.

Before the explosion there had been anxiety on the part of some of those present lest an uncontrollable chain reaction might be started in the atmosphere, though this was contrary to all the known facts about the energies latent in the active substance. One of the younger scientists was so unnerved that he was removed from the scene on the advice of the doctors present.

Darkening heavens poured forth rain and lightning right up to the zero hour. The weather blocked out aerial observation of the test. Many of Dr. Oppenheimer's assistants were disturbed by the conditions, and some even urged that the test, scheduled for four o'clock, be called off altogether for that night. General Groves and Dr. Oppenheimer kept going out of the control house into the darkness to look at the sky, constantly assuring each other that the one or two visible stars were becoming brighter.

"I attempted to shield him," General Groves said, "from the evident concern shown by many of his assistants, who were disturbed by the uncertain weather conditions. By three-thirty we decided that we could probably fire at five-thirty. By four the rain had stopped, but the sky was heavily overcast. Our decision became firmer as time went on."

As the zero hour for the explosion approached, tension in the control room, about six miles from the test spot, reached a tremendous pitch. The several observation points in the area were linked to the control room by radio, and, with twenty minutes to go, Dr. Allison, the assistant director of Los Alamos, took over the radio set and made periodic time announcements. The time signals, "Minus twenty minutes, minus fifteen minutes," and so on, increased the tension to the breaking point. The last few seconds were described by General Farrell as much worse than any he had experienced during zero hour in the front-line trenches in World War I. Dr. Conant said he had never imagined seconds could be so long.

In a report to the War Department General Farrell gave his impressions of those last long seconds before zero, and the eternal moments that followed:

As the time interval grew smaller and changed from minutes to seconds, the tension increased by leaps and bounds. Everyone in that room knew the awful potentialities of the thing that they thought was about to happen. The scientists felt that their figuring must be right and that the bomb had to go off, but there was in everyone's mind a strong measure of doubt. The feeling of many could be expressed by "Lord, I believe: help Thou mine unbelief."

We were reaching into the unknown and we did not know what might come of it. It can safely be said that most of those present were praying and praying harder than they had ever prayed before. If the shot were successful, it was a justification of the several years of intensive effort of tens of thousands of people—statesmen, scientists, engineers, manufacturers, soldiers, and many others in every walk of life.

In that brief instant in the remote New Mexico desert, the tremendous effort of the brains and brawn of all these people came suddenly and startlingly to the fullest fruition. Dr. Oppenheimer, upon whom had rested a very heavy burden, grew tenser as the last seconds ticked off. He scarcely breathed. He held on to a post to steady himself. For the last few seconds he stared directly ahead, and then when the announcer shouted "Now!" and there came this tremendous burst of light followed shortly thereafter by the deep growling roar of the explosion, his face relaxed into an expression of tremendous relief. Several of the observers standing back of the shelter to watch the lightning effects were knocked flat by the blast.

The tension in the room let up and all started congratulating each other. . . . No matter what might happen now all knew that the impossible scientific job had been done. Atomic fission would no longer be hidden in the cloisters of the theoretical physicists' dreams. It was almost full grown at birth. It was a great new force to be used for good or for evil. . . .

Dr. Conant reached over and shook hands with General Groves. Dr. Bush, who was on the other side of the General, did likewise. Dr. Kistiakowsky threw his arms around Dr. Oppenheimer and embraced him with shouts of glee. Others were equally enthusiastic. All the pent-up emotions were released in those few minutes and all seemed to sense immediately that the explosion had far exceeded the most optimistic expectations and wildest hopes of the scientists. . . .

As to the present war, there was a feeling that no matter what else might happen, we now had the means to ensure its speedy conclusion and save thousands of American lives. As to the future, there had been brought into being something big and something new that would prove to be immeasurably more important than the discovery of electricity or any of the other great discoveries which have so affected our existence.

The town nearest to the spot where the bomb was tested was Carrizozo, about thirty miles to the east; 1,500 people lived there. If the wind at the time of the test were to change in any easterly direction, there would have been a real danger that the radioactive cloud might blanket the sleeping town and expose its unsuspecting inhabitants to deadly fallout.

To prepare for this emergency, several hundred Army trucks, each manned with carefully briefed personnel, surrounded Carrizozo during the night and waited silently. If the wind showed signs of blowing in that direction, the men in the trucks were to go into action at a radio signal. Each group had been assigned a block of houses in advance, and their orders were to enter them, awaken the inhabitants and carry them to safety—by force if necessary—without giving them time to dress and without taking time to explain.

While the citizens of Carrizozo were no doubt aroused from their slumbers by the blast, they do not know to the present day what greater surprise was in store for them had there been a change in the wind. The only casualties, outside of rattlesnakes and the small animals of the desert, were found among a herd of red cows grazing several miles away, which developed gray spots from radioactive dust.

These radioactive cows and their progeny were carefully studied for the genetic and other effects of radiation. They became the nearest equivalent to "sacred cows" in the United States.

All the military personnel stationed around the test site had been warned in advance to leave their barracks at the appointed time and lie down in the deep trenches that had been especially dug for the occasion. They were told that a powerful new explosive was about to be tested—without, of course, being told of the nature of the experiment.

In the midst of all the activities over the weekend, no one remembered a soldier from Tennessee who had been given a three-day pass that expired, of all times, at five o'clock that Monday morning, just a half hour before the test. As he returned, after celebrating his three days of liberty in wine, women and song, he failed to notice the strange emptiness of the barracks and piled into bed in a drunken stupor. The next thing he knew, he was lifted out of his bunk with the violence of an earthquake. He opened his eyes and was immediately blinded by a light that was not of this world.

When he was discovered about an hour later, his astonished buddies found a raving madman, speaking incoherently about the "wrath of the Lord," and the "Day of Judgment," and about the sin of getting drunk on the Sabbath. Medical examination diagnosed the case as hysteria brought about by shock. It was also found that he had been totally blinded by the light of many suns concentrated in the flash.

Luckily the soldier's mind and vision returned to normal after a few weeks of careful medical and psychiatric nursing in the hospital. When he returned to duty he announced that he had taken the pledge never to drink again—a rather drastic cure for alcoholism.

The atomic bomb was the product of the greatest concentration of brain power on any single device in history. Millions of man-hours were spent to develop a "gadget" that would yield its energy in a millionth of a second. Yet none of the scientists could be certain that it would work.

I remember only too well the spirit of uncertainty that pervaded the atmosphere of Los Alamos up to the very last minute of the test. Here was a "two-billion-dollar baby" brought to term, but none of the obstetricians present could be sure that it would not be still-born.

Everyone in Los Alamos was haunted by the nightmare of a possible "fizzle," a term which meant anything from a complete dud to a test that yielded the equivalent of only a score or more of ordinary blockbusters.

Confidence among the scientists was subject to violent fluctuations. One day when confidence in the successful outcome of the scheduled test shot was very low someone composed the following quatrain which became known as the "Los Alamos Blues":

From this crude lab that spawned the dud
Their necks to Truman's axe uncurled
Lo the embattled savants stood
And fired the flop heard round the world.

To relieve the tension, which grew greater as the time of the test drew nearer, a pool was organized, in which, after paying one dollar, we recorded a guess on the ultimate power of the explosion in terms of TNT.

While the atomic bomb was designed to yield an explosive force equal to twenty thousand tons of TNT, no one there dared predict that amount. Dr. Oppenheimer's guess was a mere three hundred tons. The winner, Nobel Prize physicist Dr. I. I. Rabi of Columbia University, who arrived on the scene late, when all the low numbers had already been taken up, took what everyone, including himself, regarded as a wild gamble, with a guess of eighteen thousand tons. He was still two thousand tons—two hundred wartime blockbusters —below the actual figure.

When the test succeeded beyond all expectations, Fermi returned triumphantly to his home in Los Alamos in his battered jalopy, happily bouncing along the perilous road on the edge of precipitous canyons on a tire that had been inflated with precious argon gas. It was the only spare tire he had to replace a blowout.

There were a number of hard-boiled practical engineers on the project who looked upon university scientists as longhairs and regarded many of their ideas as coming close to being crackpot. This led to a certain amount of friction until the matter was brought to the attention of General Groves, himself a very able engineer, who at once called a meeting of all the top engineers on the project and delivered a short, characteristic speech.

"Listen," he said, "it has taken a lot of trouble to bring all these screwballs together and to get them to work for us. Now you work with them!"

Under the watchful eye of General Groves things went on more or less smoothly from then on, yet beneath the surface the age-old disdain of the "practical man" for the "dreamer" and vice versa kept smoldering, and each side was quietly preparing its lists of alibis in advance for placing the blame on the other in case of failure. All this, however, vanished in that great cloud of atomic dust that rose more than forty thousand feet above the New Mexico desert.

On that occasion, one of the engineers, who watched the test from a deep trench about ten miles away, paid the scientists the highest compliment ever paid by a "practical man" to a "dreamer." As soon as he regained his power of speech, after watching the tremendous ball of fire and the unearthly mushroom-topped mountain of many colors that kept rising and expanding, and hearing the mighty thunder that kept reverberating from the mountains all around him, he was overheard to exclaim, "Jesus Christ, the longhairs have let it get away from them!"

The vision of the apocalyptic cloud I had seen at Alamogordo had left me in a state of shock which seemed to grow worse with time. I could not get the vision in the desert out of my mind. And on top of it all I was greatly worried about the job ahead.

There were several things I worried about, in the following order:

Would I be able to write a story worthy of the occasion?

Would I survive to write the story?

Even if I got there and did a creditable job, would my story ever see the light of day?

As a newspaperman honored above all others to report the greatest news story of all time, these professional worries naturally came first. But I also had other, more personal worries. I had been forbidden to tell anyone, even my wife, where I was going. I was also told that there would be a blackout period of several weeks, during which I would not be permitted even to write to her.

To allay any fears she may have that I was involved in some dangerous war mission, I was ordered to tell her that I was going on a top-secret mission to London, that she should not expect to hear from me for some time, but that she would be kept informed about me from Washington.

To make the story about my going to London authentic, some clever individual in Washington arranged with *The New York Times* to have my byline appear over some story datelined from London. I didn't know about this until I returned home and Florence showed me the clipping, which she still carries around with her.

I don't know to the present day how that was arranged, but someone in the Manhattan District in Washington no doubt had asked Mr. James for this bit of co-operation to bolster up Florence's peace of mind. It was a thoughtful act on the part of someone, and I shall always be grateful for this touch of human kindness.

CHAPTER SEVENTEEN

To Use or Not to Use?

On MARCH 15, 1945, the late Henry L. Stimson had luncheon at the White House with President Roosevelt. Mr. Stimson was then Secretary of War and also the Cabinet member directly responsible to the President for the administration of the two-billion-dollar Manhattan Project. At the same time he was President Roosevelt's senior adviser on the military employment of atomic energy. He had come at the President's invitation to talk over several important matters about the project, which was then approaching its climax.

First he took up with Mr. Roosevelt a "rather jittery and nervous memorandum" from an unidentified "distinguished public servant" sent him by the President. The author of the memorandum expressed his alarm at the rumors of extravagance in the Manhattan Project, suggested that "it might become disastrous" and urged that a body of outside scientists be called in to pass upon the project "because rumors are going around that Vannevar Bush and Jim Conant have sold the President a lemon."

Similar views were expressed later to President Truman by Admiral William D. Leahy. After Vannevar Bush had explained to the President how the bomb worked, Leahy told Mr. Truman, "This is the biggest fool thing we have ever done. This bomb will never go off, and I speak as an expert on explosives."

Mr. Stimson assured President Roosevelt that the rumors were wholly unfounded and, indeed, "rather silly." He gave him a list of the scientists engaged on the project, which included four Nobel Prize winners in physics and practically every physicist of standing. Only those not fully informed, he told him, held such views.

Next he outlined to the President the future of the project. He told him with uncanny accuracy that the bomb was expected to be ready in four months, and it was exactly four months to the day, on July 15, that the bomb stood ready for testing on its steel tower in the New Mexico desert. On many earlier occasions President Roosevelt had spoken to Mr. Stimson "of his awareness of the catastrophic potentialities of our work" and of the "terrible responsibility involved in our attempt to unlock the doors to such a devastating weapon." Now that "the doors were about to be unlocked" at last, Mr. Stimson pointed out to the President "how important it was to get ready."

He then informed the President about the existence of two schools of thought in respect to the future control of atomic energy and of the atomic bomb after the war, in case it was successful. One school held that it should remain a secret, with control to be left in the hands of those "who control it now," namely, the United States, Britain and Canada. The other school urged international control "based upon freedom of both science and of access." Those things, Mr. Stimson told the President, "must be settled before the first projectile is used." Furthermore, he added, he [the President] "must be ready with a statement to the people to come out just as soon as that is done." The President agreed.

The question of the use of the bomb was not even mentioned during that conversation. Nor had it been discussed on earlier occasions. In a historic article in *Harper's Magazine* for February 1947, Mr. Stimson wrote:

At no time, from 1941 to 1945, did I ever hear it suggested by the President, or by any other responsible member of the government, that atomic energy should not be used in the war. . . . It was our common objective, throughout the war, to be the first to produce an atomic weapon and use it. The possible atomic weapon was considered to be a new and tremendously powerful explosive, as legitimate as any other of the deadly explosive weapons of modern war. The entire purpose was the production of a military weapon; on no other ground could the wartime expenditure of so much time and money have been justified. . . .

The policy adopted and steadily pursued by President Roosevelt and his advisers was a simple one. It was to spare no effort in securing the earliest possible successful development of an atomic weapon. The reasons for this policy were equally simple. . . . In 1941 and 1942 they [the Germans] were believed to be ahead of us, and it was vital that they should not be the first to bring atomic weapons into the field of battle. Furthermore, if we should be the first to develop the weapon, we should have a great new instrument for shortening the war and minimizing destruction.

Secretary Stimson never saw Franklin Roosevelt again. The next time he went to the White House to discuss atomic energy was April 25, 1945, to initiate President Truman into the mysteries of the atomic-bomb project. Truman had actually learned first about the bomb unofficially from James F. Byrnes, who at that time held no official position, but it was Stimson who first told the new President the entire fantastic story of the Manhattan Project, which had been kept a secret from Truman, and from nearly all other members of Congress, while he was Senator.

As was the case with Stimson's last meeting with Roosevelt, his first meeting with Truman dealt largely with the political and diplomatic consequences that would follow the use of the bomb. It did not deal with the questions of how, when and where it would be used, or whether it would be used at all. The exact circumstances in which the bomb might be used were unknown at the time. It was not even known that the bomb would work at all, all concerned being haunted by the nightmare that when the time for testing came, sometime in the middle of July 1945, it would turn out to have been a two-billion-dollar failure. The only thing that was known for certain was that the bomb would not be ready in time to be used against Germany.

Stimson's first talk with Truman on that day in April hinged on the assumption that the bomb would be successful, in which case it would create enormous problems of postwar national policy. For it was already recognized at that early date that, unless effective methods of international control could be devised, the unleashing of the greatest destructive force in history would threaten the very existence of civilization.

Meantime, while waiting for the completion and testing of the bomb, and assuming that it would be successful, Stimson recommended, and the President approved, the appointment of a special advisory committee of civilians and scientists to advise, among other things, on whether or not the bomb should be used, and, if so, how, when and where.

Stimson's talk that day with Mr. Truman, who had succeeded to the Presidency less than two weeks before, is outlined in the following memorandum, which must rank as one of the great historic documents of our time:

1. Within four months we shall in all probability have completed the most terrible weapon ever known in human history, one bomb of which could destroy a whole city.

2. Although we have shared its development with the United Kingdom, physically the United States is at present in the position of controlling the resources with which to construct and use it and no other nation could reach this position for some years.

3. Nevertheless it is practically certain that we could not remain in this position indefinitely.

> a) Various segments of its discovery and production are widely known among many scientists in many countries, although few scientists are now acquainted with the whole process which we have developed.

> b) Although its construction under present methods requires great scientific and industrial effort and raw materials, which are temporarily mainly within the possession and knowledge of U.S. and U.K., it is extremely probable that much easier and cheaper methods of production will be discovered by scientists in the future, together with the use of materials of much wider distribution. As a result, it is extremely probable that the future will make it possible for atomic bombs to be constructed by smaller nations or even groups, or at least by a larger nation in a much shorter time.

4. As a result, it is indicated that the future may see a time when such a weapon may be constructed in secret and used suddenly and effectively with devastating power by a willful nation or group against

an unsuspecting nation or group of much greater size and material power. With its aid even a very powerful unsuspecting nation might be conquered within a very few days by a very much smaller one. . . .

5. The world in its present state of moral advancement compared with its technical development would be eventually at the mercy of such a weapon. In other words, modern civilization might be completely destroyed.

6. To approach any world peace organization of any pattern now likely to be considered, without an appreciation by the leaders of our country of the power of this new weapon, would seem to be unrealistic. No system of control heretofore considered would be adequate to control this menace. Both inside any particular country and between the nations of the world, the control of this weapon will undoubtedly be a matter of the greatest difficulty and would involve such thoroughgoing rights of inspection and internal controls as we have never heretofore contemplated.

7. Furthermore, in the light of our present position with reference to this weapon, the question of sharing it with other nations and, if so shared, upon what terms, becomes a primary question of our foreign relations. Also our leadership in the war and in the development of this weapon has placed a certain moral responsibility upon us which we cannot shirk without very serious responsibility for any disaster to civilization which it would further.

8. On the other hand, if the problem of the proper use of this weapon can be solved, we would have the opportunity to bring the world into a pattern in which the peace of the world and our civilization can be saved.

9. As stated in General Groves's report, steps are under way looking toward the establishment of a select committee of particular qualifications for recommending action to the executive and legislative branches of our government when secrecy is no longer in full effect. The committee would also recommend the actions to be taken by the War Department prior to that time in anticipation of the postwar problems. All recommendations would of course be first submitted to the President.

The next step was the appointment by the President of the "select committee." This committee, which became known as the Interim Committee, was charged with advising the President on the various questions raised, in Mr. Stimson's words, "by our apparently imminent success in developing an atomic weapon." Mr. Stimson himself was chairman of the committee, but the principal labor of guiding its deliberations fell to George L. Harrison, president of the New York Life Insurance Company and special consultant in Secretary Stimson's office, who acted as chairman in Mr. Stimson's absence.

The other members were:

James F. Byrnes, then a private citizen, who served as President Truman's personal representative.

Ralph A. Bard, Under Secretary of the Navy.

William L. Clayton, Assistant Secretary of State.

Vannevar Bush, director, Office of Scientific Research and Development (O.S.R.D.), and president of the Carnegie Institution of Washington.

Karl T. Compton, chief of the Office of Field Service in the O.S.R.D., and president of the Massachusetts Institute of Technology.

James Bryant Conant, chairman of the National Defense Research Committee (N.D.R.C.) and president of Harvard University.

To assist the Interim Committee, Mr. Stimson selected a scientific panel of four nuclear physicists of the first rank, all of whom had played a major role in the atomic project since its inception. The panel included Drs. Arthur H. Compton, Enrico Fermi and Ernest O. Lawrence, all Nobel Prize winners in physics, and J. Robert Oppenheimer, scientific director of the Los Alamos Scientific Laboratory, where the atomic bomb was nearing completion.

The climactic meeting of the committee concerning the bomb's use was held in Secretary Stimson's office on May 31, 1945. In addition to the committee members and the scientific panel, those present were General George C. Marshall, Chief of Staff of the United States Army, and General Leslie R. Groves, military commander in chief of the Manhattan Project, both of whom served as military advisers.

As Dr. Compton recollects it in his personal narrative, *Atomic Quest* (Oxford University Press), Mr. Stimson opened that historic meeting with the following preamble:

"Gentlemen, it is our responsibility to recommend action that may turn the course of civilization. In our hands we expect soon to have a weapon of wholly unprecedented destructive power. Today's prime fact is war. Our great task is to bring this war to a prompt and successful conclusion. We may assume that our new weapon puts in our hands overwhelming power. It is our obligation to use this power with the best wisdom we can command. To us now the matter of first importance is how our use of this new weapon will appear in the long view of history."

"Both General Marshall and I at this meeting," Mr. Stimson reports, "expressed the view that atomic energy could not be considered simply in terms of military weapons but must also be considered in terms of a new relationship of man to the universe."

In its deliberations on the question of the bomb's military use, the Interim Committee also carefully considered several alternative methods of using it, other than its being dropped without prior warning over a military target. One alternative was a detailed warning in advance. The other was a demonstration of the bomb in some uninhabited area. These suggestions were rejected as both impractical and involving serious risks.

The reasons were obvious. At that time the first test bomb was still four months away and no one could tell whether the test would be successful. Even assuming the first bomb tested were to be a success, that would by no means be a guarantee that the second one might not be a complete dud. Furthermore, even a successful, carefully controlled stationary test in New Mexico would not give final proof that the bomb was certain to explode when dropped from an airplane.

Moreover, one of the principal advantages of the bomb was the element of surprise. Since the one and only reason for its use was to bring the war to an end as quickly as possible and to save as many lives as possible, both American and Japanese, the element of surprise was expected to play a highly important role in providing the Emperor and his military advisers with a face-saving excuse for accepting surrender on honorable terms.

In the words of Secretary Stimson, "I felt that to extract a genuine surrender from the Emperor and his military advisers, they must be administered a tremendous shock which would carry convincing proof of our power to destroy the Empire. Such an effective shock would save many times the number of lives, both American and Japanese, that it would cost."

On June 1, 1945, after carefully weighing all the alternatives, and following discussions with the Scientific Panel, the interim committee unanimously adopted the following recommendations:

1. The bomb should be used against Japan as soon as possible.

2. It should be used on a dual target—that is, a military installation or a war plant surrounded by, or adjacent to, houses or other buildings most susceptible to damage.

3. It should be used without prior warning [of the nature of the weapon]. Mr. Bard later changed his view and dissented from the third recommendation.

The Interim Committee also considered various suggestions from other scientists working on the project, particularly a report from the atomic laboratory at the University of Chicago, which seriously questioned the use of the bomb against the enemy. The scientific panel, after careful discussion, commented, in part, as follows:

The opinions of our scientific colleagues on the initial use of these weapons are not unanimous: they range from the proposal of a purely technical demonstration to that of the military application best designed to induce surrender. Those who advocate a purely technical demonstration would wish to outlaw the use of atomic weapons, and have feared that if we use the weapons now our position in future negotiations will be prejudiced. Others emphasize the opportunity of saving American lives by immediate military use, and believe that such use will improve the international prospects, in that they are more concerned with the prevention of war than with the elimination of this special weapon. We find ourselves closer to these latter views; *we can propose no technical demonstration likely to bring an end to the war; we see no acceptable alternative to direct military use.* [Italics by the author.]

With regard to these general aspects of atomic energy, it is clear that we, as scientific men, have no proprietary rights. It is true that we are among the few citizens who have had occasion to give thoughtful consideration to these problems during the past few years. We have, however, no claim to special competence in solving the political, social and military problems which are presented by the advent of atomic power.

In addition to advising about the use of the bomb, the Interim Committee also agreed upon a statement that the President was to make immediately after the bomb's first use. That statement had been prepared by me on May 16. It was "a tentative draft of a radio address by President Truman to be delivered at the time of use of the atomic bomb over Japan." It announced to the world that we had "released upon Japan the most destructive weapon in history, a bomb so powerful that one of them has the equivalent effect of 20,000 tons of TNT. . . . It is an atomic bomb. Its explosive force comes from the vast energy inside the atom, an energy millions of times greater than any form of energy known on earth. . . . It will shorten the war by months, and possibly even years. It will save many precious American lives . . ."

President Truman was aboard the cruiser *Augusta* on his way home from the Potsdam Conference when Hiroshima was bombed. My tentative draft formed the basis of two previously prepared releases given out in Washington that same day, August 6, one from the White House on behalf of President Truman, the other from the War Department in the name of Secretary Stimson.

The Interim Committee played a vital role in the decision to use the bomb, but its recommendations were only advisory. The final decision was to be made by President Truman and two months were to pass before the great decision was made. It was not made until the last minute, after much discussion with his military leaders and with British Prime Minister Winston Churchill, all of whom were decidedly in favor of the bomb's use.

But the final decision was in fact made by Japan, when Premier Suzuki declared to the press on July 28 that Japan would ignore the Potsdam Declaration of July 26 offering her the choice between surrender and hope for an honorable future, on the one hand, and "inevitable and complete destruction," on the other. It was actually this statement to the press, addressed only to the Japanese people, but interpreted by the Allies as a rejection of the Potsdam Declaration, that finally persuaded Truman and Churchill that the use of the bomb was the only course left open to them for bringing the war to the speedy end.

A theory has been built up that we really used the bomb when we did for political, not for military, reasons, being in a hurry to bring the war with Japan to an end before the Soviet Union had a chance to enter it. Those who champion this view, particularly Professor P. M. S. Blackett, British Nobel Prize-winning physicist, point to the fact that the invasion of Japan, estimated to cost the lives of a million Americans and two million Japanese, which the use of the bomb was intended to save, was not scheduled until November 1, 1945. That being the case, Professor Blackett argues, why could we not have waited until Nov. 1 before using the bomb? In the meantime we could have used intensive air bombardment and a naval blockade, and if these did not bring surrender we could then have used the bomb before resorting to invasion.

This reasoning is superficially plausible, but it completely ignores the facts of the case.

We have it on the authority of W. Averell Harriman, then special assistant to the President, in testimony before the Committee on Armed Services and the Committee on Foreign Relations, United States Senate, that "at Potsdam, more than five months after Yalta, the Joint Chiefs of Staff were still planning an invasion of the Japanese home islands and still considered Soviet participation in the Pacific war essential." President Truman himself, in telling the story of Potsdam to Dr. Arthur H. Compton, "laid special emphasis on the fact that the Americans wanted Russia's help now." Dr. Compton relates:

Almost every time he [Truman] saw Stalin [at Potsdam] he asked him how soon he could begin the attack by the Russian armies in Manchuria. If, as now seemed possible, the Russian attack could come together with devastating demonstrations of these powerful new bombs, even the determined Japanese warlords might be brought to their senses. The date of August 8, Stalin explained, was the soonest that it would be possible for their forces to be ready on the Manchurian front.

This was the carefully considered American strategy as Mr. Truman has explained it to me.

The fact is that we could by no means be certain that the atomic bombs alone, even if successful, would be sufficient to bring the war to a speedy end. As Dr. Compton points out: "Even with both the atomic bombing and the Russian declaration of war it was nearly impossible for the Japanese government to achieve surrender."

Moreover, even if the atomic bombing had brought about Japan's surrender before the Soviet Union's official declaration of war, there was no way we could have stopped them from invading Manchuria. As Harriman told Admiral Leahy, "Russia would come into the war regardless of what we might do."

Even so, one may ask, why could we not have waited until November 1 in hopes that Japan might surrender before the date set for the invasion? One answer is, as Secretary Stimson pointed out, that conventional bombardment during the three months of August to November would have caused greater destruction than the bomb. And another answer is that during that period we would have run the risk of sacrificing some thousands of American lives.

As Secretary Stimson put it:

My chief purpose was to end the war in victory with the least possible cost in the lives of the men in the armies which I had helped to raise. In the light of the alternatives which, on a fair estimate, were open to us I believe that no man, in our position and subject to our responsibilities, holding in his hands a weapon of such possibilities of accomplishing this purpose and saving those lives, could have failed to use it and afterward looked his countrymen in the face.

There were even those who asserted that a desire to justify the expenditure of two billion dollars on the Manhattan Project played a part in the decision to use the bomb. But that was too much even for Professor Blackett. "The wit of man," he declared in his *Fear, War, and the Bomb* (Whittlesey House), "could hardly devise a theory of the dropping of the bomb, both more insulting to the American people, or more likely to lead to an energetically pursued Soviet Defense policy."

When detailed plans of the atomic mission against Japan were brought to Secretary Stimson for approval, he struck off the list of suggested targets, "with President Truman's warm support," the city of Kyoto. "Although it was a target of considerable military importance," he wrote in *Harper's*, "it had been the ancient capital of Japan and was a shrine of Japanese art and culture. We determined that it should be spared." He approved four other targets— Hiroshima, Kokura, Nagasaki and Niigata.

Truman first told Stalin about the atomic bomb on July 24 during the Potsdam Conference, which had opened the day after the test in New Mexico, about which Truman had been informed at once. On the advice of his chief advisers, he told Stalin "casually" that the Americans had "a new weapon of unusual destructive force." Stalin, Truman recalled, "showed no special interest. All he said was that he was glad to hear it and hoped that we would make 'good use of it against the Japanese.'" As we learned about five years later, Stalin had known all about it even before Truman did.

It was on the same day that Truman sent orders to the War Department to instruct General Carl ("Tooey") Spaatz, Commanding General of the United States Army Strategic Air Forces in the Pacific, to drop the bomb on Japan as soon after August 3 as weather permitted. This order, however, was subject to change, pending Japanese last-minute acceptance of the Potsdam Declaration of July 26. Truman waited until August 2 or 3 before he gave his final authorization. He was then on his way to Washington on the *Augusta*.

The decision to use the atomic bomb [Secretary Stimson wrote] was a decision that brought death to over a hundred thousand Japanese. No explanation can change that fact and I do not wish to gloss it over. But this deliberate, premeditated destruction was our least abhorrent choice. The destruction of Hiroshima and Nagasaki put an end to the Japanese war. It stopped the fire raids, and the strangling blockade; it ended the ghastly specter of the clash of great land armies.

In this last great action of the Second World War we were given final proof that war is death. War in the twentieth century has grown steadily more barbarous, more destructive, more debased in all its aspects. Now, with the release of atomic energy, man's ability to destroy himself is very nearly complete. The bombs dropped on Hiroshima and Nagasaki ended a war. They also made it wholly clear that we must never have another war. This is the lesson men and leaders everywhere must learn, and I believe that when they learn it they will find a way to lasting peace. There is no other choice.

CHAPTER EIGHTEEN

Death of a City

I ARRIVED in Tinian three days behind schedule. I had been first delayed at Hamilton Field, near San Francisco, waiting for transportation, and then had lost another precious day when the C-54 taking me to Hickam Field, Hawaii, on the first leg of my journey, was forced to turn back after flying half the distance. I was traveling under sealed orders and did not know until I arrived in Guam the morning of Sunday, August 5, what my final destination was.

At two-thirty that afternoon the first atomic bomb destined for use over a living city was taken from its air-conditioned assembly house for loading into the B-29 that was to take it to its destination. The funerallike cortege was led by a command car loaded with M.P.s and was followed by a truck carrying the bomb, now covered by a tarpaulin, which made it look like a giant corpse. This was followed by a Navy staff car, carrying General Farrell and Rear Admiral William Parnell, Navy liaison officer, and a jeep with Captain James Nolan, radiological expert, and Group Captain G. Leonard Cheshire, a famous Royal Air Force pilot, then a member of the British military mission to the United States.

On my arrival I learned from General Farrell, who was in command, that I had arrived too late to join the mission. I was in despair. I had missed the Big Chance. General Farrell told me I would go along on the next mission, at that time scheduled for Saturday, August 11, but that appeared aeons away.

By late afternoon the bomb was hanging in the bomb bay of the specially remodeled B-29 the *Enola Gay,* named by Colonel Paul W. Tibbets, Jr., its commanding officer, after his mother. It carried many inscriptions, ribald and otherwise.

That evening I attended the briefing in the barnlike assembly hall. The room was tense and one could hear the silence as Colonel Tibbets took the platform.

"This is the night we have all been waiting for," he told the men of the 509th Composite Group of the Twentieth Air Force. "Our long months of training are to be put to the test. We will soon know if we have been successful or failed. Upon our efforts tonight it is possible that history will be made. We are going on a mission to drop a bomb different from any you have ever seen or heard about. This bomb contains a destructive force equivalent to twenty thousand tons of TNT. Because this bomb is so powerful we must use different tactics from those we have employed when using ordinary bombs."

He then explained the tactics. The mission had three alternate targets, depending on the weather. The first target was Hiroshima. The second was the city of Kokura, on the island of Kyushu. The third was Nagasaki, also on Kyushu. Three weather planes were to leave one hour ahead, each one to scout the visibility over one of the three chosen targets, since, for the sake of absolute accuracy, the bomb was to be dropped only visually.

At midnight there was another briefing. The men were told what had happened in the test at Alamogordo. Each member of the three B-29s that were to go on the mission was given a pair of dense arc welder's lenses and cautioned not to look with their naked eyes at the flash following the bomb's explosion. The briefing was concluded with a prayer for the success of the mission by the chaplain, Captain William B. Downey, of the Hope Lutheran Church in Minneapolis.

We silently filed out into the night and proceeded to the mess hall for the traditional preflight supper.

At exactly 2:45 A.M., Marianas time, three B-29s took off from parallel runways. We watched breathless as Colonel Tibbets held the *Enola Gay* to the ground almost to the last few feet of the runway. It then climbed gracefully and disappeared into the northern sky.

We spent agonizing hours of waiting through the night. We

knew that the schedule called for making the drop on Hiroshima at 9:15 A.M., if the weather plane ahead had reported good visibility, and, in that case, we expected a coded message from Colonel Tibbets shortly thereafter.

And then, exactly at 9:30, two words winged across the vast distances of the Pacific: *"Mission successful!"*

Shortly before three that Monday afternoon we saw the *Enola Gay* approaching from the north. It was a thing of beauty to behold between the blue Pacific and the clear blue sky, its great silver body shimmering in the sun. We glanced at our watches to time its landing.

It was exactly three o'clock on the afternoon of Monday, August 6, 1945, Marianas time. The first successful atomic bomb mission had come to an end after a round-trip flight of three thousand miles in an elapsed time of twelve hours and fifteen minutes.

The *Enola Gay* reached the main island of Japan at 8:50 and headed toward its I.P., the initial point of a straight course to the target. It reached this point at 9:11. Major Thomas W. Ferebee, of Mocksville, North Carolina, the bombardier, Captain Theodore J. ("Dutch") Van Kirk, of Northumberland, Pennsylvania, the navigator, and Sergeant Joe A. Stiborik, of Taylor, Texas, the radar operator, here began their final few minutes of co-ordinated teamwork, a job of synchronization fearful and wonderful to contemplate.

The *Enola Gay* had a four-minute run on a perfectly open target. Major Ferebee manipulated the cross hairs in his bomb sight until the target was at the intersection between his course line and his rate line. The great moment had come. He synchronized on Hiroshima and let go.

Those inside the *Enola Gay* first saw a little pinpoint of light, purplish red. In an instant the pinpoint grew into a giant ball of purple fire, half a mile in diameter. The great fireball suddenly exploded into a huge mass of swirling flames and purple clouds. Out of it came gigantic concentric white rings of fog, as though the earth itself were blowing mighty smoke rings.

The mass seemed to hesitate for a brief instant. Suddenly out of the swirling purple clouds came a huge white column of smoke. Up it went, higher, ever higher, until it reached 10,000 feet.

Then came another phase. The 10,000-foot column suddenly grew into a giant mushroom, with tremendous clouds of dust swirling about its base for a distance of three miles. The mushroom kept rising, growing to tremendous heights before the incredulous eyes of those who watched it from the *Enola Gay* and the other B-29s that followed along as instrument and photographic planes. It kept climbing upward until it reached a height of 45,000 to 50,000 feet, breaking into several layers of a creamy white mass with a purplish tinge, distinguishable from the white clouds through which it penetrated.

With the flash came a blast that was heard for hundreds of miles around. It reverberated from the hills east and west of Hiroshima. Both the original blast and the echo hit the *Enola Gay* and made it tremble, though it was several miles away from the scene by the time the blast reached it.

The men in the *Enola Gay* could still see the great column of swirling dust and smoke at a distance of more than four hundred statute miles. "It was solid enough to walk on," one of the crew members said.

Here is how the late Captain (later Rear Admiral) William S. ("Deke") Parsons reported it immediately on his return:

It was a terrific spectacle. The huge dust cloud covered everything. The base of the lower part of the mushroom, a mass of purplish-gray dust about three miles in diameter, was all boiling—the entire area was boiling. A huge white cloud got separated from the top of the mushroom and went upward. Then a second white cloud rose into the air and started chasing the first one. The mushroom top was also boiling, a seething turbulent mass. The mushroom smoke reached our altitude; then another mushroom came up, also very turbulent. There was also another column of smoke off to one side, different in character from the main mass, at a forty-five-degree angle from the ground. It looked as though it was coming from a huge burning fire, and seemed to settle back to earth again. The purple clouds and flames were whirling around. It seemed as though the whole town got pulverized.

Along with preparations to give the Japanese militarists a second taste of atomic bombing, should they fail to heed the lesson of the first, measures were also taken to inform the Japanese people of what was in store for them unless they petitioned their Emperor to end the war. The following is the text of a leaflet dropped by the million over Japan:

To the Japanese People

America asks that you take immediate heed of what we say on this leaflet.

We are in possession of the most destructive explosive ever devised by man. A single one of our newly developed atomic bombs is actually the equivalent in explosive power to what 2,000 of our giant B-29s can carry on a single mission. This awful fact is one for you to ponder and we solemnly assure you it is grimly accurate.

We have just begun to use this weapon against your homeland. If you still have any doubt, make inquiry as to what happened to Hiroshima when just one atomic bomb fell on that city.

Before using this bomb to destroy every resource of the military by which they are prolonging this useless war, we ask that you now petition the Emperor to end the war. Our President has outlined for you the thirteen consequences of an honorable surrender. We urge that you accept these consequences and begin the work of building a new, better, and peace-loving Japan.

You should take steps now to cease military resistance. Otherwise, we shall resolutely employ this bomb and all our other superior weapons to promptly and forcefully end the war.

The major part of the explosive material for the Hiroshima bomb had been delivered by the cruiser *Indianapolis* to Tinian Island in the Marianas at the end of July 1945. A few days later, her precious cargo delivered, the *Indianapolis* was sunk with the loss of nearly all the men aboard while on her way to the Philippines. This gave rise later to the erroneous report that the Japanese had sunk a Navy ship carrying an atomic bomb. As we learned subsequently, the Japanese had no knowledge of the *Indianapolis'* mission, and its sinking was the result of a tragic chance.

The news of the sinking reached Tinian just as the atomic bomb for Hiroshima was being assembled. At take-off the bomb carried in large letters the inscription: "From the boys of the *Indianapolis*."

About a week before the first bomb took off for Japan, General Farrell called on Admiral Chester W. Nimitz at his headquarters in Guam, to acquaint him with the mission and to arrange for Navy co-operation. At the end of the conference, Admiral Nimitz called General Farrell to the window and pointed to an island a few miles away.

"That island over there," said the Navy commander in chief, "is Rota. There are about three thousand Japs on it. They observe our activities and send information about them back home. They are a great nuisance, but they do not warrant an amphibious operation. How about dropping a small atom bomb on Rota?"

"Unfortunately, Admiral," General Farrell replied, "all our atomic bombs are big ones."

Captain Parsons, Navy ordnance expert who served as the "weaponeer" for the bomb, became greatly perturbed one evening, about one day before the scheduled take-off for Hiroshima, when he watched four B-29s in a row crash at the end of the runway and burn. Suppose that happened to the B-29 carrying the atomic bomb. That might lead to one of the greatest catastrophes of the war. All of Tinian, our largest air base in the Pacific, with two thousand B-29s and 150,000 picked Air Force personnel, might go up in a cloud of radioactive dust.

So he went to General Farrell with the proposition that the final assembly of the bomb, the fusing, should not be done until after the plane had taken off, at a point several hundred miles away from Tinian. This would make it impossible for a nuclear explosion to take place if the plane crashed and caught fire at take-off.

"Have you ever assembled the fusing mechanism of a bomb like this before?" asked General Farrell.

"No, but I have all day to learn," was the answer.

By Sunday afternoon, August 5, Marianas time, Deke Parsons felt confident that he had mastered the intricate mechanism of the A-bomb's final assembly stages. But General Farrell and the rest of us in the know stayed up all night worrying about whether or not Parsons would succeed in doing the job in mid-air. And as we learned later, it was not until 7:30 that morning, just one hour and forty-five minutes before the bomb was dropped, that Captain Parsons had finished the job.

Just before the take-off, Captain Parsons borrowed an automatic pistol from one of the security officers. He was the only man aboard who knew all the top secrets of the bomb's mechanism, and in case of a forced landing in enemy territory he was not going to be taken alive.

The fliers and crews of the fifteen B-29s assigned to carry the atomic bomb were for several months the butt of the jibes and sneers of all the other Air Force personnel at Tinian. Only Colonel Tibbets knew what it was all about. And while Tinian was the major base for the heavy bombing of the Japanese homeland, from which hundreds of B-29s took off every night, Colonel Tibbets' group, the 509th, had to be satisfied with small practice missions of no more than three B-29s at a time, in which they carried simulated atomic bombs. Even the Japanese started making fun of them, not knowing that these missions were to get them off guard against similar future A-bomb missions of no more than three B-29s.

But on the afternoon of August 7, when President Truman's announcement was heard over the Tinian radio, the 509th became the glamour group of Tinian.

CHAPTER NINETEEN

12:01 over Nagasaki

I<small>T WAS</small> Wednesday evening, August 8, in Tinian. In the quonset hut that served as the officers' club a hot crap game was in progress. I was seated at a table drinking beer with Dr. William G. Penny, one of the group of eminent British scientists at Los Alamos, who later became the director of the British nuclear-weapons program, and several members of the American scientific group, when I was notified by a messenger from General Farrell to get ready to go along as official reporter on the second atomic-bomb mission that was to get under way early next morning.

Dr. Penny and I almost stopped the crap game by the loud whoops with which we greeted the news. Dr. Penny, now Sir William Penny, and Group Captain Cheshire had been designated by Winston Churchill (when he was still Prime Minister) as observers of the atomic bomb in action and were then the official representatives of the new Prime Minister, Clement Attlee.

When he heard that I was going, Major Ferebee, who two and a half days before had dropped the bomb on Hiroshima, at once took me under his wing. He drove me in his jeep to the supply room and saw to it that I was properly equipped with the special paraphernalia carried by fliers on a combat mission in a B-29, which included a Mae West, a parachute, a lifeboat, an oxygen mask, a flak suit and a survival vest. He lent me his personal survival belt and showed me how the equipment was used. He then transported me to the briefing, after which he drove me to the flying field. I shall never forget Tom Ferebee's kindness to me that night.

I climbed into the nose of the B-29, the instrument plane which was to follow directly behind the strike plane, No. 77. The quarters were cramped and the only place I could find to sit was a hard metal box. The pilot of my ship was Captain Frederick C. Bock, of Greenville, Michigan, who had majored in philosophy at the University of Chicago. The night outside was dark and uncertain.

It was 3:50 Thursday morning, August 9, when I became airborne. Seated on the metal box, I took out a small notebook and began writing a play-by-play account of the mission. The dateline read: "With the Atomic Bomb Mission to Japan, Thursday, August 9." It was the first and only dateline of its kind in history.

The lead paragraph read:

We are on our way to bomb the homeland of Japan, in a formation equivalent to 2,000, and possibly 4,000, B-29 Superbombers. Actually our flying contingent consists of only three specially designed B-29s, and two of them carry no bombs. But our lead plane, about 3,000 feet directly ahead, is on its way with another atomic bomb, the second in three days, concentrating in its active substance an explosive energy equivalent to 20,000, and under favorable conditions 40,000, tons of TNT.

We were headed northwest on a straight course for Japan. Only a few stars were visible through the overcast, and from time to time a flash of lightning would illuminate the sky. The weather report had predicted storms ahead part of the way, but clear weather for the final stages. The storm broke just about one hour after we had left Tinian.

On we went through the night. We rode out the storm. On and on we went on a straight course to the Empire. The first signs of dawn came shortly after five o'clock. By 5:50 it was light outside.

The bombardier, First Lieutenant Charles Levy of Philadelphia, came over and offered me his front-row seat in the transparent nose of the ship. From that vantage point in space, 17,000 feet above the Pacific, I could see hundreds of miles on all sides, horizontally and vertically. At that height the ocean below and the sky above appear to merge into one great sphere.

In my notebook I wrote:

I am on the inside of that firmament, riding above the giant mountains of white cumulus clouds, feeling myself suspended in infinite space.

One hears the whir of the motors behind one, but it soon becomes insignificant against the immensity all around and is before long swallowed by it. There comes a point where space also swallows time and one lives through eternal moments filled with an oppressive loneliness, as though all life had suddenly vanished from the earth and you are the only one left, a lone survivor traveling endlessly through interplanetary space.

My mind soon returns to the mission I am on. Somewhere beyond these vast mountains of white clouds ahead lies Japan, the land of our enemy. In about four hours from now one of its cities, either Kokura, our primary target, or Nagasaki, our secondary target, will be wiped off the map by the greatest weapon ever made. In a fraction of time immeasurable by any clock a whirlwind from the skies will pulverize thousands of its buildings and tens of thousands of its inhabitants. But at this moment no one yet knows which of the two cities chosen as targets is to be annihilated.

The final choice lies with destiny. The winds over Japan will make the decision. If they carry heavy clouds over Kokura, that city will be saved, at least for the time being. Its inhabitants will not know that a wind of a benevolent destiny had passed over their heads. But that same wind will doom Nagasaki.

Our weather planes ahead of us are on their way to find out where the wind blows. Half an hour before target time we shall know what the winds have decided.

We reached our altitude of about 32,000 feet at nine o'clock. We were then over Japanese waters, close to the mainland. The navigator motioned to me to look through his radarscope. Before me was the outline of our assembly point. We would soon meet our strike ship and proceed on the final stage of our journey.

At 9:12 we reached Yakoshima, our assembly point, a little island southeast of Kyushu, and there, about four thousand feet ahead of us, was No. 77 with its atomic load. I saw Lieutenant Leonard A. Godfrey of Greenfield, Massachusetts, the navigator, and Sergeant Ralph D. Curry of Hoopeston, Illinois, the radio operator, strap on their parachutes, and I did likewise.

We started circling. The little towns on the coast line were heedless of our presence. We kept on circling, waiting for the third ship in our formation.

From the time we reached Yakoshima fate started playing a grim game with us. Our troubles started when the third plane in our group, which was to make the official photographs of the bombing, did not join us within the expected time limit. We circled and circled, endlessly it seemed, around the little island. More than forty-five minutes had passed when the lead ship decided not to wait any longer.

It was 9:56 when we began heading for the coast line. The weather planes, half an hour ahead of us, had signaled good visibility over Kokura as well as Nagasaki. But our arrival over Kokura had been delayed by more than three quarters of an hour, and when we got there the weather had changed and thick clouds covered the target. We had located the city by radar, but the orders were to make only a visual drop, which has the advantage of greater accuracy. This meant circling until we found an opening through the clouds over the selected target area. But the winds of destiny decreed otherwise.

Round and round in wide circles went No. 77. Round and round went our ship close behind. But Kokura remained hidden from our view. All we needed was a small peephole though the white curtain stretching for miles below us, but the curtain remained impenetrable. Clouds were matched against man's mightiest weapon.

What was at stake was the ending of the war as quickly as possible. Turning back for another try the following morning might mean prolonging the war by at least one day, and every day the war went on meant the loss of many lives. And too much time had passed since the weather plane's report on the visibility over Nagasaki. The chances were therefore about even that it was by then no better than over Kokura.

We were making our third run over Kokura and had flown over Japan for about two hours when I suddenly saw large black rings come shooting through the white sea of clouds. I watched them in a dreamlike state of semiawareness, seeing them come higher and nearer, yet in no way realizing what they meant.

Suddenly, I came to. "That's flak!" I exclaimed. "The Japs are shooting at us!"

I counted fifteen black rings in rapid succession, all too low. Eight more followed, right up to our altitude, but too far to the left.

I began fingering the ring of my parachute. Would I ever make it? I had never made a parachute jump and at that time we were flying over water at an altitude of more than thirty thousand feet. I was by far the oldest man in the plane and I knew that my chances of making a safe landing in the water, or of surviving even if I did make a landing, were certainly not as good as they would be for the young crew members in the prime of life.

I turned to Sergeant Curry, the twenty-year-old radio operator. I showed him the notebook in which the story of the mission up to that moment had already been scribbled down by me in pencil.

"If we have to jump," I said, "would you be good enough to take this notebook? Give it to the first American officer you see as soon as you get back to an American camp and tell him it's the story of the mission over Kokura and Nagasaki up to the minute we were forced to bail out."

"Don't worry," Sergeant Curry said, apparently less concerned than I was.

On leaving Washington I had been given an impressive-looking official card, bearing my fingerprints and photograph, which stated that I was the bearer of the rank of "simulated colonel," entitling me to all the privileges of a full colonel. But stamped across the card in bold red letters was the line, "Valid only if captured by the enemy."

What a helluva way to become a colonel, I said to myself as I caressed the ring of my parachute. I could see myself waving the card as I landed and proclaiming to the enemy, "Here comes Colonel Laurence!"

As the black rings came ever nearer, as it seemed, I said to myself, Any minute now you may become a colonel!

Just after we had got out of the range of the flak, we noticed a squadron of Japanese fighter planes emerging from the clouds, spiraling upward toward us. The approach of the fighter planes and the flak from Kokura finally forced the pilot of the strike plane to change course. Destiny had chosen Nagasaki.

A careful check on the fuel supply revealed that No. 77, which started 700 gallons short (no one knows how this shortage came about), had enough fuel left for only one run on the target, and that if the bomb were not dropped, thus lightening the load, there would not be enough fuel to reach our emergency landing field at Okinawa.

We flew southward down the channel and at 11:33 crossed the coast line and headed straight for Nagasaki, about 100 miles to the west. And the nearer we came the greater grew our dejection. Nagasaki too was hidden under a curtain of clouds.

Would we drop the bomb by radar if we could not find an opening on the first and only possible run, and thus risk being off the mark, or would we continue looking for an opening until we had only enough gas left to reach our naval rescue craft in Japanese waters? Maybe we would go even farther—keep on looking for an opening until the last drop and then bail out over enemy territory. What were the misfortunes, or lives, of a handful of men in two B-29s against the chance of shortening the war?

It was up to the pilot and the weaponeer to make the decision, and they would have to make it fast. In the aircraft ahead of us two men were just then weighing our fate, and their own, in the balance.

We were then approaching the end of the first run. In a few minutes we would know the answer. The clouds below were still as impenetrable as ever.

And then, at the very last minute, there came an opening. For a few brief moments Nagasaki stood out clearly in broad noontime daylight.

Our watches stood at noon. The seconds ticked away. One, two, three. Ten, twenty, thirty, forty. Fifty. Fifty-seven, fifty-eight, fifty-nine . . .

It was 12:01 over Nagasaki.

We heard the prearranged signal on our radio, put on our arc welder's glasses and watched tensely the maneuverings of the strike ship about half a mile in front of us.

"There she goes!" someone said.

Out of the belly of No. 77 a black object went downward.

Our B-29 swung around to get out of range; but even though we were turning away in the opposite direction, and despite the fact that it was broad daylight in our cabin, all of us became aware of a giant flash that broke through the dark barrier of our arc welder's lenses and flooded our cabin with intense light.

After the first flash we removed our glasses, but the light lingered on, a bluish-green light that illuminated the entire sky all around. A tremendous blast wave struck our ship and made it tremble from nose to tail. This was followed by four more blasts in rapid succession, each resounding like the boom of cannon hitting our plane from all directions.

Observers in the tail of our ship saw a giant ball of fire rise as though from the bowels of the earth, belching forth enormous white smoke rings. Next they saw a giant pillar of purple fire, ten thousand feet high, shooting skyward with enormous speed.

By the time our ship had made another turn in the direction of the atomic explosion the pillar of purple fire had reached the level of our altitude. Only about forty-five seconds had passed.

Awestruck, we watched it shoot upward like a meteor coming from the earth instead of from outer space, becoming ever more alive as it climbed skyward through the white clouds. It was no longer smoke, or dust, or even a cloud of fire. It was a living thing, a new species of being, born right before our eyes.

At one stage of its evolution, covering millions of years in terms of seconds, the entity assumed the form of a giant square totem pole, with its base about three miles long, tapering off to about a mile at the top. Its bottom was brown, its center amber, its top white.

Then, just when it appeared as though the thing had settled down into a state of permanence, there came shooting out of the top a giant mushroom that increased the height of the pillar to a total of 45,000 feet.

The mushroom top was even more alive than the pillar, seething and boiling in a white fury of creamy foam, sizzling upward and then descending earthward, a thousand geysers rolled into one.

It kept struggling in an elemental fury, like a creature in the act of breaking the bonds that held it down. In a few seconds it had freed itself from its gigantic stem and floated upward with tremendous speed, its momentum carrying it into the stratosphere to a height of about sixty thousand feet.

But at that instant another mushroom, smaller in size than the first one, began emerging out of the pillar. It was as though the decapitated monster was growing a new head.

As the first mushroom floated off into the blue it changed its shape into a flowerlike form, its giant petals curving downward, creamy white outside, rose-colored inside. It still retained that shape when we last gazed at it from a distance of about two hundred miles.

The boiling pillar of many colors could also be seen at that distance, a giant mountain of jumbled rainbows, in travail. Much living substance had gone into those rainbows.

The quivering top of the pillar protruded to a great height through the white clouds, giving the appearance of a monstrous prehistoric creature with a ruff around its neck, a fleecy ruff extending in all directions, as far as the eye could see.

We landed in Okinawa in the afternoon, our tanks nearly empty, and there, to our great relief, was No. 77. On landing, two of its motors had stopped dead halfway down the runway for lack of fuel.

As No. 77 approached Okinawa, the pilot had signaled that he was coming in for an emergency landing without circling the field. To get immediate clearance he sent down the proper flare, which, however, failed to work. So his crew shot off all the flares in the B-29 vocabulary, including the one signifying "Wounded aboard." They were met by all the emergency paraphernalia and personnel on the field—ambulances, crash wagons, doctors, Red Cross workers, and priests.

While we were refueling we learned that the Soviet Union had entered the war against Japan.

The feeling of incredulity that two small bombs had devastated Hiroshima and Nagasaki persisted even in the highest military circles. Shortly after the Nagasaki mission, I was present when Lieutenant General Spaatz, then commander of the Pacific Strategic Air Forces, and several other high-ranking Air Force officers were being guided by young Dr. Charles P. Baker of Cornell University through the bomb assembly building. They were shown, among other things, the container in which the explosive material for the Nagasaki bomb had been delivered. Its small size puzzled General Spaatz.

"You mean," he said, "this container carried the fuse that set off a chain reaction in the atmosphere?"

"Oh no, General," said the very much surprised Dr. Baker. "This was it. The entire explosion came from the material in this container."

"Young man," said General Spaatz in the manner of a man too wise to be taken in, "you may believe it. I don't."

One of the strangest letters in history was written by three University of California physicists, members of the scientific crew on Tinian Island which assembled the atomic bombs for delivery. The writers of the document, the first and only letter sent with an atom bomb, were Dr. Alvarez, Dr. Robert Serber (now at Columbia), and Dr. Philip Morrison (now at Cornell), and the addressee was Dr. Ryokichi Sagane, professor of physics at the Imperial University in Tokyo, who had studied with them at the University of California at Berkeley in 1935.

Just before the plane carrying the Nagasaki bomb took off, Alvarez made three copies of the letter in longhand. These were attached to radio sondes that were dropped over Nagasaki simultaneously with the bomb.

The text of the letter was as follows:

Headquarters
Atomic Bomb Command
August 9, 1945

TO: PROFESSOR R. SAGANE
FROM: THREE OF YOUR FORMER SCIENTIFIC COLLEAGUES
DURING YOUR STAY IN THE UNITED STATES

We are sending this as a personal message to urge that you use your influence as a reputable nuclear physicist, to convince the Japanese General Staff of the terrible consequences which will be suffered by your people if you continue in this war.

You have known for several years that an atomic bomb could be built if a nation were willing to pay the enormous cost of preparing the necessary material. Now that you have seen that we have constructed the production plants, there can be no doubt in your mind that all the output of these factories, working 24 hours a day, will be exploded on your homeland.

Within the space of three weeks, we have proof-fired one bomb in the American desert, exploded one in Hiroshima, and fired the third this morning.

We implore you to confirm these facts to your leaders, and to do your utmost to stop the destruction and waste of life which can only result in the total annihilation of all your cities if continued. As scientists, we deplore the use to which a beautiful discovery has been put, but we can assure you that unless Japan surrenders at once, this rain of atomic bombs will increase manyfold in fury.

One of the three copies came into the hands of a Japanese naval officer and Sagane assured him of its authenticity. Early in 1946 Sagane gave the letter to Dr. Wilson Compton, one of the three famous Compton brothers, who was then in Japan on an educational mission, with the request to trace it to the writers. It was finally returned to Alvarez, who inscribed it "To my friend Sagane, with best regards," signed it and sent it back to him.

In due time Alvarez received an acknowledgment from Sagane.

"Dear Luis," he wrote, "it was a great excitement for me to receive a letter which actually noticed the end of the war. . . ."

CHAPTER TWENTY

9:15 over Hiroshima

THE DAY OF Monday, August 6, 1945, began as a bright, clear summer morning in Hiroshima. An air raid alarm sounded about seven o'clock, Hiroshima time, when a lone American plane came circling high overhead. It was the weather plane that had preceded the *Enola Gay* to check on the conditions of visibility over the city. No one paid any attention, and at eight o'clock (it was then nine o'clock, Tinian time, in the *Enola Gay*) the all clear was sounded. The people of Hiroshima, young and old, went about their normal pursuits. It was then fifteen minutes to doomsday.

Up to that Monday morning, occasional bombs, which did no great damage, had fallen on Hiroshima. While many cities roundabout had been destroyed, one after another, Hiroshima had not been subjected to any serious bombing from the air. There were almost daily observation planes over the city, but to everyone's astonishment none of them dropped a bomb that did much damage. People wondered why they alone had been spared for so long a time, and there were fantastic rumors that the enemy had something special in store for the city. But no one really took such rumors seriously.

Actually, those daily observation planes had a mission with a dual purpose. One was purely psychological, to condition the people of the city, and of the three other cities selected as targets for atomic bombs—Kokura, Nagasaki and Niigata—getting them accustomed to the fact that a formation of no more than three planes flying at a high altitude of about thirty thousand feet did not drop highly explosive bombs. The second purpose was to give the select group of our highly experienced bombardiers, the elite of our Air Force, needed additional practice for dropping an atomic bomb with the greatest of accuracy. The bombs that these "observation" planes dropped were actually exact models of the atomic bomb in every detail, the exact weight, size and shape of the real thing, with the sole exception that, instead of the atomic charge, they carried a small quantity of an ordinary explosive. These simulated atomic bombs were, furthermore, dropped from the exact altitude determined for the dropping of the real thing, a much higher altitude than the one to which our bombardiers had been accustomed, requiring considerable adjustment in their skills.

So well did this plan work out that it became a subject of derision in the regular broadcasts beamed to the United States by Tokyo Rose. "You are now reduced to small missions of three planes," she taunted us, "and the bombs they drop are just duds."

By the window in his room at the novitiate of the Society of Jesus in Nagatsuka, the Reverend John A. Siemes, S.J., a thirty-nine-year-old German-born Jesuit priest, sat in contemplation that Monday morning. During the past six months the philosophical and theological section of the Jesuit mission in Japan had been evacuated to this place from ruined Tokyo, where Father Siemes had served as professor of philosophy at the Catholic University. The novitiate is situated a little over a mile from Hiroshima, half-way up the side of a broad valley that stretches from the town at sea level into a mountainous hinterland, through which courses a river. From his window, Father Siemes had a clear view down the valley to the edge of the city.

Suddenly—the time was approximately 8:14 Hiroshima time, 9:14 by the watches inside the *Enola Gay*—the whole valley was illuminated by a garish yellow-green light, resembling the light of a huge magnesium flare, while at the same time Father Siemes became conscious of a wave of heat. He jumped to the window to find out the cause of the remarkable phenomenon, but saw nothing more than the brilliant green-yellow light. As he made for the door it did not occur to him that the light might have something to do with a bomb.

On the way from the window, he heard a moderately loud explosion which seemed to come from a distance, and at the same time the windows were broken in with a loud crash. There had been an interval of perhaps ten seconds since the flash of light. He was sprayed with fragments of glass. The entire window frame had been forced into the room. He realized now that a bomb had burst and he was under the impression that it had exploded directly over the house or in its immediate vicinity.

He was bleeding from cuts about the hands and head. As he attempted to get out of the door, he found that it had been forced outward by the air pressure and was jammed. He forced an opening in the door by means of repeated blows with his hands and feet and entered a broad hallway onto which the various rooms opened. He found everything in a state of confusion. All the windows were broken and all the doors were forced inward. The bookshelves in the hallway had tumbled down. Most of his colleagues had been injured by fragments of glass. A few were bleeding, but none had been seriously injured. The wall of Father Siemes's room, opposite the window at which he had sat, had been lacerated by long fragments of glass.

They proceeded to the front of the house to see where the bomb had landed. There was no evidence of a bomb crater, but the southeast section of the house had been very severely damaged. Not a door nor a window remained. The blast of air had penetrated the entire house from the southeast, yet the house still stood. It was constructed in Japanese style, with a wooden framework, but had been greatly strengthened by the labor of Brother Gropper. Only along the front of the chapel which adjoined the house, three supports had given way.

Down in the valley, perhaps half a mile toward the city from the novitiate, several peasant homes were on fire, and the woods on the opposite side of the valley were aflame. A few of the Jesuit fathers went over to help control the flames. While they were attempting to put things in order, a storm came up and it began to rain. Over the city, clouds of smoke were rising and they heard a few slight explosions. Father Siemes came to the conclusion that an incendiary bomb with an especially strong explosive action had gone off down in the valley. A few of the other Jesuits had seen three planes at great altitude over the city at the time of the explosion, but Father Siemes had seen no aircraft whatsoever.

Perhaps a half hour after the explosion, a procession of people began to stream up the valley from the city. The crowd thickened continuously. A few came up the road to the novitiate. The Jesuits gave them first aid and brought them into the chapel, which they had in the meantime cleaned and cleared of wreckage, and put them to rest on the straw mats which constitute the floors of Japanese houses. A few displayed horrible wounds of the extremities and the back. The small quantity of the scarce fat which the mission possessed was soon used up in the care of the burns. Father Rektor, who, before taking holy orders, had studied medicine, ministered to the injured, but the bandages and drugs were soon gone, and he had to be content with merely cleansing the wounds.

More and more of the injured came. The least injured dragged the more seriously wounded. There were wounded soldiers, and mothers carrying burned children in their arms. From the houses of the farmers in the valley came word: "Our houses are full of wounded and dying. Can you help, at least by taking the worst cases?" The wounded came from the sections at the edge of the city. Those who had been in the open had suffered instantaneous burns, particularly on the lightly clothed or the unclothed parts of the body. Numerous fires had sprung up and soon consumed the entire district. The Jesuit fathers now concluded that the epicenter of the explosion was at the edge of the city near the Jokogawa station, about two miles away from them. They became concerned about Father Kopp, who, that same morning, had gone to hold Mass at the children's home of the Sisters of the Poor at the edge of the city and had not yet returned.

Toward noon, the large chapel and the library were filled with the seriously injured. The procession of refugees from the city continued. Finally, about one o'clock, Father Kopp returned together with the sisters. Their house and the entire district where they lived had burned to the ground. Father Kopp was bleeding about the head and the neck, and he had a large burn on the right palm. He had been standing in front of the nunnery ready to go home. All of a sudden he became aware of the light and felt the wave of heat, and a large blister formed on his hand. The windows were torn out by the blast. He thought that the bomb had fallen in his immediate vicinity. The nunnery, also a wooden structure made by Brother Gropper, still remained, but soon it was noted that the house was as

166

good as lost because the fire, which had begun at many points in the neighborhood, was sweeping closer and closer, and water was not available. There was still time to rescue certain things from the house and to bury them in an open spot. Then the house was swept by flame, and they fought their way back to the mission along the shore of the river and through the burning streets.

Soon news came that the entire city had been destroyed by the explosion and that it was on fire. What had become of Father Superior and the three other fathers who were at the center of the city at the central mission and parish house? Up to that time those at the novitiate had not given them a thought, because they had not believed that the effects of the bomb encompassed the entire city. Also, they did not want to go into town except under pressure of dire necessity, because they feared that the population was greatly perturbed and that it might take revenge on any white foreigners.

Father Stolte and Father Erlinghagen went down to the road, which was still full of refugees, and brought in the seriously injured who had collapsed by the wayside, to the temporary aid station at the village school. There iodine was applied to the wounds, but they were left uncleansed. Neither ointments nor other therapeutic agents were available. Those who were brought in were laid on the floor; no one could give them further care.

What could one do [Father Siemes wrote in the only eyewitness account of the bombing of Hiroshima], when all means are lacking? Under such circumstances, it is almost useless to bring them in. Among the passers-by, there are many who are uninjured. In a purposeless, insensate manner, distraught by the magnitude of the disaster, most of them rush by and none conceives the thought of organizing help on his own initiative. They are concerned only with the welfare of their own families.

It became clear to us during these days that the Japanese displayed little initiative, preparedness, and organizational skill in preparation for catastrophes. They failed to carry out any rescue work when something could have been saved by a co-operative effort, and fatalistically let the catastrophe take its course. When we urged them to take part in the rescue work, they did everything willingly, but on their own initiative they did very little.

At about four o'clock in the afternoon a theology student and two kindergarten children, who lived at the parish house and adjoining buildings, which had burned down, came in and said that Father Superior La Salle and Father Schiffer had been seriously injured and that they had taken refuge in Asano Park on the riverbank. They were too weak to walk.

Hurriedly the fathers got together two stretchers, and seven of them rushed toward the city. Father Rektor came along with food and medicine. The closer they got to the city, the greater was the evidence of destruction and the more difficult it became to make their way. The houses at the edge of the city were all severely damaged. Many had collapsed or burned down. Farther in, almost all the dwellings had been damaged by fire. Where the city had stood there was a gigantic burned-out scar.

The Jesuit fathers made their way along the street on the riverbank among the burning and smoking ruins. Twice they were forced into the river itself by the heat and the smoke.

Frightfully burned people beckoned to them. Along the way, there were many dead and dying. On the Misasa Bridge, which leads into the inner city, they were met by a long procession of soldiers who had suffered burns. They dragged themselves along with the help of staves or were carried by their less severely injured comrades—an endless procession of human misery.

Abandoned on the bridge, there stood with sunken heads a number of horses with large burns on their flanks. On the far side, the cement structure of the local hospital was the only building that remained standing. Its interior, however, had been burned out. It served as a landmark to guide them on their way.

Finally they reached the entrance of the park. A large proportion of the city's population had taken refuge there, but even the trees of the park were on fire in several places. Paths and bridges were blocked by the trunks of fallen trees and were almost impassable. They were told that a high wind, which may well have resulted from the heat of the burning city, had uprooted the large trees.

It was now quite dark. Only the fires, which were still raging in some places at a distance, gave out a little light.

At the far corner of the park, on the riverbank itself, they came at last upon their colleagues. Father Schiffer was on the ground, pale as a ghost. He had a deep incised wound behind the ear and had lost so much blood that they were concerned about his chances for survival. The Father Superior had suffered a deep wound of the lower leg. Father Cieslik and Father Kleinsorge had minor injuries but were completely exhausted.

While they were eating the food that their colleagues had brought, they told of their experiences. They had been in their rooms at the parish house—it was a quarter after eight, exactly the time when those in Nagatsuka had heard the explosion—when the intense light came, followed immediately by the sound of breaking windows, walls and furniture. They were showered with glass splinters and fragments of wreckage. Father Schiffer was buried beneath a portion of a wall and suffered a severe head injury. The Father Superior received most of the splinters in his back and lower extremity, and he bled heavily. Everything was thrown about in the rooms themselves, but the wooden framework of the house remained intact, thanks again to the labors of Brother Gropper.

They had the same impression their colleagues had had in Nagatsuka: that the bomb had burst in their immediate vicinity. The church, the school and all buildings in the immediate area collapsed at once. Beneath the ruins of the school, the children cried for help. They were freed with great effort. Several others were also rescued from the ruins of nearby dwellings. Even the Father Superior and Father Schiffer, despite their wounds, rendered aid to others and lost a great deal of blood in the process.

In the meantime, the fires which had begun some distance away were raging ever closer, so that it became obvious that everything would soon burn down. Several objects were rescued from the parish house and were buried in a clearing in front of the church, but certain valuables and necessities which had been kept ready in case of fire could not be found because of the confusion. It was high time to flee, since the oncoming flames would soon leave open no way of escape. Fukai, the secretary of the mission, was completely out of his mind. He did not want to leave the house and explained that he did not want to survive the destruction of his fatherland. He was completely uninjured. Father Kleinsorge dragged him out of the house on his back and he was forcibly carried away.

Beneath the wreckage of the houses along the way, many had been trapped and they screamed to be rescued from the oncoming flames. They had to be left to their fate. Fukai did not want to go any farther and remained behind. He was never heard from again.

In the park, they took refuge on the bank of the river. A violent whirlwind now began to uproot large trees, lifting them high in the air. As the wind reached the water, a water spout approximately three hundred feet high formed. The violence of the storm luckily passed them by. Some distance away, however, where numerous refugees had taken shelter, many were blown into the river. Almost all who were in the vicinity had been injured and had lost relatives who had been pinned under the wreckage or who had been lost sight of during the flight. There was no help for the wounded and many died.

The transportation of the priests' own wounded was difficult. It was not possible to dress their wounds properly in the darkness, and their wounds reopened upon slight motion. As they were carried on the shaky litters in the dark over the fallen trees of the park, they suffered unbearable pain as the result of the movement and lost dangerously large quantities of blood.

Our rescuing angel in this difficult situation [Father Siemes wrote] is a Japanese Protestant pastor. He has brought up a boat and offers to take our wounded upstream to a place where progress is easier. First we lower the litter containing Father Schiffer into the boat and two of us accompany him. We plan to bring the boat back for the Father Superior. The boat returns about one half hour later and the pastor requests that several of us help in the rescue of two children whom he had seen in the river. We rescue them. They have severe burns. Soon they suffer chills and die in the park.

The Father Superior was conveyed in the boat in the same manner as Father Schiffer. The theology student and Father Siemes accompanied him. Father Cieslik considered himself strong enough to make his way on foot to Nagatsuka with the rest of them but Father Kleinsorge could not walk that far and they left him and the housekeeper behind, to be picked up in the morning. From the other side of the stream came the whinny of horses threatened by the fire.

They landed on a sandspit that jutted out from the shore. It was crowded with the wounded who had taken refuge there and who were screaming for help, as they were too weak to move and were in danger of drowning when the river rose with the incoming tide. But the relief party had to press on, and it finally reached the spot where the group which included Father Schiffer was waiting.

An earlier relief party had brought a large case of fresh rice cakes, but there was no one to distribute them to the numerous wounded lying all about. The missionaries distributed them to those who were nearby and also helped themselves. The wounded called for water, but the fathers could come to the aid of only a few. They could hear cries for help from a distance but could not approach the ruins from which the cries came.

A group of soldiers came along the road and their officer noticed that the group spoke a foreign language. He at once drew his sword and demanded to know who they were, threatening to cut them down. Father Laures seized his arm and explained that they were German, and he calmed down. He had suspected that they were Americans, for rumors of parachutists were spreading in the city.

The Father Superior, who was clothed only in shirt and trousers, complained of feeling freezing cold, despite the warm summer night and the heat of the burning city. The one man among them who possessed a coat gave it to him, and Father Siemes gave him his own shirt. "It seemed more comfortable," he wrote, "to be without a shirt in the heat."

It was midnight. Since there were not enough of them to man both litters with four strong bearers, they determined to remove Father Schiffer first to the outskirts of the city. From there, another group of bearers was to take them to Nagatsuka; the others were to turn back to rescue the Father Superior.

Father Siemes was one of the bearers. The theology student went in front to warn them of the numerous wires, beams and fragments of ruins which blocked the way and which were impossible to see in the dark. Despite all precautions, their progress was stumbling and their feet got tangled in the wire. Father Kruger fell and carried the litter with him. Father Schiffer became half unconscious from the fall and vomited. They passed an injured man sitting all alone among the hot ruins, whom Father Siemes had seen on the way down.

On the Misasa Bridge they met Father Tappe and Father Luhmer, who had come from Nagatsuka to meet them. They had dug a family out of the ruins of their collapsed house some fifty yards off the road. The father of the family was already dead. They had dragged out two girls and placed them by the side of the road. Their mother was still trapped under some beams. They had planned to complete the rescue and then to press on to meet their colleagues.

At the outskirts of the city, they put down the litter and left two men to wait until those who were to come from Nagatsuka appeared. The rest of them turned back to fetch the Father Superior.

Most of the ruins had by then burned down. The darkness hid the many bodies that lay on the ground. Only occasionally did they hear calls for help. The air was filled with the pungent smell of incinerated corpses. The sitting form they had passed by previously was still there.

Transportation on the litter, which had been constructed out of boards, was very painful to the Father Superior, whose entire back was full of fragments of glass. In a narrow passage at the edge of town, a car forced them to the edge of the road. The litter bearers on the left side fell into a six-foot-deep ditch, which they could not see in the darkness. Father Superior hid his pain with a dry joke, but the litter, which was no longer in one piece, could not be carried farther. They decided to wait until a handcart could be brought from Nagatsuka. A man named Kinjo soon came back with one he had requisitioned from a collapsed house. They placed Father Superior on the cart and wheeled him the rest of the way, avoiding whenever possible the deeper pits in the road.

About half past four in the morning, they finally arrived at the novitiate. Their rescue expedition had taken almost twelve hours. Normally one could go back and forth to the city in two hours. Their two wounded were now, for the first time, properly dressed.

Father Siemes got two hours' sleep on the floor; someone else had taken his bed. Then he read a Mass *in gratiarum actionem,* as it was the seventh of August, the anniversary of the founding of the Jesuit order. After that they prepared to bring Father Kleinsorge and others needing help out of the city.

They started again with the handcart. The day now revealed the frightful picture which the previous night's darkness had partly concealed. Where the city had stood, everything, as far as the eye could see, was a waste of ashes and ruin. Only several skeletons of gutted buildings remained. The banks of the river were covered with dead and wounded. On the broad street in the Hakushima district, naked burned bodies were particularly numerous.

Frightfully injured forms beckoned to them and then collapsed. An old woman and a girl whom she was pulling along with her fell down at their feet. They placed them on their cart and wheeled them to the hospital, at the entrance of which a dressing station had been set up. Here the wounded lay on the hard floor, row on row. Only the worst wounds were dressed. The missionaries conveyed another soldier and an old woman to the place, but they could not move everybody who lay exposed in the sun.

"It would have been endless and it was questionable whether those whom we could drag to the dressing station could come out alive, because even here nothing really effective could be done," Father Siemes wrote. Later they ascertained that the wounded lay for days in the burned-out hallways of the hospital and there they died.

They had to proceed to their goal in the park and were forced to leave the wounded to their fate. They made their way to the place where their church had stood and dug up those few belongings they had buried the day before, finding them intact. Everything else had been completely burned. In the ruins they found a few molten remnants of the holy vessels.

At the park, they loaded the housekeeper and a mother with her two children onto the cart. Father Kleinsorge felt strong enough, with the aid of Brother Nobuhara, to make his way home on foot. The way back took them once again past the dead and the wounded in Hakushima. Again no rescue parties were in evidence.

At the Misasa Bridge lay the family which Fathers Tappe and Luhmer had rescued from the ruins the day before. A piece of tin had been placed over them to shield them from the sun. The Jesuits could not take them along, as their cart was full. They gave them, and those nearby, water to drink and decided to rescue them later. At three o'clock in the afternoon they were back in Nagatsuka.

After having a little food and drink, Fathers Stolte, Luhmer, Erlinghagen and Siemes left again to bring in the family. Father Kleinsorge requested that they also rescue two children who had lost their mother and who had lain near him in the park. On the way, they were greeted by strangers who had noted that they were on a mission of mercy and who praised their efforts. They now met groups carrying the wounded about on litters.

When they arrived at the Misasa Bridge, the family that had been there was gone. There was a group of soldiers at work taking away those who had been left to die the day before. More than thirty hours had gone by before the first official rescue party had appeared on the scene.

Father Siemes's party found both children and took them out of the park: a six-year-old boy who was uninjured, and a twelve-year-old girl who had been burned about the head, hands and legs, and who had lain in the park for thirty hours without care. The left side of her face and the left eye were completely covered with blood and pus, so that they thought she had lost the eye. When the wound was later washed, they noted that the eye was intact and that the lids had just become stuck together.

On the way home, they took another group of three refugees with them. First, however, the latter wanted to know what nationality the missionaries were. They, too, feared that the fathers might be Americans who had parachuted.

The Jesuits took under their care fifty refugees who had lost everything. The majority of them were wounded and not a few had dangerous burns. Father Rektor treated the wounds as well as he could with the few medicaments that they could, with effort, gather up. He had to confine himself in general to cleansing the wounds of purulent matter. Even those with smaller burns were very weak, and all suffered from diarrhea. In the farmhouses in the vicinity, there were also wounded almost everywhere. Father Rektor made daily rounds and acted in the capacity of a painstaking physician, and a great Samaritan.

Three of the severely burned died within the next few days; suddenly the pulse and the respiration ceased. It was, indeed, remarkable that so few died. In the official aid stations and hospitals a good third or half of those who had been brought in died. They lay about almost without care, and a very high percentage succumbed. Everything was lacking: doctors, assistants, dressings, drugs. In a nearby village a group of soldiers for several days did nothing but collect the dead and cremate them behind the aid station.

During the next few days, funeral processions passed the novitiate from morning to night, bringing the dead to a small valley nearby. There, in six places, the dead were burned. People brought their own wood and carried out the cremation themselves. Father Luhmer and Father Laures found in a nearby house a dead man whose body was already bloated and stinking. They brought him to the valley and incinerated him themselves. Even late at night, the little valley was lit up by the funeral pyres.

The missionaries made systematic efforts to trace their acquaintances and the families of the refugees whom they sheltered. Frequently after the passage of several weeks someone was found in a distant village or a hospital, but of many there was no news, and these were apparently dead. They were happy to discover the mother of the two children whom they had found in the park, who had been given up for dead. After three weeks, she saw her children once again. In the tears of great joy at the reunion were mingled tears for those they would never see again.

The magnitude of the disaster that befell Hiroshima on August 6 was only slowly pieced together in Father Siemes's mind. He lived through the catastrophe and saw it only in flashes, which gradually merged to give him a total picture. In his classic report he wrote:

What actually happened simultaneously in the city as a whole is as follows: As a result of the explosion of the bomb at 8:15 almost the entire city was destroyed at a single blow. Only small outlying districts in the southern and eastern parts of the town escaped complete destruction. The bomb exploded over the center of the city. As a result of the blast the small Japanese houses in a diameter of five kilometers [three miles], which comprised 99 per cent of the city, collapsed or were blown up. Those who were in the houses were buried in the ruins. Those who were in the open sustained burns resulting from contact with the substance or rays emitted by the bomb. Where the substances struck in quantity, fires sprang up. These spread rapidly.

The heat which rose from the center created a whirlwind which was effective in spreading fire throughout the whole city. Those who had been caught beneath the ruins and who could not be freed rapidly, and those who had been caught by the flames, became casualties. As much as six kilometers [3.7 miles] from the center of the explosion, all houses were damaged and many collapsed and caught fire. Even fifteen kilometers [9.3 miles] away, windows were broken.

It was rumored that the enemy fliers had spread an explosive and incendiary material over the city and then had created the explosion and ignition. A few maintained that they saw the planes drop a parachute which had carried something that exploded at a height of 1,000 meters [3,000 feet]. The newspapers called the bomb an atomic bomb and noted that the force of the blast had resulted from the explosion of uranium atoms, and that gamma rays had been sent out as a result of this, but no one knew anything for certain concerning the nature of the bomb.

How many people were a sacrifice to this bomb? Those who had lived through the catastrophe placed the number of the dead at least 100,000. Hiroshima had a population of 400,000. Official statistics place the number who had died at 70,000 up to September 1, not counting the missing . . . and 130,000 wounded, among them 43,500 severely wounded.

Estimates made by ourselves on the basis of groups known to us show that the number of 100,000 dead is not too high. Near us there are two barracks, in each of which forty Korean workers lived. On the day of the explosion, they were laboring on the streets of Hiroshima. Four returned alive to one barracks and sixteen to the other. Six hundred students of the Protestant girls' school worked in a factory, from which only thirty to forty returned. Most of the peasant families in the neighborhood lost one or more of their members who had worked at factories in the city. Our next-door neighbor, Tamura, lost two children and himself suffered a large wound, since, as it happened, he had been in the city on that day. The family of our reader suffered two dead, father and son; thus a family of five members suffered at least two losses, counting only the dead and severely wounded.

There died the Mayor, the President of the central Japan district, the Commander of the city, a Korean prince who had been stationed in Hiroshima in the capacity of an officer, and many other high-ranking officers. Of the professors of the University, thirty-two were killed or severely injured. Especially hard hit were the soldiers. The Pioneer Regiment was almost entirely wiped out. The barracks were near the center of the explosion.

[Supreme Allied Headquarters announced in February 1946, that the casualties in Hiroshima as the result of the atomic bomb were: dead, 78,150; missing, 13,983; seriously wounded, 9,428; slightly injured, 27,997.]

Thousands of wounded who died later could doubtless have been rescued had they received proper treatment and care, but rescue work in a catastrophe of this magnitude had not been envisioned; since the whole city had been knocked out at a blow, everything which had been prepared for emergency work was lost, and no preparation had been made for rescue work in the outlying districts. Many of the wounded also died because they had been weakened by undernourishment and consequently lacked strength to recover. Those who had their normal strength and who received good care slowly healed the burns which had been occasioned by the bomb.

There were also cases, however, whose prognosis seemed good who died suddenly. There were also some who had only small external wounds and died within a week or later, after an inflammation of the pharynx and oral cavity had taken place. We thought at first that this was the result of inhalation of the substance of the bomb. Later, a commission established the thesis that gamma rays had been given out at the time of the explosion, following which the internal organs had been injured in a manner resembling that consequent upon Roentgen [X-ray] irradiation. This produces a diminution in the numbers of the white blood corpuscles.

Only several cases are known to me personally where individuals who did not have external burns later died. Father Kleinsorge and Father Cieslik, who were near the center of the explosion, but who did not suffer burns, became quite weak some fourteen days after the explosion. Up to this time small incised wounds had healed normally, but thereafter the wounds which were still unhealed became worse and are to date [in September 1945] still incompletely healed. The attending physician diagnosed leucopenia [white-cell deficiency]. There thus seems to be some truth in the statement that the radiation had some effect on the blood. I am of the opinion, however, that their generally undernourished and weakened condition was partly responsible for these findings.

It was noised about that the ruins of the city emitted deadly rays, that workers who went there to aid in the clearing died, and that the central district would be uninhabitable for some time to come. I have my doubts as to whether such talk is true and myself and others who worked in the ruined area for some hours shortly after the explosion suffered no such ill effects.

None of us in those days heard a single outburst against the Americans on the part of the Japanese, nor was there any evidence of a vengeful spirit. The Japanese suffered this terrible blow as part of the fortunes of war . . . something to be borne without complaint.

During this war, I have noted relatively little hatred toward the Allies on the part of the people themselves, although the press has taken occasion to stir up such feelings. After the victories at the beginning of the war, the enemy was rather looked down upon, but when the Allied offensive gathered momentum and especially after the advent of the majestic B-29s, the technical skill of America became an object of wonder and admiration.

The following anecdote indicates the spirit of the Japanese: A few days after the atomic bombing, the secretary of the University came to us asserting that the Japanese were ready to destroy San Francisco by means of an equally effective bomb. It is dubious that he himself believed what he told us. He merely wanted to impress upon us foreigners that the Japanese were capable of similar discoveries. In his nationalistic pride, he talked himself into believing this.

The Japanese also intimated that the principle of the new bomb was a Japanese discovery. It was only lack of raw materials, they said, which prevented its construction. In the meantime, the Germans were said to have carried the discovery to a further stage and were about to initiate such bombing. The Americans were reputed to have learned the secret from the Germans, and they had then brought the bomb to a stage of industrial completion.

We have discussed among ourselves the ethics of the use of the bomb. Some consider it in the same category as poison gas and are against its use on a civil population. Others were of the view that in total war, as carried on in Japan, there was no difference between civilians and soldiers, and that the bomb itself was an effective force tending to end the bloodshed, warning Japan to surrender and thus to avoid total destruction.

It seems logical to me that he who supports total war in principle cannot complain of war against civilians. The crux of the matter is whether total war in its present form is justifiable, even when it serves a just purpose. Does it not have material and spiritual evil as its consequences which far exceed whatever the good that might result? When will our moralists give us a clear answer to this question?

CHAPTER TWENTY-ONE

The Secrets of the Atom Bomb

THE SECRET of the atom bomb, which we had believed was carefully kept, turned out, alas, to have been no secret at all. It was given away to the Soviet Union by Klaus Fuchs, a German-born physicist who had been given asylum in Britain.

No one suspected he was a spy, although a more careful scrutiny of his record might have aroused suspicion. Because of his brilliance as a physicist he was admitted to the inner circle of scientists who were then investigating the possibilities of building an atomic bomb.

When President Roosevelt and Prime Minister Churchill agreed that the two countries should work together on the project, Fuchs was chosen a member of the British scientific team that came to this country. Because it was taken for granted that all the members of the British group had been thoroughly checked by their own security officers, no investigation was made by the American authorities. So it came about that this most dangerous of spies smuggled himself into our midst and was given access to our most intimate secrets.

At the first opportunity he sought out Soviet agents in this country and began feeding them the secrets of the atom bomb and the early theories about the hydrogen bomb. Even before we had tested the first atomic bomb at Alamogordo, the Soviet Union knew its most intimate details. For Fuchs had served in Oak Ridge, where the plants for concentrating uranium 235 were located, as well as in Los Alamos.

When the bomb was tested in the New Mexico desert Fuchs was one of the select few who watched, for he was one of the highly gifted young scientists whose talents aided greatly in the development of the bomb. His betrayal came as a great shock to his associates when they learned about it five years later.

There were other traitors who gave atomic secrets to the Russians, but it was Fuchs who gave them the vital secrets of the atom bomb. It was he alone who made it possible for them to possess an atomic bomb as early as 1949, at least three years ahead of the time estimated by most scientists.

It was not until early in 1950, after Fuchs had been working for five years as a member of the British Atomic Center at Harwell, England, that his role as a spy for the Soviet Union was revealed. He confessed and was given a fourteen-year prison term. But it will take many more years to undo the damage he has done to the free world.

By a strange irony, however, Fuchs's treachery saved us from falling behind in the development of the hydrogen bomb.

Following the end of the war there developed a debate among our scientists as to the wisdom of spending great resources, scientific and material, on such a weapon. In the first place, no one knew at the time that a hydrogen bomb could be made at all. And in the second place, there were many who believed that the atomic bomb was good enough and that our best interests would be served by devoting our resources to improving the weapon we already had.

But the picture changed overnight when President Truman announced on September 23, 1949, that the Russians had exploded an atomic bomb. It soon became evident that we were in a race for our very existence, and that the Soviet Union, already in possession of our preliminary explorations of the hydrogen bomb—given to her by Fuchs—would undoubtedly go all out on building such a weapon if there was the remotest possibility of success.

So, late in January 1950, President Truman issued his historic order to the Atomic Energy Commission "to continue with the development of the so-called hydrogen, or super-bomb." And, as we learned three and a half years later, Russia was already well ahead of us in the development of the hydrogen bomb. It was in the summer of 1953 that she announced to a startled world that she had successfully tested the first airborne thermonuclear (hydrogen fusion) weapon, exploded from a great height after being dropped from a giant bomber, whereas our tests in November 1952 and in March 1954 were of clumsy earthbound devices each the size of an enormous structure that occupied the major part of an island. Indeed, it was not until May 1956, nearly three years after the Soviet Union's successful test of an actual weapon, that we finally succeeded in exploding a hydrogen bomb dropped from a B-52.

In those three fateful years between August 1953 and May 1956 the Soviet Union was the only power in the world possessing a stockpile of hydrogen bombs. During those three years we did not have even one weapon in the megaton range. Those who demanded in 1956 that we call a halt to our testing of hydrogen bombs were unaware of the fact—kept secret from our people and from the world—that the Russians had had three years in which to accumulate a multimegaton stockpile of intermediate ballistic missiles with thermonuclear warheads, whereas at that time we had just begun to build up such a stockpile. And it is well to keep in mind that even as late as 1958 they had had five years in which to design and test improved thermonuclear weapons for both offense and defense, as against only two years on our side.

It is one of the ironies of our time that though we knew that Russia had the secrets of our atom bomb, we waited four years before the secrets known to her were given to the American people.

An order of President Eisenhower, issued on December 15, 1953, requested that all enforcement officers, both Federal and state, report all information relating to violations of the Atomic Energy Act to the nearest field representative of the F.B.I. Pursuant to this White House request, a description of atomic devices and component parts, including a description of the two principal types of atomic bombs, was sent out to all law enforcement officials on January 1, 1954, by J. Edgar Hoover, the F.B.I.'s director.

The release of the description of the "atomic devices," Mr. Hoover wrote, "has been approved by the Atomic Energy Commission, the National Security Council, and the President in order that you may be better able to recognize atomic devices or parts of atomic devices which might come to your attention."

The main purpose of Mr. Hoover's action was to warn all police agencies that it is now possible for enemy agents to smuggle compact atomic sabotage bombs into the United States.

There is one basic fact about atomic bombs that must be kept in mind in order to understand the principles involved in their design. It is known as the critical mass, and it relates to a definite quantity of fissionable material. Any quantity below this mass will not explode. As soon as the critical mass is reached the explosion takes place automatically in about a millionth of a second.

The actual amount of the critical mass is still kept secret, but Oliphant, the British physicist, has estimated that it would be somewhere between ten and thirty kilograms (about twenty-two to sixty-six pounds).

If, for example, the critical mass is ten kilograms, such an amount could not be put in one piece, for it would explode automatically. Hence, in one type of bomb, the ten kilograms are divided in two parts, say eight and two kilograms respectively, and placed in opposite parts of a gun barrel. At the proper moment the two parts are brought together by a gun mechanism, thus forming a critical mass that explodes automatically.

Another way to bring about a critical mass is to increase the density of the fissionable material by the application of sudden and equal pressure at all points. For example, a mass of nine kilograms would be subcritical at normal density, but by the application of great pressure, evenly distributed, on all sides of the mass, we would increase the density of the material from subcritical to critical.

Such a sudden increase in density by the application of pressure on all sides is known as an implosion. The word means a bursting inward, as contrasted with an explosion, which means a bursting outward.

With this in mind, the description of the atomic bombs sent to all police agents by Mr. Hoover makes very interesting reading. Here is the text in full:

December 21, 1953

In order that citizens of the United States may intelligently assist in the defense of our country, they should have sufficient information regarding atomic weapons to enable them to recognize bombs or parts of bombs which might be smuggled into the United States by enemy agents.

It is impossible to describe exactly what a foreign atomic bomb will look like. On the other hand, it is possible to explain the basic ideas which will govern their design. For this explanation it is then possible to designate and describe those materials which must be essential to the construction of any atomic bomb.

Atomic explosions result when (1) certain amounts of fissionable material in two pieces or more are brought quickly together to form one piece of such material and when (2) a certain amount of fissionable material is quickly made more dense by squeezing it together.

The important thing about each of these methods is that masses of fissionable material must be placed into rapid motion. We know that high explosives are capable of giving any material such necessary rapid motion.

In the first case we would look for some kind of a gun-barrel device using high explosive to blow one piece of fissionable material from the breech end of the gun down through the barrel into another piece of fissionable material firmly anchored in the muzzle end of the gun.

In the second case we would look for a device using high explosive to squeeze fissionable material. To explain how such a device will work we must understand what is meant by "implosion."

The significance of the word explosion is familiar to most people. Implosion signifies a bursting inward as contrasted with the bursting outward of an explosion. In order to obtain an implosion, however, strange as it may seem, explosive material is necessary.

The scientists who worked on the first atomic bomb needed an implosion in order to compress nuclear material enough to get an atomic "explosion." They solved their problem by forming a large sphere of explosive material. In a hole in the center of this sphere they placed the fissionable material they wanted to squeeze.

Then instead of using one detonator to ignite the explosive sphere, they placed many detonators around it. These detonators were connected electrically in such a way that they could be fired simultaneously.

If only one detonator had been used, one can easily understand that the sphere, having been ignited at only one point, would have exploded in the ordinary way; that is, with the exploding wave burning through the sphere from one side to the other. However, with many detonators igniting the sphere from all sides, the fast-burning wave is essentially spherical in shape and burns inward toward the center of the sphere.

When this fast-burning imploding wave reaches the sphere of fis-

183

sionable material, this mass has no place to be pushed except in upon itself and is thus compressed.

We have now explained very simply the basic ideas which govern atomic bomb design. Looking back at these ideas, we note that two essential features of the gun-type device are the gun barrel itself and fissionable material, and two essential features of the implosion-type device are high explosive charges that could be used to build a sphere and again fissionable material.

We see by this that we will be able to help protect ourselves and our country, if we can recognize any one of three essential components; namely:

1. Fissionable material.
2. Gun-barrel-type device.
3. High explosives for implosion.

In order to help us in our recognition of these essential components, we must learn something about them. Fissionable material is uranium and/or plutonium, which are extremely heavy metals weighing half again as much as lead of the same size. Fifty pounds of these heavy fissionable materials would be approximately five inches in diameter, if in the shape of a sphere—about the size of a softball.

Since both of these metals can be coated with other metals or plastics and can be machined into all sorts of shapes, we should be especially alert regarding any article that is extremely heavy for its size. Pieces which might be smuggled would probably be of a size that could be carried on the person.

The gun-barrel-type device will probably be made of steel. The diameter of the bore of such a gun barrel would probably not be less than two inches or more than ten inches. With such a range of inner diameters for the bore, we may expect the outer diameter of the gun barrel to range from about five inches as a minimum to about twelve inches as a maximum. Both ends of the barrel may be closed by breech-block-type devices so that the bore of the gun will not be visible.

It is possible, of course, that the gun tube and the two breech blocks may be carried as three separate pieces; in this case the inner bore may be visible. The fissionable material for this gun-type weapon may be concealed within, and usually at the ends of, the gun barrel or it may be carried in separate packages for later assembly with the barrel.

We may visualize the gun-type device then as one in which a projectile of fissionable material is fired down a gun barrel into another plug of fissionable material in the muzzle of the gun barrel. The length of the entire device need not exceed about two and one half feet.

The high explosives of implosion will probably be in specially fabricated shapes one side of which will be a part of a spherical surface. Most high explosives are light tan in color, have a soapy feel and are half again as heavy as an equal quantity of water.

PART TWO

The Hydrogen Bomb

CHAPTER TWENTY-TWO

We Are Catapulted

into the Hydrogen Age

THERE HAS NEVER BEEN any great mystery, from a theoretical point of view, about the H-bomb. Its principles were known long before the principles of the A-bomb. For years physical theory had predicted that, under certain circumstances, light elements such as hydrogen would fuse and release fantastic amounts of energy.

A month before the discovery of uranium fission, for example, Professor Hans Bethe of Cornell University had produced the first satisfactory theory of the source of the sun's light and heat. This called for the fusion of four atoms of hydrogen into one atom of helium at the rate of 500 million tons of hydrogen a second, producing 496 million tons of helium. The energy liberated each second by this reaction is equivalent to the energy content of 12 quadrillion tons of coal—a million times as great as the entire coal reserve of the United States.

While all this was known, it was also realized that this vast treasure house of cosmic energy would, according to the knowledge available at the time, remain forever beyond our reach under conditions then existing on earth. For this fusion of hydrogen in the sun, and in other stars of the same family, takes place at a temperature of 20 million degrees Centigrade, whereas the highest temperature that could be realized on earth was in the vicinity of 6,000 degrees Centigrade. We had a vast supply of the cosmic fuel, hydrogen, but, alas, we had no match to light it with—no match that would provide a flame at least 20 million degrees hot.

When the men of Los Alamos, of whom Dr. Bethe was one of the leaders, were building the atomic-fission bomb of U-235 or plutonium, they knew that a successful fission bomb would give them possession of a key to the cosmic treasure house of fusion energy, until then possessed only by the sun and the main-sequence stars. For their experiments and calculations revealed to them that the U-235, or plutonium, fission bomb, at the instant of its explosion, would generate a temperature of 100 million degrees Fahrenheit, three times the temperature of the sun's interior. Here at last was the match with which to light the cosmic fire of hydrogen fusion.

What this meant was that the fission bomb, when perfected, could serve as the trigger for setting off the much more powerful hydrogen bomb, a bomb whose explosive power would be practically limitless.

Yet there was one fundamental difference between the sun and the fission bomb that placed a tremendous, and at first seemingly insuperable, obstacle in the way of achieving fusion on earth on a practical scale. In the interior of the sun, the 20-million-degree temperature is constant, so that the hydrogen fusion process can go on at a leisurely pace and a steady rate. Although the temperature within an A-bomb is three times hotter than in the interior of the sun, it lasts much too short a time to permit the fusion of common hydrogen into helium.

The case is analogous to the lighting of a cigarette with a match in a high wind, when one has only one match. If the wind is of hurricane strength, there is obviously no hope of keeping the match going long enough to light the cigarette.

This inexorable time factor made it evident at the very outset that it would never be possible to duplicate on earth the fusion process in the sun with common, light hydrogen of atomic weight one. To do so would require keeping the fission bomb assembly together for too long a time—many minutes, if not hours—against an internal pressure of tens of thousands of tons.

In January 1950, when President Truman ordered the Atomic Energy Commission to "continue work," the order actually meant that the A.E.C. should investigate the possibility of whether a hydrogen bomb could be made.

The studies at Los Alamos in 1944 and 1945 had indicated that the fusion reaction could be achieved only by the fusion of the two heavy variants of hydrogen. These are known as deuterium (hydrogen of atomic mass 2) and tritium (hydrogen of atomic mass 3).

This at once presented a tremendous difficulty, for tritium does not exist in nature, and to produce it in quantity would be extremely costly both in money and in precious strategic materials.

For example, it was realized that it would require the sacrifice of eighty kilograms of plutonium, the man-made atomic-bomb fissionable element, to produce one kilogram of tritium.

What made it worse was that tritium is a radioactive element that decays at the rate of 50 per cent every twelve years. In other words, a pound of tritium in 1958 would be only half a pound in 1970.

Another major obstacle was the fact that both deuterium and tritium could not be fused in their normal gaseous state but had to be liquefied first before they would undergo a fusion reaction.

Liquid hydrogen boils (that is, reverts to gas) at a temperature of minus 423 degrees Fahrenheit under a pressure of one atmosphere (fifteen pounds per square inch). To liquefy it, the gas must be cooled in liquid air at minus 313.96 Fahrenheit, while it is kept at the same time under a pressure of 180 atmospheres.

To be transported, liquid hydrogen must be placed in a vacuum vessel surrounded by an outer vessel of liquid air. Such requirements presented enormous engineering difficulties in production, transportation and storage.

Here indeed was one of the strangest of paradoxes. Before the fusion of the two hydrogen variants at a temperature of 100 million degrees could be brought about, the hydrogen had to be first reduced to a liquid at a temperature close to absolute zero. The obvious question, of course, was whether the liquid state could be maintained, even for as long as a fraction of a millionth of a second, in the face of the temperature of 100 million degrees at which fusion could take place.

By June 1951 we had reached a serious crisis in our hydrogen bomb program. It was then that the late Gordon Dean, then chairman of the Atomic Energy Commission, decided to call a meeting of the high command of the project. To that meeting, held at the Institute for Advanced Study at Princeton, New Jersey, "came Drs. John von Neumann, Fermi, Bethe and Teller, Wheeler, Norris Bradbury, Lothar Nordheim, and every man that could conceivably have made a contribution." All the top men from every laboratory sat around the table, presided over by Dr. Oppenheimer.

In the midst of general gloom, Dr. Teller arose quietly and went to the blackboard. "Out of his own head he brought to the meeting something that was an entirely new approach to the thermonuclear weapon," according to Mr. Dean.

"It was just a theory at this point," Mr. Dean related. "Pictures were drawn on the board. Calculations were made." A new hope was injected among the participants. At the end of two days "everyone in the room was convinced that we had something for the first time that looked feasible in the way of ideas." Gloom had turned into enthusiasm, and everyone was impressed with the fact that at last "we had something foreseeable."

From that day on, the hydrogen bomb project went into full swing. "It then began to roll and it rolled very fast." Within four days the Atomic Energy Commission made a commitment for building a new plant, though at the time the A.E.C. had "no money in the budget to do it with," Mr. Dean said.

Within just one year after that day in June we were able, in the words of Mr. Dean, "to have that gadget ready." It was shipped to Eniwetok in the Pacific and was fired on November 1, 1952. It was that "gadget" that exploded with a force of five megatons (five million tons) of TNT. It was followed in March and April 1954 by at least three others of much greater power. And many more new designs have been tested since.

While the revolutionary approach that at last made the hydrogen bomb possible is still top secret, the basic principle involved may be easily surmised. It was obviously ridiculous on the face of it to try to bring about a reaction that required a temperature of 100 million degrees with ingredients that had to be kept at the same time at a temperature close to absolute zero. The only way to eliminate this impossible requirement was to do away with the necessity of reducing the hydrogen to a liquid state.

This could be done only by incorporating the hydrogen gas into some compound, in which the hydrogen would become part of a solid that could be kept at ordinary room temperatures.

There are many such hydrogen-containing solid compounds. One in particular appears to be the most logical one, indeed the only one, to serve as the principal ingredient of the hydrogen bomb.

This compound, a brand-new substance especially created for the purpose, is named lithium 6 deuteride. It is a combination of the rare, light isotope of the metal lithium, composed of three protons and three neutrons, with deuterium, or heavy hydrogen, the nucleus of which consists of one proton and one neutron.

The lithium-deuterium compound is a solid at room temperature. One atom of lithium 6 in the compound is combined with one atom of deuterium (hydrogen 2), giving the compound a molecular weight of 8. In other words, eight pounds of the compound contains six pounds of the light lithium 6, and two pounds of the heavy hydrogen 2.

Now, lithium 6 is not found in nature as a separate entity. Like the fission element, U 235, lithium comes in nature in a mixture of two variants, one of atomic mass 6 and the other of atomic mass 7. As much as 92.5 per cent of nature's lithium is the heavier lithium 7, while only 7.5 per cent is the lighter variant.

Since variants of the same element cannot be separated by chemical means, a special isotope separation plant would have to be built to isolate the lithium 6 in pure form. This, very likely, is the "new plant" which, Mr. Dean said, the Atomic Energy Commission contracted to build within four days following the June 1951 meeting at Princeton, though the A.E.C. had "no money in the budget to do it with."

The lithium 6 deuteride is of tremendous importance for two reasons. It not only makes it possible to keep the deuterium at room temperature, doing away with the requirement to reduce it to a liquid at a temperature near absolute zero, it also makes possible the miracle of producing tritium (hydrogen 3), the second essential hydrogen bomb element, within the assembly of the bomb itself at the very moment of its detonation. Thus, lithium 6 deuteride contains not only hydrogen 2 in the solid state but potentially hydrogen 3 as well.

This miracle is performed by neutrons emitted from the fission bomb trigger. A neutron entering the nucleus of lithium 6 creates a compound element of three protons and four neutrons. The entry of the high-energy neutron makes the compound nucleus highly unstable, so that the newly formed nucleus of three protons and four neutrons breaks up immediately into two gases, hydrogen 3 (tritium), with a nucleus of one proton and two neutrons, and helium with a nucleus of two protons and two neutrons.

In a fraction of a millionth of a second the explosion of the fission trigger bomb liberates both deuterium and tritium and, at the same time, produces a temperature of more than 100 million degrees, at which the deuterium and tritium undergo fusion in billionths of a second.

There is another possible fusion reaction, though this is less likely. The two nuclear particles in the deuterium (one proton, one neutron) may fuse, under the influence of the high fission temperature, with the six particles (three protons, three neutrons) in the lithium 6 nucleus, giving a nucleus of four protons and four neutrons. Such a nucleus represents a highly unstable form of beryllium, which breaks up at once into two nuclei of helium, of two protons and two neutrons each. This would release an enormous explosive fusion energy equivalent to 60,000 tons of TNT per kilogram, three times the explosive force of the fission bomb.

The new chemical compound that revolutionized the production of the hydrogen bomb made it certain that the most dreaded weapon of all—the cobalt bomb—also could be successfully built.

The cobalt bomb is a hydrogen bomb of the same fundamental type as the one that was tested successfully in the Pacific. The principal difference lies in the material of the shell surrounding the active ingredients.

Instead of a shell of steel, which becomes only mildly radioactive as it turns into a cloud of vapor, a shell of cobalt encases the fission and fusion substances. On being vaporized in the explosion, it is transformed into a deadly radioactive cloud 320 times more powerful than radium.

It is this type of hydrogen bomb of which Albert Einstein said, "If successful, radioactive poisoning of the atmosphere, and hence annihilation of any life on earth, will have been brought within the range of technical possibilities."

Whereas the fission process yields only one per cent of the weight of the fissionable elements—uranium 235 or plutonium—in free neutrons, the fusion of the nuclei of deuterium and tritium (the D-T reaction) yields as much as 20 per cent of the total weight of the two hydrogen isotopes as neutrons. The fusion of the nuclei of

600 grams of tritium with the nuclei of 400 grams of deuterium—that is, one kilogram, or 2.2 pounds—would thus yield 200 grams of free neutrons.

This small amount of neutrons would create an amount of deadly radioactive cobalt (atomic mass 60) equal to 12,000 grams. This is equal in its radioactivity to the tremendous quantity of 8,448 pounds of radium.

Because the cobalt bomb could be exploded from an unmanned barge in the middle of the ocean it could be made of any weight desired. It could, for example, in addition to its normal fission and fusion constituents, incorporate as much as a ton of deuterium in a solid compound.

Such a monster would, on being fused into helium, yield as much as 250 pounds of free neutrons. These would produce 7.5 tons of radioactive cobalt, equal to nearly five million pounds of radium.

According to Professor Harrison Brown, nuclear chemist at the California Institute of Technology, a cobalt bomb incorporating a ton of deuterium, could be set on a north-south line in the Pacific about a thousand miles west of California. The radioactive dust would reach California in about a day, and New York in four or five days, killing most life as it traverses the continent.

He added, "Similarly, the Western powers could explode hydrogen-cobalt bombs on a north-south line about the longitude of Prague that would destroy all life within a strip fifteen hundred miles wide, extending from Leningrad to Odessa, and three thousand miles deep, from Prague to the Ural Mountains. Such an attack would produce a 'scorched earth' unprecedented in history."

Professor Szilard has estimated that 400 one-ton deuterium-cobalt bombs would release enough radioactivity to extinguish all life on earth.

CHAPTER TWENTY-THREE

Why There Cannot Be Another War

Aʙᴏᴜᴛ ᴏɴᴇ ʜᴏᴜʀ ʙᴇꜰᴏʀᴇ sᴜɴʀɪsᴇ on Monday, May 21, 1956, in the northern Pacific, I stood on the flag bridge of the *U.S.S. Mount McKinley* and watched the test explosion of America's first airborne hydrogen bomb.

It had been dropped from a B-52, then the world's fastest bomber, in the vicinity of the island of Namu in the Bikini atoll, and was exploded at a height of more than fifteen thousand feet after being released from an altitude of about ten miles.

While hydrogen fusion bombs of immense destructive power had been exploded before in our Pacific proving ground in the Marshall Islands, the one I saw that Monday morning was the first portable one, the first that could actually deliver its catastrophic blow to the land of any aggressor.

It was the first one that could carry to a potential enemy an apocalyptic concentrate of megatons of devastation, the equivalent of millions of tons of TNT.

Through high-density goggles I saw a supersun rise over the vastness of the blue-black Pacific, with a dazzling burst of green-white light estimated to equal, for a brief instant, the light of five hundred suns at high noon. Awestruck, I watched the enormous fireball expand in a matter of seconds to a diameter of about four miles, more than twenty times the diameter of the fireball of the now antiquated atomic-fission bombs that had devastated Hiroshima and Nagasaki.

For nearly an hour after the fireball had faded I watched incredulously the great many-colored cloud that had been born in a gigantic pillar of fire. This cloud rose and spread until the boiling mushroom at its top had reached about twenty-five miles into the stratosphere and covered a stretch of sky, now tinged by the rising sun to the east of it, about a hundred miles long.

Having seen what a much smaller fireball and mushroom-topped cloud had done to the city of Nagasaki, I was momentarily staggered by the thought of what the fireball and mushroom I was then watching would do to any of the world's great cities—New York, Washington, Chicago, Paris, London, Rome or Moscow. But then, as I kept on watching, a second, more reassuring thought became uppermost in my mind, a thought that has kept growing ever more reassuring in the years that have followed that historic morning.

This great iridescent cloud and its mushroom top, I found myself thinking as I watched, is actually a protective umbrella that will forever shield mankind everywhere against the threat of annihilation in any atomic war.

This rising supersun seemed to me the symbol of the dawn of a new era in which any sizable war had become impossible; for no aggressor could now start a war without the certainty of absolute and swift annihilation.

This world-covering, protective umbrella, I have since become convinced, will continue shielding us everywhere until the time comes, as come it must, when mankind will be able to beat atomic swords into plowshares, harnessing the vast power of the hydrogen in the world's oceans to bring in an era of prosperity such as the world has never even dared dream about.

To those who would have us stop our tests in the Pacific, I would therefore say, "These tests, and others of improved models to come, serve as an effective substitute for war. History will record, I am sure, that World War III was fought and won on the Pacific proving ground in the Marshall Islands without the loss of a single life and without the slightest damage to any inhabited locality anywhere in the world."

That this is not mere wishful thinking can be proved by a few simple facts. The single atomic-fission bomb I saw tested in the desert of New Mexico on the morning of July 16, 1945—the same model that I watched three weeks later transform the city of Nagasaki into an atomic cloud that rose sixty thousand feet—packed a destructive power equal to that of twenty thousand tons of TNT, namely, an explosive force of twenty kilotons.

Nowadays, when we talk in terms of megatons—the equivalent of millions of tons of TNT—a bomb of only kilotons is a mere outdated trifle by comparison.

Nevertheless, that now antiquated atomic weapon was in its day the equal of no less than 2,000 ten-ton blockbusters, which were considered veritable monsters in the first years of World War II.

To carry the equivalent of just one Nagasaki-type bomb, it will thus be seen, would then have required no less than two thousand B-29s, World War II's largest bombers, each costing about $1,000-000. With a crew of nine men per bomber, such a mission would have required eighteen thousand highly trained young American fliers. The Nagasaki-type bomb, on the other hand, was carried by just one B-29 and one crew of nine.

A few years later, this equivalent of 2,000 ten-ton blockbusters of World War II was so obsolete that it was not even fit to be used as a trigger for the multimegaton hydrogen bomb. To set off a hydrogen fusion bomb of the type I watched explode on May 21, we now have improved models of ordinary atomic-fission bombs (using uranium 235 or plutonium) yielding an explosive force as high as five hundred kilotons (the equivalent of 500,000 tons of TNT), or smaller ones of much higher efficiency than the models dropped on Japan.

With the successful testing of our first portable multimegaton hydrogen bomb, we have entered the megaton age, in which a single plane, carrying just one hydrogen bomb, can deliver on a target a cargo of destructive force exceeding by far all the explosives dropped on Germany, Japan and Italy combined throughout all of World War II.

In fact, a ten-megaton bomb, about the size of the one I saw explode over Bikini, would equal about five times the total load of explosives dropped in the whole of World War II by the air forces of all the combatants.

What would such a ten-megaton bomb do if dropped over a city? We can get an idea from the official data given out by the Atomic Energy Commission on the results of the test of a device that yielded an explosive force of only five megatons—the equivalent of five million tons of TNT—in the November 1952 test. That shot, known as "Mike," produced the greatest lateral destructive effects up to that time from a single explosive device—complete annihilation within a radius of three miles, severe to moderate damage out to seven miles, light damage as far as ten miles.

In Washington, with the Capitol as Ground Zero (detonation point), there would have been complete annihilation west to Arlington Cemetery, east to the Anacosta River, north to the Soldiers' Home, and south to Bolling Field.

That five-megaton bomb created the largest nuclear explosive fireball produced up to that time—three and a half miles in diameter at its maximum, enough to engulf about one quarter of Manhattan Island, the heart of New York City. With the Empire State Building as Ground Zero, the fireball would have extended from Washington Square to Central Park.

That blast caused the particular test island, named Elugelab, to disappear, leaving a crater roughly a mile in diameter, into which fourteen Pentagon Buildings could have fitted easily. The crater sloped down to 175 feet—equivalent to the height of a seventeen-story building.

Within two minutes after the explosion, the mushroom cloud soared to forty thousand feet—the height of thirty-two Empire State Buildings. Nearing its maximum ten minutes later, the cloud stem pushed upward twenty-five miles, deep into the stratosphere, while the mushroom cap portion, ten miles high, spread laterally for a hundred miles.

Yet even this apocalyptic weapon was dwarfed by the two high-altitude hydrogen bombs detonated over Johnston Island, 700 miles southwest of Honolulu, during the Hardtack series in 1958. The first shot, named Teak, was detonated near midnight on July 31, 1958, at an altitude in excess of 200,000 feet. The second one, named Orange, was detonated at an altitude of about 100,000 feet shortly before midnight on August 11, 1958. Both thermonuclear devices, carried aloft by missiles, were the first megaton devices ever detonated in the stratosphere by the United States.

Teak and Orange were by far the most spectacular shots ever fired by the United States. Teak produced a bright fireball which grew rapidly and immediately started to rise at a rate of approximately

½ to one mile per second. An aurora, the first man-made aurora in history, developed from the bottom of the fireball and spread rapidly to the north. The fireball reached a diameter of approximately 11 miles in 0.3 of a second and a diameter of better than 18 miles in 3.5 seconds. It glowed brightly for five minutes. The fireball of the Orange shot developed much more slowly, and the aurora, which was somewhat less pronounced than that of Teak, did not appear until after the fireball had risen.

The explosions disrupted radio communications for thousands of miles, beclouded radar sets and partly blinded rabbits more than 300 miles away.

These earth-destroying weapons, now being constantly reduced in size and increased in power, thus make it certain that no nation, no matter how powerful, could dare risk a thermonuclear war.

CHAPTER TWENTY-FOUR

The "Clean" Hydrogen Bomb

During 1954 and 1955 the free world passed through, without knowing it, a major crisis that threatened to cripple its defenses by depriving it of its most potent deterrent weapon against totalitarian aggression. During those two fateful years we came pretty close to losing the hydrogen bomb. In fact, to all intents and purposes we had practically lost it, though neither we nor the Russians fully realized it at the time. Only now, when the danger is fortunately past, can the story of the crisis, one of the most fateful in modern times, be told, within the limits of security.

By one of the strangest of paradoxes, our near-loss of our most powerful defensive weapon, the only weapon that counterbalances the overwhelming superiority of the totalitarians in manpower, did not come about as the result of espionage or sabotage on the part of any potential enemy, nor because of any negligence or carelessness on our part. It came about, incredible as it may sound, because the weapon was much too good—so good, in fact, that it threatened to kill hundreds of millions of people without discrimination between friend and foe. Even more dreadful, the weapon turned out to be so "dirty" that it threatened to contaminate the hereditary endowment of future generations.

Obviously, a weapon so dirty that it would indiscriminately maim and kill untold millions of human beings, as well as generations yet unborn, could not under any conceivable circumstances be used. Even if we did not openly renounce it, the Soviet Union and the rest of the world would know that the use by us, or any nation, of such a terrible weapon would be unthinkable. This, of course, meant that the weapon could no longer be regarded as a deterrent against aggression, so its possession became totally meaningless.

As Lieutenant General James M. Gavin, Army chief of research and development, testified in secret before a Senate subcommittee on May 25, 1956 (made public on June 28), an all-out nuclear attack by our Air Force on the Soviet Union would result in "several hundred million deaths, that would be either way, depending upon which way the wind blew."

Our stockpile of hydrogen bombs was not only in danger of becoming useless as a deterrent but was actually being transformed into a most potent propaganda weapon against us.

This propaganda has gained millions of adherents not only in the Communist world but also among neutral nations and in our own country, where the subject of the banning of further tests of large hydrogen bombs was made one of the major issues of the 1956 Presidential election campaign. A joint Indian-Soviet declaration on December 13, 1955, stated that "the leaders of both countries wish to emphasize again their strong conviction that there should be unconditional prohibition of the production, use and experimentation of nuclear and thermonuclear weapons." Pope Pius XII, in his Christmas 1955 message, said, "We propose to direct our attention to a recent proposal which aims at putting a check on experiments in nuclear weapons by means of an international agreement." And Adlai Stevenson, speaking in April and May 1956, some months before he was nominated as the Democratic Party's candidate for President, suggested that "we announce that we would voluntarily suspend further tests of H-bombs and ask Russia to do likewise," a suggestion he later modified to a proposal for an agreement between the Soviet Union and ourselves to discontinue testing of high-yield hydrogen bombs.

The true nature of the question "to test or not to test" was outlined by the distinguished foreign-affairs authority, our former ambassador to the Soviet Union, Mr. George F. Kennan, now a professor at the Institute for Advanced Study at Princeton. Writing on October 19, 1956, Professor Kennan said:

There are hundreds of millions of people who are not yet convinced that Washington, in its treatment of these questions [the ban on H-bomb tests], has their interests, those of their children and, in short, the future of civilization, adequately at heart. The feelings of these millions cannot be safely ignored.

That the dreadful fallout did, indeed, worry our leaders was revealed by President Eisenhower in his press conference a few days before the scheduled Pacific tests of 1956. One of the main objectives of the forthcoming nuclear testing program, he told the conference, was the making of weapons with "reduced fallout."

That we have actually succeeded in designing a "cleaner" type of hydrogen bomb was indicated later in a statement by then Chairman Lewis L. Strauss of the Atomic Energy Commission, and, in the course of the 1956 Presidential election campaign, by President Eisenhower himself.

It was the successful test explosion of a cleaner weapon that I witnessed on the morning of Monday, May 21, from the flag bridge of the *U.S.S. Mount McKinley,* off Bikini atoll.

On July 19, less than two months after that event, Chairman Strauss announced that "the mass hazard from fallout" has been proved by the 1956 tests not to be "a necessary complement to the use of large nuclear weapons." The weapons tested in the Pacific in the spring and summer of 1956, Mr. Strauss told the world, achieved "maximum effect in the immediate area of a target with minimum widespread fallout hazard." The tests have "confirmed," Mr. Strauss added, "that there are many factors, including operational ones, which do make it possible to localize to an extent not heretofore appreciated the fallout effect of nuclear explosions."

Mr. Strauss concluded: "Thus the current [1956] series of tests has produced much of importance not only from the military point of view but also from a humanitarian aspect."

The "operational factors" mentioned by Mr. Strauss refer to the explosion of a multimegaton hydrogen bomb from a high altitude, in the vicinity of thirty thousand feet—that is, above the radius of the huge fireball formed at the instant of the explosion. When exploded from a height greater than its radius (about three to four miles) the fireball is prevented from touching the ground, or the ocean surface, and hence from lifting thousands of tons of either earth or water, contaminated with deadly radioactive particles, into a gigantic fallout-producing cloud.

However, Mr. Strauss's suggestion that there are "many factors" in addition to the purely operational ones "which do make it possible to localize the fallout effect of nuclear explosions" could only mean a reduction in the fissionable material—largely heavy uranium—responsible for the major part of the dangerous fallout.

This was further suggested in a statement by President Eisenhower on October 23, 1956.

"The most recent tests," the President said, "enable us to *harness* and *discipline* our weapons more precisely and effectively, *drastically reducing their fallout* and making them more easy to concentrate, if ever used, upon military objectives. Further progress along these lines is confidently expected."

Does this mean that we have a 100 per cent clean hydrogen bomb? Since all hydrogen bombs require an ordinary atomic bomb as a trigger to set them off, and since all atomic bombs produce a certain amount of fallout, depending on their size, it is obvious that no hydrogen bomb completely free from fallout is possible.

On the other hand, the hydrogen bomb may be designed, on the basis of new principles recently discovered, so that only a "small" atomic bomb, say one of a power equivalent to fifty thousand tons of TNT, could set off a hydrogen bomb of a power of five megatons (five million tons in terms of TNT), derived from fusion. This would mean a reduction of the fallout to only one per cent of the total, instead of more than 80 per cent of dangerous fallout from a dirty bomb of equivalent yield.

The construction of the clean hydrogen weapons is, of course, top secret. But certain facts that have come to light leave no doubt about what is involved in the cleaning-up process. Briefly stated, these facts have revealed that from 80 to 90 per cent of the dangerous radioactive fallout comes from the fission (i.e., splitting) of the atoms of a dirty element. Hence it becomes obvious that to make a clean bomb the thing to do is to eliminate the dirty element from the bomb's assembly. But, as will be presently explained, this entailed tremendous difficulties that appeared insurmountable.

The identity of the dirty element was first revealed in a study by Japanese physicists, who recently published a monumental two-volume report on their careful analysis of the deadly radioactive ashes that landed on their fishing vessel following the explosion of the dirty hydrogen bomb at Bikini on March 1, 1954.

These studies revealed that the greatest proportion of the gigantic poisonous cloud of radioactive dust that contaminated an area of seven thousand square miles did not come from the hydrogen elements in the bomb, nor, indeed, from either of the two fissionable elements—uranium 235 or plutonium—that serve as the explosive elements in ordinary atomic bombs.

By some strange miracle of transformation, the giant poisonous mushroom cloud, as well as more than 90 per cent of the explosive force of some fifteen megatons (the equivalent of fifteen million tons of TNT) came, the Japanese studies revealed, from the otherwise very peaceful, nonexplosive form of uranium known as uranium 238, the cheap and most abundant form of the element, which constitutes more than 99 per cent of all the uranium found in nature.

The Japanese analyses revealed that it was the successful transformation of the uranium "Dr. Jekyll" into a uranium "Mr. Hyde" that constituted the true secret of the dirty hydrogen bomb. What the fusion of the hydrogen elements in the bomb's assembly actually accomplished, these vital studies revealed, was to release, in the tenth of a millionth of a second during which the bomb's assembly was held together, a vast supply of neutrons of such tremendous energies that they are capable of cracking the atoms of the non-explosive type of uranium.

What makes the uranium 238 so much more frightful and threatening to the human race is that, unlike the ordinary A-bomb elements that explode automatically after reaching a rather small critical mass, there is no critical limit to the amount of material that can be incorporated into a hydrogen bomb. Since uranium 238 is by nature a gentle Dr. Jekyll until the moment of explosion, any amount can be put into the bomb, depending on how much of an explosive force is desired. A one-megaton bomb would be designed to explode fifty kilograms (110 pounds) of this Jekyll-and-Hyde element, while a bomb of twenty megatons would require the explosion of a thousand kilograms (about a ton) of the dirty element.

Since the Jekyll-and-Hyde substance is the one responsible for almost all the dirty character of the weapon known as the hydrogen bomb (which is mainly a uranium-238 bomb), it becomes obvious that the only way to make a clean hydrogen bomb is to eliminate the dirty element. Alas, in view of the fact that not only 80 to 90 per cent of the fallout but also about 80 per cent of the explosive force comes from the dirty element, the solution on the face of it looks like a recipe for making an omelet without eggs, or an apple pie without apples.

The only way possible to produce a clean hydrogen bomb entirely free from fallout, save for the small amount from the A-bomb trigger, is to produce a weapon that derives its explosive force entirely from the fusion of hydrogen. But here nature interposed a seemingly insurmountable roadblock. To produce a pure hydrogen bomb requires two heavy forms of hydrogen, hydrogen 2 and hydrogen 3. Hydrogen 2, known as deuterium, which has a weight twice that of common hydrogen 1, constitutes 0.02 per cent of the world's waters, from which it is concentrated cheaply by electricity. But hydrogen 3, known as tritium, which weighs three times as much as hydrogen 1, disappeared from the earth aeons ago.

Tritium can be re-created in a nuclear reactor out of light lithium of atomic mass 6, which must first be separated from the heavy lithium 7, the variety that constitutes 92.5 per cent of the lithium found in nature. A neutron from the fission of uranium 235 in the reactor enters the nucleus of lithium 6, which consists of three protons and three neutrons. The entry of the fission neutron in the nucleus of lithium 6 results in the creation of two gases, tritium, the nucleus of which consists of one proton and two neutrons, and helium, the nucleus of which consists of two protons and two neutrons. The combined total of the tritium and the helium nuclei thus accounts for the three protons and three neutrons of the original lithium 6 nucleus, plus the extra fission neutron that had entered it.

To create the tritium in the relatively enormous quantities that would be required for a stock pile of clean hydrogen bombs of megaton yield, in which the explosive force would be derived, with the exception of the trigger fission bomb, entirely from the fusion of hydrogen 2 (deuterium) and hydrogen 3 (tritium), would be prohibitively costly, requiring many multibillion-dollar nuclear reactors.

However, as already stated, there are strong indications that our scientists have perfected a method that creates tritium simply and cheaply inside the bomb itself. This is done by incorporating into the bomb a special solid compound, named lithium 6 deuteride, which consists of a combination of lithium 6 and hydrogen 2.

When the fission bomb trigger explodes, the neutrons released in the process enter the lithium 6 and transmute it into tritium and helium, as explained earlier. The tritium thus created then fuses, as the result of a 100-million-degree temperature created by the explosion of the fission trigger, with the hydrogen 2 in the compound, and this leads to a tremendous explosion due mostly to the clean tritium-deuterium fusion process, which yields fewer dangerous radioactive-fallout products.

As was indicated in the A.E.C.'s July 1956 report to Congress, the reduction in fallout, and the promise of still greater reduction to come, has to be paid for by a reduction of the power of the bomb. But a bomb of even one or two megatons would still be great enough to cripple any large city, and is thus still good enough to serve its purpose as the most powerful deterrent in our defensive arsenal. Furthermore, the elimination of the dirty element makes the bomb much lighter.

In fact, the 1956 Pacific tests included the testing not only of high-yield hydrogen weapons in the megaton range but also of much smaller hydrogen bombs, made possible by the elimination of the heavy dirty element. These small hydrogen bombs greatly enlarge the potentialities of the clean weapon for defensive purposes. They can be used as warheads in ground-to-air missiles as powerful defenses against air attack, and as portable weapons that can be delivered by supersonic jet-powered fighter planes.

All the known facts thus make it clear that we are succeeding in humanizing the hydrogen bomb by limiting its enormous destructive power to blast and fire, thus transforming it from a radioactive monster, deriving most of its power from a dirty element, into a concentrated weapon deriving most of its explosive force from the fusion of two forms of hydrogen in which fallout is reduced to a minimum.

CHAPTER TWENTY-FIVE

Alice in Thunderland

A BABY GIRL was born to a native of the Marshall Islands at the moment of the explosion of a multimegaton hydrogen bomb on Eniwetok atoll a few hundred miles away. The child was named Alice, after Alice Strauss, wife of the then chairman of the Atomic Energy Commission, who had presented to the young mother a fortune of ten pigs. It was then inevitable that someone sooner or later would refer to the newborn as "Alice in Thunderland."

Thunderland is a vast stretch of deep-blue and emerald-green Pacific water covering nearly half a million square miles. Its land mass consists of two atolls, Eniwetok and Bikini, strings of tiny coral islands surrounding great lagoons covering hundreds of square miles. Visiting them, one comes upon the shattered dreams of would-be empire builders, first the Germans, then the Japanese. On one of the islands of Eniwetok atoll, for example, named Enau, there is a forest of neatly planted coconut trees, its coral base spread over several acres with a thick layer of rich black soil. The black soil, thousands of tons of it, was transported by the Germans before World War I all the way from the Black Forest in Germany as part of an ambitious plan to transform the coral islands into rich agricultural colonies.

The Japanese, in their turn, made these islands into strongholds of the Micronesian Fortress, which was to serve as one of the key-stones in their planned conquest of the Pacific world. Enau now serves as a recreation center for the American inhabitants of Thunderland, with a clubhouse and a well-stocked bar.

I well remembered these atolls from my earlier sojourn during Operation Crossroads—the first atomic tests in Bikini—in the summer of 1946. The principal island of Bikini atoll, also named Bikini, was then a little paradise, covered with large shady palms and coconut groves and surrounded on all sides by green waters that reflected the coral beneath.

I had a particular interest in one of the groves fronting the beach, for it had been named, because my prophecy of its destruction by the atomic bomb had not come true, the "William L. Laurence Memorial Grove." Sure enough, as we flew over it this time, there was the Memorial Grove still standing in its original splendor. But the erstwhile paradise was reminiscent of the original Eden in only two respects: It was forbidden ground because of its highly secret installations; and on the beach there was a large sign, "Do not eat the fruit of these trees, they are poisonous!" The soil, the trees and all their fruit had become dangerously radioactive.

There were similar signs on the trees growing on the transplanted Black Forest. They warned of the forbidden fruits of the tree of knowledge of the atomic age.

The day set for the blast was, of course, known as D day. It took a full four days to complete all the vast co-ordinated movements of ships, planes, materials and men required to carry out the test, so that the four preparatory days were known, respectively, as D minus 4, D minus 3, D minus 2, and D minus 1. As one postponement after another had to be made because the wind pattern from the surface up to 100,000 feet blew in the wrong direction, it was no longer possible to reverse the process in its entirety back to D minus 4, and so everything had to be placed on a permanent D-minus-2 basis.

As the final decision to shoot or not to shoot was to be made at the very last minute, depending on last-minute shifts in the wind, we never knew on going to bed what the night would bring. And since the test was to be held at about an hour before sunrise, we would leave word to be called at four-fifteen. The sailor assigned to get us up would arrive punctually to shake us at the appointed time and announce, "It's four-fifteen, sir, you don't have to get up!" On the morning of D day, when all he said was "It's four-fifteen," I wondered until the last minute whether the test would actually take place, or whether it would be called off. This actually happened on at least two occasions.

The pool photographers were not permitted to take pictures until after fifteen seconds had been counted off. As the security agent was counting off the quarter minute a small cloud was slowly creeping along, and by the time the fifteenth second had passed the cloud had all but hidden the magnificent spectacle of the fireball. The frustrated muttering of the photographers is still ringing in my ears.

And I shall not soon forget the lead of one of the two pool correspondents for the afternoon newspapers, a leading political reporter from Washington whose familiarity with nuclear terminology was rather elementary. It read:

"Megaton, shmegaton, it's a hell of a bomb!"

PART THREE

Looking Backward

CHAPTER TWENTY-SIX

A Light from the Depths

THE ATOMIC "SUNRISE" at Alamogordo in July 1945 was preceded by a dawn that began nearly half a century earlier. Its first faint light, invisible to human eyes, manifested itself on a photographic plate in the dark drawer of a desk, where it had been placed by an absent-minded professor of physics one sunless day in Paris in 1896. By one of the strange paradoxes of history, the dawn of a new era on earth, which reached its climax nearly fifty years later in the first light that did not have its origin in the sun, came as a result of the failure of the sun to shine that bleak winter day in Paris in 1896. But it took some years before the meaning of that light in the desk drawer was understood or its true significance recognized.

The strange revelation of the light from the inner cosmos, which had about it at the time an aspect of the supernatural, came to Henri Becquerel, who, like his father and grandfather before him, was professor of physics at the Paris Museum of Natural History. He was an international authority on fluorescence, the ability of some substances to emit light on being exposed to sunlight or other radiations, and at that particular time, the early months of 1896, he had become greatly interested in X rays, those highly penetrating radiations that had been accidentally discovered in Germany by Wilhelm Konrad Roentgen in November 1895. What interested him most was a suggestion by the great mathematician Henri Poincaré that there might be a direct connection between the X rays and the fluorescence shown by the glass of the vacuum tube at the spot from which the X rays emerged. If that were so, Becquerel reasoned, then the fluorescence of natural substances might also be accompanied by X rays, which would mean that X rays could be produced much more simply and economically without vacuum tubes and high-voltage current.

The news of the discovery of X rays had electrified the world. Here were mysterious rays that possessed the power to penetrate flesh, cloth, wood and metal. In the popular belief they literally "saw" through everything. They could remove walls of houses and partitions between rooms. They could undress women. Every attractive Victorian lady would become a Lady Godiva, helpless before the gaze of peeping Toms everywhere, armed with long-range X-ray spyglasses. Victorian maidens blushed at the very mention of the term "X ray" and elderly gentlemen talked about it with relish in the privacy of their clubs.

Newspapers all over the world published all sorts of fantastic stories illustrated with ghastly skeleton pictures of hands and legs of living persons. Sunday supplements had a field day. Some New York newspapers speculated that the new rays might lead to photography of departed spirits and of the soul. One newspaper reported that X rays were used at the College of Physicians and Surgeons to reflect anatomic diagrams directly into the brains of students, thereby making a much more enduring impression than by ordinary methods of learning.

One assemblyman in New Jersey introduced a bill in the House prohibiting the use of X rays in opera glasses at theaters. In London a firm advertised "X-ray-proof clothing." And the London *Pall Mall Gazette* thundered editorially, "We are sick of the Roentgen rays. Perhaps the best thing would be for all civilized nations to combine to burn all the Roentgen rays, to execute all the discoverers, and to corner all the equipment in the world and to whelm it in the middle of the ocean. Let the fish contemplate each other's bones if they like, but not us."

But to Henri Becquerel the X ray held promise of a powerful new searchlight for probing deeper into the dark caverns of nature. His first task was to find out whether these X radiations were in any way related to fluorescence. Two rather simple steps were to give the answer. The first would be to expose a suitable substance to sunlight until it became strongly fluorescent. He could then determine whether the fluorescent radiations possessed the power of X rays to fog a photographic plate wrapped in thick dark paper opaque to ordinary light.

It so happened that Henri's father, Edmond Becquerel, had carried out extensive investigation into the phenomenon of fluorescence, as well as of the related phenomenon of phosphorescence, and as a result the museum had a large collection of substances exhibiting either one of these properties. And out of this large collection Henri picked, of all things and for reasons not known, a salt of uranium as the substance for testing, the very element that forty-three years later brought in the atomic age.

What made him pick the uranium salt? Was it just a hunch? Scientific intuition? Pure chance? Nobody knows. But whatever the reason, it must go down as one of the strangest coincidences in history that Becquerel happened to choose the one and only natural element that can be used as an atomic fuel or explosive, the one and only element without which neither the atomic bomb nor the hydrogen bomb nor atomic power plants would be possible.

Out of the hundreds of samples he had picked the only one that held the key for unlocking the atom.

Having picked his sample he exposed it to sunlight until it showed strong fluorescence and placed it against a photographic plate wrapped in black paper impenetrable to ordinary light. Then came the thrill that comes only to a seeker after knowledge on the rare occasion when nature reveals to him an important secret. For upon developing the plate that had been so securely shielded against exposure by ordinary light, he saw to his delight that it had been blackened by some mysterious rays that penetrated the dark paper as only X rays could. There was no doubt that strong fluorescence could produce X rays. All one had to do was to expose a fluorescent substance to sunlight.

But as he was about getting ready to repeat his crucial experiment, heavy black clouds denied him the sunlight that he needed to make his uranium salt fluorescent.

Here came another of those strange accidents of history in which a little thing led to tremendous consequences. Since there was no sunlight the experiment had to wait for another day, so Becquerel put the unopened package of new photographic plates he had ordered, wrapped as usual in thick dark paper to prevent exposure, into a drawer in his desk. And on top of the package of plates, for no particular reason, and without actually being aware of what he was doing, he placed the sample of uranium salt.

But when the sun failed to shine the next day and the next Henri Becquerel grew impatient. He remembered that the uranium sample had been exposed to sunlight for a few moments before the sun went under a cloud. He also knew that some salts of uranium are phosphorescent, that is, they continue to glow in the dark for some time after they have been exposed to sunlight. And so he decided to find out whether even the short exposure to sunlight might not have induced the uranium salt to emit X radiations.

His amazement was great when, on developing the plates, he found that the blackening effect was much more striking than it had been the first time, when the uranium had been exposed to brighter sunlight for a much longer period. Another experiment with new plates and a uranium sample that had not been exposed to sunlight soon made it clear that exposure to sunlight had nothing to do with the blackening of the photographic plate through the dark paper. There was another "sun" within the uranium giving off rays much more powerful than sunlight.

Further experiments revealed that the rays, at first named Becquerel rays, were entirely unaffected by external conditions. Even more amazing, they seemed to persist with undiminished strength indefinitely. "The bush burned with fire, and the bush was not consumed."

Becquerel had discovered radioactivity, the phenomenon that gave man the most important key to the universe and opened for him gates of new worlds so dazzling that to this day his eyes have not as yet been able to discern them except in very faint outline.

CHAPTER TWENTY-SEVEN

The Vision in the Cadaver Shed

THOSE MYSTERIOUS RAYS from uranium seen by Becquerel gave the first hint of the existence of a new force in nature, a force recognized years later as the prime force of the cosmos, dwelling within the heart of matter, the nucleus of the atoms of which the universe is made.

But man's eyes beheld much more awesome rays from the inner cosmic fire some six years later, in 1902, when the first few grains of radium were finally extracted by Marie and Pierre Curie out of a ton of pitchblende, the principal uranium-bearing ore.

Indeed, it was the discovery of radium in 1898 by the most famous scientific couple in all history, and the concentration of the first infinitesimal bits of that magic element after nearly four years of herculean labors, that led inevitably, step by step, by devious routes in the course of the following thirty-six years, to the arrival of the atomic age.

Marie Curie, nee Sklodowska, a native of Poland, was then thirty-one. Pierre, a brilliant chemist and a professor at the municipal School of Physics and Chemistry, was eight years older. They had been married in 1895, and their first daughter, Irène, had been born in 1897; their second daughter, Ève, was to be born in 1904. For eleven years, until April 1906, when Pierre was run over and killed by a beer wagon, they lived among the stars. Theirs was one of the world's great love stories. It was a consecration, to each other and to the search for knowledge.

217

They had discovered the new element, in fact two new elements, after observing that the remnants of pitchblende left over after the uranium had been extracted gave off radiations more powerful than the radiations from the uranium. Breaking up the pitchblende residue by painful chemical distillation, and tracing the unknown radioactive substance by its power, Marie first came upon a fraction of the residue in which the radiations appeared to be most heavily concentrated. Since the radiations appeared to be more powerful than those emanating from any element known at the time, Marie concluded that they must come from an element as yet unidentified. She named the new element polonium, after her native Czarist-oppressed Poland, which she had left seven years before to seek freedom and knowledge in France.

At this point she was joined by her husband. In their joint labors, they soon found that the radiations in the pitchblende residue came not from one but from two distinct fractions, chemically different from each other. This, they concluded, could mean only one thing: In addition to polonium, pitchblende contained a second unknown radioactive element. In a note published by them in the *Proceedings* of the French Academy of Science on the day after Christmas of 1898 they announced that they proposed to give the name of "radium" to the new radioactive element.

"The radioactivity of radium must be enormous," they informed the Academicians, who, in the manner of academicians from time immemorial, were skeptical.

"We will show them," said Marie and Pierre Curie.

They then set out on one of the greatest adventures of all time, Argonauts in search of a treasure vastly more precious than the Golden Fleece. They were searching for two mysterious and extremely rare elements that were constantly sending out signals in a language never before heard by man. But before they could even attempt to decipher the cosmic code hidden in the messages of the two elements, they had to wrest at least a few tangible grains of polonium or radium out of the mountains of ore in which nature had hidden them.

It took Marie and Pierre nearly four years of unremitting toil in a miserable shed under the most disheartening conditions before they had succeeded in concentrating a minute quantity of the elusive radium. When they had started, early in 1899, with a ton of pitchblende residue, then a waste product of uranium concentration, a gift of the Austrian government, they had hoped that it might yield as much as one per cent, or something like ten kilograms, of radium and polonium. As it turned out, all they got after four backbreaking years of labor was a puny decigram, one tenth of a gram, of radium salt, out of the whole ton, a yield of one part in ten million.

As we know today, pitchblende contains 3.4 parts of radium in ten million parts. In one ton of the mineral, if it contains 60 per cent uranium, there is only 0.2 grams of radium. Small as this quantity is, it is still five thousand times the pitchblende content of polonium, so the Curies found it impossible to isolate it in anywhere near pure form. That they managed to find it at all was due to the fact that its radiations are four thousand times as intense as those of radium, which means that one part of polonium would emit radiations equal to those of four thousand parts of radium.

The wooden shack with the leaky roof which served as the birthplace of the new age had been used by the Faculty of Medicine of the Sorbonne as a dissecting room in the teaching of anatomy, but it had been abandoned for a long time as not fit to house the cadavers. In the summer the shack was stifling hot and in the winter it was miserably cold. When it rained, the water fell drop by drop through the leaky skylight onto the worktables and on the ground. The old cast-iron stove with its rusty pipe gave no heat unless one came near enough to touch it. Since their makeshift installations were not equipped with chimneys to carry off the noxious gases, much of their work had to be carried on in the open air of a courtyard.

"It was in this miserable old shed," Marie wrote later, "that the best and happiest years of our lives were spent, entirely consecrated to work. I sometimes passed the whole day stirring a boiling mass with an iron nearly as big as myself. In the evening I was broken with fatigue."

In addition to serving as midwives at the birth of two new elements, Pierre and Marie had their infant daughter to raise.

And so the years passed. A new century began and it reached the age of two years and little Irène Curie the age of four. The great mountain of pitchblende ore had been distilled, bit by bit, into highly concentrated, strongly radioactive solutions in many glass receptacles on the old tables and shelves in the abandoned cadaver shed. And as the solutions in the glassware daily grew richer in radium Marie grew more impatient, while the miserable shack became more and more like a shrine.

"I wonder what It will be like, what It will look like, what form It will take," she kept saying, and Pierre answered, "I should like it to have a very beautiful color."

Then came an evening in the autumn of 1902 that Marie was to remember forever, an evening in which stars fell on that shack in the Rue Lhomond. Marie had fed and bathed Irène, put her to bed and sat a long time in the darkness until the child had gone to sleep. She then tiptoed down the stairs to Pierre, who had been pacing about the room, and busied herself with stitches on Irène's new apron, but somehow she felt too restless.

"Suppose we go down there for a moment?" she heard herself say.

Pierre, for his part, had also been longing to go back to the shed they had left two hours before. As Ève Curie was to write later in her famous biography of her mother, *Madame Curie,* "Radium, fanciful as a living creature, endearing as a love, called them back to its dwelling."

With Grandfather Curie, a retired physician, who came to live with the young Curies after the death of his wife, serving as babysitter, Marie and Pierre walked arm in arm to their rendezvous with destiny.

Let Ève tell the story of that night:

. . . they arrived in the Rue Lhomond and crossed the little courtyard. Pierre put the key in the lock. The door squeaked, as it had squeaked thousands of times, and admitted them to their realm, to their dream.

"Don't light the lamps!" Marie said in the darkness. Then she added with a little laugh:

"Do you remember the day when you said to me: 'I should like radium to have a beautiful color'?"

The reali~~ ~~ more entrancing than the simple wish of long ago.
~~thing better than "a beautiful color": it was spon-
~~. And in the somber shed where, in the absence of
~~ecious particles of their tiny glass receivers were

placed on tables or on shelves nailed to the wall, their phosphorescent bluish outlines gleamed, suspended in the night.

"Look. . . . Look!" the young woman murmured.

She went forward cautiously, looked for and found a straw-bottomed chair. She sat down in the darkness and silence. Their two faces turned toward the pale glimmering, the mysterious sources of radiation, toward radium—their radium. Her body leaning forward, her head eager, Marie took up again the attitude which had been hers an hour earlier at the bedside of her sleeping child.

Her companion's hand lightly touched her hair.

She was to remember forever this evening of glowworms, this magic.

Nor can mankind ever forget that vision in the cadaver shed.

CHAPTER TWENTY-EIGHT

Citadel of the Cosmos

THE EERIE GREEN-BLUE LIGHT that Pierre and Marie Curie saw that night in 1902 was in every respect a signal flashing from another world. Though they could not possibly have realized the full meaning of the strange glow in the abandoned cadaver shed, they nevertheless sensed intuitively that they had arrived at the shores of a new realm of matter never before penetrated by man.

As we have realized only recently, nearly half a century later, the light in that miserable shed signaled the blazing on earth of a new fire, millions of times more powerful than the old. It came from the same cosmic source as the supersun that flashed over the desert of New Mexico in July 1945. From the moment it was first seen the atomic age became inevitable. It was at that moment that man arrived at a turning point which may well turn out to have been the most crucial in the million years of his existence.

The light seen by the Curies was soon picked up by thirty-one-year-old New Zealand-born Ernest Rutherford, then a member of the physics faculty of McGill University in Montreal, Canada. In the hands of this brilliant scientist, the light that emerged from the minute residue of the mountain of pitchblende became a powerful searchlight for probing into the darkest labyrinth of matter, the heart of the atoms, building blocks of the cosmos.

By the light of that searchlight Rutherford made a great discovery

—that nearly all the matter of the atoms of which the universe is constituted is concentrated in an infinitesimally small, positively charged core in the atom's center. He had discovered the inner citadel of the material universe—the nucleus of the atom.

The nucleus, young Rutherford soon recognized, contained 99.98 per cent of the atom's substance, and yet, marvel of marvels, it occupied but a trillionth of the atom's volume. This meant that the atom, and hence the entire material universe made of atoms, consisted almost entirely of empty space. And that, in turn, meant that the density of the matter in the nucleus was some hundred trillion times the density of matter as we know it on earth.

The atom as a whole, the radium searchlight suggested, was a minuscule solar system. The positive nucleus was its "sun," and around it, like planets, revolved the negatively charged electrons in definite orbits. These orbits were at relatively vast distances from the "sun," their diameter being some ten thousand times larger than the diameter of the nucleus.

Further explorations of the new frontiers of the cosmos thus opened up by Rutherford, explorations led by Albert Einstein, Max Planck and Niels Bohr, soon revealed that the nucleus was the very fountainhead of energy that keeps the cosmos going in all its infinite variety, the source of the power without which the universe, and the matter of which it is constituted, could never have come into being.

Man had thus arrived at the Ultimate Frontier beyond which he may never pass.

Yet long before the discovery of the nucleus and the fountainhead of cosmic energy within it, it became evident that the fires burning in radium and the light that emanated from it came from a source until then unknown on earth.

From the beginning, the Curies became aware that radium was endowed with properties that seemed to defy well-established laws of nature. The Biblical miracle of the burning bush—"And he looked, and, behold, the bush burned with fire, and the bush was not consumed"—seemed to re-enact itself before their astonished gaze. Here was a substance giving off light and heat at a rate that seemed to go on indefinitely without any sign of diminishing. Day in, day out, week after week and month after month, it kept radiating away light and heat at a steady rate without the slightest indication that any part of it was being burned up.

They could neither speed up the process nor slow it down, nor effect it in any way by any change in the environment. Neither increasing nor decreasing the temperature or the pressure affected it in the least. Nor did it make any difference whether it was deprived of oxygen, the element without which no ordinary fuel would burn.

Out of that twentieth-century version of the burning bush of Exodus came a new promise, not to just one people, but to all the peoples of the world—"to bring them out . . . unto a good land and a large, unto a land flowing with milk and honey."

The first glimpse of that new Promised Land came to a young man of twenty-five named Albert Einstein, two years after the Curies saw the light in the cadaver shed.

CHAPTER TWENTY-NINE

One of the "Makers of the Universe"

In 1904, Albert Einstein, then an obscure young man of twenty-five, could be seen daily in the late afternoon wheeling a baby carriage on the streets of Bern, Switzerland, pausing now and then, unmindful of the traffic around him, to scribble down some mathematical symbols in a notebook that shared the carriage with his infant son, also named Albert.

Out of those symbols came the most explosive ideas in the age-old strivings of man to fathom the mystery of his universe. Out of them, incidentally, also came the atomic bomb, which, viewed from the long-range perspective of mankind's intellectual and spiritual history, may turn out, as Einstein fervently hoped, to have been just a minor by-product.

With those symbols Einstein was building his theory of relativity. In that baby carriage with his infant son was the record of Einstein's universe-in-the-making, a vast, finite-infinite four-dimensional universe, in which the conventional universe—existing in absolute three-dimensional space and in absolute three-dimensional time of past, present and future—vanished into a mere subjective shadow.

Einstein was then building his universe in his spare time, on the completion of his day's routine work as a humble $600-a-year examiner in the Government Patent Office in Bern.

A few months later, in 1905, the entries in the notebook were published in epoch-making scientific papers. One paper that year, entitled "Electrodynamics of Moving Bodies," a short article of thirty-one pages, was the first presentation of what became known as the special theory of relativity. Neither Einstein nor the world he lived in, nor man's concept of his universe, was ever the same again.

Many other scientific papers, of startling originality and intellectual boldness, were published by Einstein in the succeeding years. The fellowship of physicists, particularly the leaders of the group, recognized from the beginning that a new star of the first magnitude had appeared in its firmament. But with the passing of time his fame spread to other circles, and by 1920 the name of Einstein had become synonymous with relativity, a theory which only twelve men in the entire world could understand, according to a widespread legend.

When the atom bomb exploded with a blinding flash over Japan it did more than bring the greatest war in history to an end. It flashed to the minds of men the most spectacular proof of the theory of relativity, which provided the key to the vast treasure house of energy within the atom.

It is the special theory of relativity that contains what has become the world's most famous mathematical equation: $E = mc^2$, in which E stands for energy, m for mass and c^2 for the square of the velocity of light.

This equation, so simple that any average schoolboy could work it out, represented one of the boldest intellectual concepts in history —that matter and energy, up to 1905 believed to be totally separate and distinct entities, were actually different manifestations of one and the same reality.

Matter, the Einstein formula revealed to a startled, and at first incredulous, scientific world, is energy in a frozen state, while, conversely, what we know as energy (such as heat, light, electricity, motion) is ponderable matter in fluid form, just as ice is water in a solid state while water is ice in a liquid state.

This means that all energy, no matter in what form it appears, whether as a beam of light, or a current of electricity, or an object in motion, actually is a material substance that has a definite weight according to its quantity—the greater the energy the greater its weight.

An object in daylight weighs more than the same object in the dark. A lighted electric bulb weighs more than the same bulb unlighted. A cup of hot tea weighs more than the same tea when cold. The energy of motion imparted to a ball thrown by the pitcher makes the ball heavier than the same ball at rest. When the ball comes to a stop, the extra weight of its energy of motion is transferred to the catcher's glove in the form of heat. The two halves of a broken doughnut weigh less than the whole doughnut, the difference being the weight of the energy that held the two parts together. And, for the same reason, the two halves of a split atom weigh less than the whole atom, the difference again being the energy it takes to hold the two halves of the atom together in one piece.

More specifically, the formula revealed that a mass (m) of one gram has locked up within itself in a frozen state an energy (E) equivalent in ergs (energy units) to the square of the velocity of light in centimeters a second. Since light travels with a velocity of 30 billion centimeters a second, one gram of matter contains in the frozen state an energy of 900 billion billion ergs, or 25 million kilowatt-hours. This is equivalent to the Grand Coulee Dam working at full capacity for twelve and a half hours.

First substantiation of the formula, suggested by Einstein himself, came from the apparently inexhaustible energy emanated from the then newly discovered radioactive elements radium and polonium. The formula formed one of the keystones in the construction of the modern concept of the atom, which led to the knowledge that most of the energy of the universe is locked up within the atomic nucleus.

But the greatest proof of all, the most spectacular confirmation ever given to an intellectual concept, came on the morning of July 16, 1945, when the first atomic bomb exploded on the desert of New Mexico. To the world at large it came three weeks later with the destruction of Hiroshima and Nagasaki.

For the explosion of the atomic bomb marked for the first time the grand-scale conversion on earth of matter into energy. In each of the atomic bombs a small amount of matter (uranium 235 or plutonium) was "unfrozen" and made "fluid." The total amount of matter so converted was in the vicinity of one gram, about two-fifths the mass of a dime, but the energy thus released was the equivalent of more than twenty thousand tons of TNT.

By one of the strangest ironies in history, it was Einstein, the outstanding pacifist of his age, who signed the historic letter to President Roosevelt urging him to initiate the development of the atomic bomb. And while action was agonizingly slow in starting, it is doubtful whether any other man except Einstein could have moved the President to pay any attention at all to a matter that at the time sounded more fantastic than anything in Jules Verne or H. G. Wells or a comic strip.

To no other man in his lifetime had come the universal acclaim that had been accorded Albert Einstein. From an unknown patent clerk in Switzerland he suddenly streaked, meteorlike, across the intellectual firmament of his day and was at once recognized by the scientific elite and the world at large as one of the giants in the history of human thought.

Einstein was only twenty-six years old when he first announced to the world his special theory of relativity, which revolutionized man's concepts of space and time, of matter, energy and light, and gave him an entirely new and much more profound understanding of his universe. He was thirty-six when he announced his general theory of relativity, which vastly expanded the scope of the special theory and provided a revolutionary new concept of gravitation. But these were by no means the only great contributions he made in those years to human knowledge.

Modern science has made its tremendous strides during the last fifty years because of two concepts of transcendent importance. One of these is the theory of relativity. The other is the quantum theory, which deals with the fundamental nature of matter and radiation and their interaction. While Max Planck was the founder of the quantum theory, which revealed that radiation, instead of being continuous, comes in discrete packages, or quanta, it was Einstein who developed the theory into one of the fundamental pillars of modern science and laid the foundation for the modern concept of the forces that bind the universe together.

It was also Einstein who provided the first explanation of what is known as the photoelectric effect, the principle underlying the photo tubes that made possible the long-distance telephone, talking motion pictures, radio, television, the electron microscope and many other great modern inventions. It was he also who first explained the phenomenon known as Brownian motion, which provided the best direct proof of the existence of the molecule and enabled man to observe accurately for the first time the motions of molecules and to determine their number in any given unit of volume.

Einstein's theory of relativity, wrote Bertrand Russell in 1924,

is probably the greatest synthetic achievement of the human intellect up to the present time. It sums up the mathematical and physical labors of more than 2,000 years. Pure geometry from Pythagoras to Riemann, the dynamics and astronomy of Galileo and Newton, the theory of electromagnetism as it resulted from the researches of Faraday, Maxwell and their successors, are all absorbed, with the necessary modifications, in the theories of Einstein.

Mankind's progress has in large measure been determined by the intellectual synthesis of what had formerly been unrelated concepts. The synthesis by Faraday of magnetism and electricity into a unified concept of electromagnetism led to his discovery of the principle of electromagnetic induction, basic principle of the dynamo, which ushered in the age of electricity. Maxwell's synthesis by pure mathematics of electromagnetism and light led to the discovery of electromagnetic waves and thus to the age of radio and television. Similarly, Einstein's formulas that united space and time, matter and energy, brought into being the atomic age, while at the same time they gave man a new vision of his universe.

In the entire course of man's recorded civilization, according to George Bernard Shaw, only eight men—Pythagoras, Aristotle, Ptolemy, Copernicus, Galileo, Kepler, Newton and Einstein—succeeded in synthesizing the sum total of the knowledge of their day and age into a new vision of the universe, vaster than the one encompassed in the visions of their predecessors.

"Even among these eight men," Shaw added, "I must make a distinction. I have called them 'Makers of the Universe,' but some of them were only repairers. Only three of them made universes." While he did not name the three, it was made clear at the time that Einstein was one of the trinity of Universe Makers, Pythagoras and Newton presumably being the two others.

Einstein dwelt all his life on a lonely scientific Sinai from which he descended from time to time with new and more comprehensive sets of laws to explain the workings of the cosmos. In his quest for new understanding of the fundamental laws governing the universe, he searched for simple unifying principles underlying the multifarious phenomena in which the cosmos manifests itself. In his special and general theories of relativity, which brought about the greatest intellectual revolution since Newton, he unified the concepts of space and time, matter and energy, gravitation and inertia—all considered at the time as independent, absolute entities —into one all-embracing cosmic concept.

But having achieved what Russell described as "the greatest synthetic achievement of the human intellect," Einstein still found himself confronted with what was to him the profoundly disturbing fact that the universe, as revealed to him through relativity, appeared to flow in two seemingly parallel streams, or "fields," the gravitational and electromagnetic fields, of which only the first could be traced directly to its source in the geometry of the world: the curvature of the four-dimensional space-time continuum. Convinced that both streams must have a common source in a larger cosmic geometrical design still hidden from him, Einstein dedicated his life from 1916 until the end to find the common origin of the two main cosmic streams.

What he was seeking with the consecrated devotion of a high priest for more than half his life was a simple set of logically coherent laws, embodied in mathematical formulas, that would unify the field of gravitation with the field of electromagnetism, a synthesis he called a "unified field theory." In doing so, he hoped to reduce the physical universe in its totality to a few simple fundamental concepts that would unify all its multifarious and seemingly unrelated manifestations into one all-embracing intellectual synthesis.

But the big prize at the end of his scientific rainbow kept eluding him like a will-o'-the-wisp and gradually led to his intellectual isolation from his fellows. He first believed he had achieved his goal in 1929, after thirteen years of concentrated effort, only to find it illusory on closer examination. In 1950 he thought he almost had it within his grasp, having overcome "all the obstacles but one." In March 1953 he felt convinced that he had at last overcome that lone obstacle and thus had attained the crowning achievement of his life's work. Yet even then he ruefully admitted that he had "not yet found a practical way to confront the theory with experimental evidence," the crucial test for any theory.

Even more serious, his field theory failed to find room in the universe for the atom and its component particles (electrons, protons and neutrons), which appeared to be "singularities in the field," like flies in the cosmic ointment. Despite these drawbacks, he never wavered in his confidence that the concept of the pure field, free from "singularities" (i.e., the particle concept of the atom and the atomic character of energy) was the only true approach to a well-ordered universe, and that eventually "the field" would find room in it for the *enfant terrible* of the cosmos—the atom and the vast forces within it.

Behind the Einstein quest for a unified field theory—actually a quest to find a uniform set of cosmic laws for the universe of the stars and the galaxies, and the universe of the atom, of which the stars and the galaxies are constituted—lay one of the greatest intellectual schisms in the history of human thought, involving fundamental questions that had divided philosophers throughout the ages: monism versus dualism, continuity versus discontinuity, causality versus chance, free will versus determinism.

Einstein believed that the physical universe was one continuous field, governed by one logical set of laws, in which every individual event is inexorably determined by immutable laws of causality. On the other hand, the vast majority of modern-day physicists champion the quantum theory, which leads to a discontinuous universe, made up of discrete particles and quanta (atoms) of energy, in which probability takes the place of causality and determinism is supplanted by chance.

According to the quantum theory, of which Einstein himself was one of the principal founders, the physical universe is dual in nature, everything in it partaking of the nature of both particle and wave. The theory—which applies to the atom, while relativity applies to the universe at large—has as one of its keystones the Heisenberg uncertainty principle, according to which it is impossible to predict individual events, so that all knowledge is based on probability and thus at best can be only statistical in nature. The uncertainty principle has, furthermore, led to the acceptance by present-day physicists (with the exception of Einstein) that there is no causality or determinism in nature.

Einstein alone stood in majestic solitude against all these concepts of the quantum theory. Granting that it had had brilliant successes in explaining many of the mysteries of the atom and the phenomena of radiation, which no other theory had succeeded in explaining, he nevertheless insisted that a theory of discontinuity and uncertainty, of duality of particle and wave, and of a universe not governed by cause and effect was an "incomplete theory"; that eventually laws would be found showing a continuous, unitary universe, governed by immutable laws in which every individual event was predictable.

"I cannot believe," he said, "that God plays dice with the cosmos!" Rather, as he said on another occasion, "God is subtle but He is not malicious."

Paradoxically, as the years passed, the figure of Einstein the man became more and more remote, while that of Einstein the legend came ever nearer to the masses of mankind. They grew to know him not as a universe maker whose theories they could not hope to understand, but as a world citizen, one of the outstanding spiritual leaders of his generation, a symbol of the human spirit and its highest aspirations.

Dr. Philipp Frank, Dr. Einstein's biographer, wrote in 1947:

The world around Einstein has changed very much since he published his first discoveries . . . but his attitude to the world around him has not changed. He has remained an individualist who prefers to be unencumbered by social relations, and at the same time a fighter for social equality and human fraternity.

Many famous scholars live in the distinguished university town [Princeton], but no inhabitant will simply number Einstein as one among many other famous people. For the people of Princeton in particular and for the world at large he is not just a great scholar, but rather one of the legendary figures of the twentieth century. Einstein's acts and words are not simply noted and judged as facts; instead each has its symbolic significance . . .

"Saintly," "noble" and "lovable" were the words used to describe him by those who knew him even casually. He radiated humor, warmth and kindliness. He loved jokes and laughed easily.

Princeton residents would see him walk in their midst, a familiar figure yet a stranger; a close neighbor yet at the same time a visitor from another world. And as he grew older his otherworldliness became more pronounced, yet his human warmth did not diminish.

Outward appearance meant nothing to him. Princetonians, old and young, soon got used to the long-haired figure in pullover sweater and unpressed slacks wandering in their midst, a knitted stocking cap covering his head in winter.

My passionate interest in social justice and social responsibility [he wrote] has always stood in curious contrast to a marked lack of desire for direct association with men and women. I am a horse for single harness, not cut out for tandem or team work. I have never belonged wholeheartedly to country or state, to my circle of friends, or even to my own family. These ties have always been accompanied by a vague aloofness, and the wish to withdraw into myself increases with the years.

Such isolation is sometimes bitter, but I do not regret being cut off from the understanding and sympathy of other men. I lose something by it, to be sure, but I am compensated for it in being rendered independent of the customs, opinions and prejudices of others, and am not tempted to rest my peace of mind upon such shiftless foundations.

It was this independence that made Einstein on occasions the center of controversy, as the result of his championship of some highly unpopular causes. He declared himself a stanch pacifist in Germany during World War I and brought down upon his head a storm of violent criticism from all sides. When, following the German invasion of Belgium in violation of treaty, outstanding representatives of German art and science signed the "Manifesto of Ninety-two German Intellectuals" asserting that "German culture and German militarism are identical," Einstein refused to sign and again faced ostracism and the wrath of the multitude.

But he never wavered when his conscience dictated that he take a course of action, no matter how unpopular.

He was a severe critic of modern methods of education. "It is nothing short of a miracle," he said, "that modern methods of instruction have not yet entirely strangled the holy curiosity of inquiry. For this delicate little plant, aside from stimulation, stands mainly in need of freedom."

His political ideal, he emphasized frequently, was democracy.

The distinctions separating the social classes, he wrote, "are false. In the last analysis they rest on force. I am convinced that degeneracy follows every autocratic system of violence, for violence inevitably attracts moral inferiors . . . For this reason I have always been passionately opposed to such regimes as exist in Russia and Italy today." This was written in 1931, two years before Hitler came to power.

His love for the oppressed also led him to become a strong supporter of Zionism.

In November 1952, following the death of Chaim Weizmann, Einstein was asked if he would accept the Presidency of Israel. He replied that he was deeply touched by the offer but that he was not suited for the position. He never undertook functions he could not fulfill to his satisfaction, he said, and he felt he was not qualified in the area of human relationships.

On August 6, 1945, when the world was electrified by the news that an atomic bomb had exploded over Japan, the significance of relativity was intuitively grasped by the millions. From then on the destiny of mankind hung on a thin mathematical thread.

Einstein devoted much of his time and energy in an attempt to arouse the world's consciousness to the bomb's dangers. He became the chairman of the Emergency Committee of Atomic Scientists, organized to make the American people aware of the potential horrors of atomic warfare and the necessity for the international control of atomic energy. He believed that real peace could be achieved only by total disarmament and the establishment of a "restricted world government," a "supranational judicial and executive body empowered to decide questions of immediate concern to the security of the nations."

He found recreation from his labors in playing the grand piano that stood in the den in the garret of his residence, and also in playing the violin. He was especially fond of playing trios and quartets with musical friends.

"In my life," he said once, explaining his great love for music, "the artistically visionary plays no mean role. After all, the work of a research scientist germinates upon the soil of imagination, of vision. Just as the artist arrives at his conceptions partly by intuition, so a scientist must also have a certain amount of intuition."

While he did not believe in a formal, dogmatic religion, Einstein, like all true mystics, was of a deeply religious nature. He referred to it as the cosmic religion, which he defined as a seeking on the part of the individual who feels it "to experience the totality of existence as a unity full of significance."

I assert [he wrote for *The New York Times* on November 9, 1930] that the cosmic religious experience is the strongest and the noblest driving force behind scientific research. No one who does not appreciate the terrific exertions and, above all, the devotion without which pioneer creation in scientific thought cannot come into being can judge the strength of the feeling out of which alone such work, turned away as it is from immediate, practical life, can grow. . . .

The most beautiful and profound emotion we can experience is the mystical. It is the source of all true art and science. He to whom the emotion is a stranger, who can no longer pause to wonder and stand rapt in awe, is as good as dead: his eyes are closed. This insight into the mystery of life, coupled though it be with fear, also has given rise to religion. To know that what is impenetrable to us really exists, manifesting itself as the highest wisdom and the most radiant beauty which our dull faculties can comprehend only in their primitive forms —this knowledge, this feeling, is at the center of true religiousness. In this sense, and in this sense only, I belong in the ranks of devoutly religious men.

I cannot imagine a God who rewards and punishes the objects of his creation, whose purposes are modeled after our own—a God, in short, who is but a reflection of human frailty. Neither can I believe that the individual survives the death of his body, although feeble souls harbor such thoughts through fear or ridiculous egotism. It is enough for me to contemplate the mystery of conscious life perpetuating itself through all eternity, to reflect upon the marvelous structure of the universe which we can dimly perceive, and to try humbly to comprehend even an infinitesimal part of the intelligence manifested in nature.

My religion consists of a humble admiration of the illimitable superior spirit who reveals himself in the slight details we are able to perceive with our frail and feeble minds. That deeply emotional conviction of the presence of a superior reasoning power, which is revealed in the incomprehensible universe, forms my idea of God.

"The most incomprehensible thing about the world," he said on another occasion, "is that it is comprehensible."

In 1921, when Einstein made his first visit to the United States, interest in his theory and its meaning was so great that Representative J. J. Kindred of New York requested the Speaker of the House for permission to insert a popular presentation of the relativity theory into *The Congressional Record.*

Representative David I. Walsh of Massachusetts had his doubts and asked, "Does the gentleman from New York expect to get the subject in such shape that we can understand the theory?"

Mr. Kindred replied, "I have been earnestly busy with this theory for three weeks and am beginning to see some light."

"What legislation will it bear upon?" Mr. Walsh asked.

To which Mr. Kindred answered, "It may bear upon the legislation of the future as to general relations with the cosmos."

PART FOUR

Looking Forward

CHAPTER THIRTY

The Promise of Tomorrow

For I dipt into the future, far as human eye could see,
Saw the Vision of the world, and all the wonder that would
*   be;*
Saw the heavens fill with commerce, argosies of magic sails,
Pilots of the purple twilight, dropping down with costly
*   bales . . .*
Till the war-drum throbb'd no longer, and the battle-flags
*   were furl'd*
In the Parliament of man, the Federation of the world.
There the common sense of most shall hold a fretful realm
*   in awe,*
And the kindly earth shall slumber, lapt in universal law.

—TENNYSON, "Locksley Hall"

ON MONDAY, August 8, 1955, the opening day of the First International Conference on the Peaceful Uses of Atomic Energy, at Geneva, Switzerland, I was one of a group, composed of atomic scientists from many nations, including the Soviet Union, that stood in hushed silence around a large circular steel tank filled with some thirteen thousand gallons of crystal-clear water. The scene was the special building, directly behind the Palace of Nations, that housed the United States' nuclear reactor, the first atomic power plant of any kind ever to be exhibited publicly anywhere on earth. All of us present, including the Russians, were aware that we were about to be witness to one of the great events in history, at which the peaceful atom, a twentieth-century version of Atlas carrying a new world on his shoulders, was to make a public appearance. Sophisticated men of science, many of them rationalists and even outright agnostics, stood wide-eyed, with an air of expectancy and wonder very like that of children around a gift-laden Christmas tree. For, consciously or subconsciously, everyone present realized that he was about to witness the arrival of a new Prometheus with a gift richer by far than the gift of Promethean fire that started man on his slow march from the cave on the road to the stars.

There was nothing unusual about the oversized fishbowl which its makers referred to as the "swimming-pool reactor." The tank was ten feet in diameter and twenty-two feet deep, but the lower eighteen feet were buried in the ground. At the bottom of the tank was a bizarre-looking contraption, a grid plate supported from below, about five and a half feet high. This was the core of the reactor, loaded with some forty pounds of uranium, enriched to contain about eight pounds of the active (fissionable) variety of the element. Rather a small amount of fuel, one might say. Not so small when one realizes that as an explosive the eight pounds would yield the equivalent of 72,000 tons of TNT, while as a source of power that rather puny amount in terms of conventional fuels would yield a total of 90,000,000 kilowatt-hours of energy.

But this reactor was not designed to give up its vast energy at an explosive rate. It was a giant under complete control, operating at a nominal power level of only ten kilowatts, with a maximum level of no more than 100 kilowatts. Inserted in the grid were three control and safety rods, used to keep the fuel burning at a slow, steady rate. The water acted in a triple capacity—as a coolant to dissipate the great quantities of generated heat; as a moderator of the speed of the uranium-splitting atomic particles (neutrons) that keep the atomic fire burning, and as a shield against the dangerous radiations emitted in the process. The water shield thus permitted complete visibility of the reactor in action, whereas other types of reactors are hidden behind a massive wall of concrete and lead.

As we stood there the lights went out and we were left in total darkness for a time that seemed very long. Then out of the depths below, which appeared to be much deeper than the actual depth of the tank, there emerged a faint blue glow. Slowly, imperceptibly, the glow became more and more luminous until the reactor lattice was enveloped in a whitish-blue light. Around it was a halo of unearthly greenish blue that ended abruptly in a haze of many-shaded purple. The haze grew ever more intense, a purple fire that seemed to penetrate through the ring of steel that confined it, enveloping all of us in a mantle of eerie cold purple light, coming, one felt, from a source not of this world, from the very bowels of the cosmos, as it were. Outward, outward, the cloud of purple haze spread into ever widening circles, until it seemed to penetrate the very walls of the room.

As the lights were turned on again, and we gradually returned to the mundane sphere of everyday life, I remembered the other occasions on which I had seen the same force from the inner core of the cosmos, the citadel of the atoms of which the material world is made. I saw once again the purple-green ball of fire, liberated in an uncontrolled burst of flame and concentrating the light of more than a hundred noontime suns, that rose over the desert near Alamogordo. I remembered the same purple-green sun as it burst over the city of Nagasaki. I remembered the underwater explosion at Bikini of a primitive atomic bomb, equivalent to a mere twenty thousand tons of TNT, and how it lifted to a height of about a mile and a half a column of water weighing ten million tons. And in my mind's eyes I saw the greatest mushroom cloud of them all—the explosion of the hydrogen bomb at Eniwetok, which released a force equal to some fifteen million tons of TNT.

By comparison with any of these, the tiny contrivance we saw that August day in Geneva, releasing a minute force of a mere ten kilowatts, was insignificant. Yet it was more powerful than all of them together.

"This is a weapon infinitely more powerful than any atomic bomb, than any hydrogen bomb, than any stockpile of atomic or hydrogen bombs," I heard myself saying to my neighbor, as we slowly filed out of the building into the Geneva sunshine. It was then that I first noticed that my neighbor was a member of the Soviet delegation of atomic scientists. He did not answer, and I do not know whether he understood English. But the smile and the nod he gave me were symbolic of more than the understanding of one individual from behind the Iron Curtain. They were a token of agreement between men of all nations, between East and West, between the free world and the world of totalitarianism. As I looked up and saw the Palace of Nations in front of me, that monumental edifice—the original home of the ill-fated League of Nations, now the UN's European headquarters—assumed a new significance.

The nuclear reactor, of which the one exhibited at Geneva was only a small prototype (reactors for power are now being built in many countries, including the United States), holds out the promise of giving man everywhere for the first time limitless power with which to build an industrial civilization with a standard of living superior to anything ever known on earth. For this reason it is infinitely more powerful than any stockpile of atomic and hydrogen bombs. It will conquer the world by building instead of destroying, by giving life instead of taking it. Instead of being a mere deterrent to war, maintaining a precarious peace with atomic- and hydrogen-bomb stockpiles that may be triggered off any time a potential aggressor sees an opportunity to deliver a knockout blow before the victim has a chance to retaliate, it is a positive force that makes peace inevitable, as it totally eliminates the basic, elemental reason that has led to all the major wars in history—the have-nots coveting the possessions of the haves. For in the nuclear reactor, as the atomic power plant is known, man has at last all the energy he needs to create wealth and leisure and spiritual satisfaction in such abundance as to eliminate forever any reason for one nation to covet the wealth of another.

This point was aptly expressed in 1956 by Harold E. Stassen, then special assistant to the President on disarmament, at a meeting in New York of the National Industrial Conference Board.

"Every country," he said, "has figuratively open to it an undeveloped nuclear country equal in size to its present territory, which it can develop and enjoy without contending with a rival claimant.

"Under these circumstances, coveting or claiming the developed territory of another nation with the inevitable risk of mutual devastation is sheer folly. This is the fundamental fact of the atomic age which is slowly penetrating the minds of men everywhere."

One of the most significant facts that came out of the atomic meeting at Geneva was the willingness of all nations, including the Soviet Union, to exchange knowledge and experience on the peaceful uses of atomic energy. This in itself promises to go a long way toward eliminating the danger of an atomic war, as it marks a big step forward toward the eventual international control of atomic energy. But the most significant fact of all for the future of mankind was the assurance that, for the first time in his existence on earth, man at last has at his disposal an unlimited supply of energy, a supply great enough to satisfy all his needs for all time.

In one scientific report after another, presented by world authorities in the field, it was made evident that the nightmare of a future without energy was a thing of the past. The highly industrialized countries need no longer worry about the exhaustion of coal and oil within a century or less. And the peoples of Asia, Africa and other underdeveloped countries need no longer worry about not being able to raise their standards of living. For the nuclear fuels, uranium and thorium—until recently believed to be rather rare—have now been found to be present in many parts of the world in relative abundance, enough to last thousands, and more likely millions, of years. And beyond that, scientists believe they will find in the relatively near future, possibly no more than twenty years from now, a way to tame the power of the hydrogen bomb for industrial power. When that day comes, and it will surely come long before the uranium and thorium supplies are exhausted, the waters of the oceans of the world will supply man with energy from their practically limitless supply of the heavy variety of hydrogen, a store estimated by authorities to be great enough to last a billion years.

It thus became clear at the Geneva atomic conference that man was on the eve of the greatest industrial, social and economic revolution in the million years of his evolution on earth. From a civilization limited and controlled by scarcity, he is about to emerge into the green pastures of a civilization built on plenty. From a world torn by strife and war, he is about to enter a new world based on peace, a world built to order with no limit to the realization of his vast potentialities, physically, intellectually and spiritually.

Ironically enough, this great potential future that man may realize only if he maintains peace with his fellows came about as the product of the greatest and most destructive war in his history. "Out of the eater came forth food, and out of the strong came forth sweetness"—a modern solution of Samson's riddle.

While 99.3 per cent of the natural uranium and fully 100 per cent of nature's thorium are not in themselves atomic fuels, both can be transmuted by modern alchemy into highly efficient nuclear fuels, one pound of each being equal in energy content to 1,500 tons of coal, a ratio of 3,000,000 to one. The useless form of uranium can be transmuted into plutonium, while the otherwise inert thorium can be transformed into a form of highly active uranium known as uranium 233. Neither plutonium nor uranium 233 is found in nature.

Both these transmutations are accomplished in the nuclear reactor, in addition to its role as an atomic power plant. What is even more miraculous, advanced designs of nuclear reactors, known as breeders, replace the fuel they consume on a compound-interest basis, some types of breeder reactors creating as much as two pounds of plutonium for each pound they burn up.

While atomic power will not supplant coal, oil or hydroelectric power in the countries where such energy supplies are abundant, it will become a vast source of new energy in those parts of the world where conventional fuels are scarce or in short supply. But even in the highly industrialized countries it will find important uses in sections where conventional fuels are costly, as well as supplement existing power supplies.

The vast power in the atom can be used to create wealth in wastelands and figuratively stretch the surface of the earth by making places now uninhabitable into fit dwelling places for man. It could be employed to bring to light treasures of mineral wealth now buried in inaccessible places; to irrigate deserts and transform them into blooming gardens; to air-condition vast stretches of the tropics and of the arctic and subarctic continents, thus providing more living space for the increasing world population.

All this is not a mere dream of a present-day Jules Verne. It is a reality. The atomic revolution is actually here, as can be seen by the fact that our leading utilities are investing many millions in the building of atomic power plants. Several such plants are already in operation here, in England and in the Soviet Union, and many more, of gigantic proportions, are now under construction. Atomic power plants have taken the *Nautilus,* our first atomic-powered submarine, and later the *Skate,* on their historic voyages under the North Pole. Large nuclear merchant ships are under construction and nuclear-powered aircraft are expected to follow. Nuclear rockets and spaceships to the moon and the planets, capable of speeds of a million miles per hour, are expected to become realities within a generation.

Because we have such an abundance of conventional fuels and falling water, we can now produce electric power more economically by conventional methods than from nuclear fuels. But the cost of nuclear energy is constantly being reduced and it is fully expected that in about another decade, circa 1970, nuclear energy will become fully competitive with power from conventional fuels.

All signs point to the realization within the next quarter century of a price so low as to make nuclear power practically free, so that only hydroelectric power, which alone is produced without fuel cost, will offer real competition.

This view was expressed by Mr. Strauss in 1954.

"It is not too much to expect," he said, "that our children will enjoy in their homes electrical power too cheap to meter, will know of great periodic regional famines in the world only as matters of history, will travel effortlessly over the seas and under them and through the air with a minimum of danger and at great speeds, and will experience a life span far longer than ours, as disease yields and man comes to understand what causes him to age. This is the forecast for an age of peace."

Does all this mean that coal and oil will become useless? By no means. Heat is only one of the products of coal. Coal tar is the major source of many valuable substances, such as nylon, perfumes, plastics and a host of other important chemicals, such as the lifesaving sulfa drugs. Aspirin is produced from coal tar, and despite an abundance of atomic wealth and power, there still are likely to be a few headaches around. The same is true of the many valuable byproducts of petroleum, among which is one of the basic ingredients for synthetic rubber.

And no matter how cheap atomic power becomes, there will always be a need for gasoline, because the heavy shielding required against radiations from atomic power makes it impractical to use it in automobiles.

In addition to producing vast quantities of power, the nuclear plants also produce an abundance of radiations offering potential use in a host of chemical and industrial processes. The fission products, the clinkers of an atomic furnace, are expected to lead to revolutionary methods in the preservation and sterilization of foods and drugs. Studies in this field have already demonstrated the possibility of increasing the fresh life of meat, vegetables and dairy products with radiations from the fragments of burned-out atoms. This may lead to great savings by preventing spoilage of vast quantities of much-needed foods.

Similarly, the use of atomic radiation for the sterilization of drugs also promises a number of important health benefits. For example, sterilization processing requiring high temperatures that often reduce the strength and effectiveness of drugs might be replaced by radiation processing at room temperature, thus preserving the drugs' potency.

But the radiations from the fission products, important as they are, are only a small part of the radiation story and the great promise it holds for future benefits for mankind. For the nuclear reactor is a veritable philosophers' stone in which all manner of new radioactive elements, each tailor-made for a specific purpose, can be created at will.

These man-made radioactive elements open up practically limitless vistas as the most powerful agents for the treatment and prevention of disease, and as searchlights to probe nature's most vital processes, including the basic processes of life itself, in health and in disease, in youth and in age.

A radioactive form of iodine, because of its special affinity for the thyroid gland, is being used to seek out and destroy cancer of that gland, the radiations from the man-made iodine serving as an internal X ray aimed exclusively at the cancer. The lives of many victims of this type of cancer already have been prolonged by this new product of the atomic oven.

In scores of institutions studies are going on to devise new methods of using radioactive elements to combat cancer of other organs. For example, at the Brookhaven National Laboratory of the Atomic Energy Commission, at Upton, New York, studies are being made on boron as a potential guided missile against a deadly type of brain tumor, as boron has an affinity for brain tumor tissue.

The nuclear reactor also can transmute common elements to serve as cheap substitutes for radium, thus making them available to hospitals which could not afford to buy the very costly substance. One of these is radioactive cobalt, which can give out radiations hundreds of times as powerful as the rays from radium. This "poor man's radium" has been found useful in the treatment of deep-seated cancers too difficult to treat by surgery or conventional forms of radiation.

But by far the greatest promise of these man-made radioelements lies in their use as the most revealing agents for probing the mysteries of nature and the myriad of chemical processes that constantly go on at tremendous rates in plants, animals and man, from the highest forms of life to the lowest bacteria and viruses.

These man-made radioelements can be introduced as tracers into the living bodies of plants, animals and human subjects, by incorporating them into food or fertilizers as substitutes for some of the normal constituents within these substances. The path taken by these radioactive substitutes can then be followed by means of Geiger counters or other devices for detecting hidden radiations, and the extremely complex processes taking place in the living organism can thus be accurately determined for the first time.

By the use of this radioactive searchlight we may expect to find out, for example, what type of fertilizer each type of plant requires at each stage of its growth, as well as the relative amounts needed for optimum development. This knowledge would lead to much better and much more abundant crops. We may expect to find out what goes wrong in a body and leads to the development of cancer, high blood pressure, heart disease, arthritis, diabetes and other serious ills, and thus be able to devise means to eliminate in plenty of time the causes responsible for their development.

Among the most fundamental secrets of nature that we may expect to solve with the aid of the man-made radioelements is the mechanism of photosynthesis, the process that makes life possible through the creation of food out of water in the soil and carbon dioxide in the air with the aid of the energy of sunlight, and also through its constant replenishment of the oxygen supply in the atmosphere. Photosynthesis has also provided us with the fossil fuels, coal and oil, by storing within them the energy of sunlight which shone on the earth some 200 to 400 million years ago.

Solution of the mystery of photosynthesis—fully expected to come within a few decades—will open the enticing prospect of duplicating the process now known only by the green plants and some lowly bacteria. This might lead to creation of food in abundance for the world's hungry millions out of plentiful carbon dioxide and water, and to the direct harnessing of the practically limitless energy of the sun.

These are but a few of the prospects that the atomic age holds out for man, and the sooner man becomes fully aware of them the quicker will come their fruition.

As Senator Clinton P. Anderson of New Mexico, then chairman of the Joint Congressional Committee on Atomic Energy and one of this country's representatives at the Geneva atomic conference, said in 1955, just before that conference,

"A century ago Victor Hugo wrote: 'The only thing that is stronger than the tramp of marching feet is an idea whose hour has come.' * I suggest that the hour for a great new idea has arrived— and that, if we are to prevail, we must now come before the world as its champion. I refer to the idea of making low-cost atomic power available in abundance to men and women everywhere in the world.

"Let us hope that when the conference has ended we will be able to say: It was in the city of Geneva that the idea which is stronger than marching feet first set mankind marching toward a new city of men—a city made rich by the power of the atom bent to the ways of peace."

* AUTHOR'S NOTE: Senator Anderson was misquoting; the actual line of Victor Hugo read: "One can resist the invasion of armies; but one cannot resist the invasion of ideas."

CHAPTER THIRTY-ONE

Atoms against Age

From where I sit I can see the coming within the next decade of a great golden era in medicine. I see progress in many fields of science—physics, chemistry and the so-called life sciences—developing at such a rapid, ever increasing pace that within the near future a way will at last be open for the control of all the terrible diseases that have maimed and killed through the centuries.

Many of the outstanding leaders in these fields are now hopeful that the four great scourges of mankind—cancer, mental illness, heart and circulatory ailments, and virus diseases—will be brought under control in the foreseeable future.

This victory—when it comes—will not be based on any one discovery, but on a new knowledge of the underlying causes of the great diseases. So swift has been recent progress toward this knowledge that any particular drug or test or research development announced today may be superseded tomorrow. But whatever its form, the ultimate result will spring from this new body of knowledge.

We are making progress toward an understanding of the inexorable process of aging. A better knowledge of this process will lead to the development of weapons, both preventive and curative, that will bring the degenerative diseases such as cancer and cardiovascular ailments under the same control as that we now have over

249

the infectious diseases through immunization, sanitation and antibiotics.

Yesterday's dreams that man will master the diseases which have harried him through history are becoming realities at a breathtaking pace. The explosive progress we are making in our knowledge of life's underlying secrets is being accelerated to such an extent that developments previously expected to take twenty-five to fifty years, if not longer, are now expected to be achieved in no more than ten years, and some of them in as little as five.

Men of science who only a short time ago took a dim view of the likelihood of any significant progress being made in less than half a century against the major degenerative diseases, are now confident of important advances in the near future. There is a feeling of victory in the air, and authorities in the field of medical research —some of whom were only yesterday most pessimistic—are now hopeful that the great scourges I have mentioned can be controlled. The most important reason for the optimism rests on the breathtaking progress being made in the explorations on the very frontiers of life, hitherto far beyond the reach of man's most skillful probings. These explorations on life's frontiers, made possible at last by the development of new techniques and weapons, including the radioactive isotopes, have made possible the illumination of some of life's darkest secrets.

All the recent triumphs of modern science, including the harnessing of atomic energy, Dr. Maurice L. Tainter said recently, "shrink to insignificance beside a greater spectacle: the explosive development of our present Golden Age of Medicine.

"Medicine today," said Dr. Tainter, a world leader in pharmacology, "is accomplishing greater miracles than, for example, atomic-energy developments. It is because, in this Golden Age of Medicine, we have consciously evolved a technique and a scientific philosophy that finally enable us to wrestle with death itself, and on increasingly even terms."

It took one major discovery to open the way to the conquest of the infectious diseases. This was the discovery by Louis Pasteur, less than a century ago, of the bacterial origin of infectious diseases. Similarly the triumphs of modern surgery are the result of the discovery of ether anesthesia a little more than a hundred years ago. But even that development, great as it was, would have been largely of no

250

avail were it not for the discovery of the bacterial origin of infections, which led directly to the great era of antiseptic surgery.

Now our new techniques have brought us to the threshold of another era, even greater in its promise than the one opened up by Pasteur. For these techniques make it practically certain that we are on the verge of another crucial discovery that, in my opinion, will provide us with a single key to all the degenerative diseases.

In fact, we already know where the major effort is to be made, and vast armies of scientific workers are getting ready with their highly refined equipment and subtle devices to make the final assault on the wall behind which nature has hidden some of her most important secrets of life. For it is by now well established that it is the process controlling the rate of aging that lies behind the deteriorative diseases that come after an individual has passed his prime. Hence, a major victory in the battle against these diseases may come by breaking through the massive wall of our ignorance about the aging process and the underlying causes that make some of us grow older at a faster pace, mentally and physically, than those who retain their youthful vitality for decades longer.

Just as the discovery of the general cause of the infectious diseases led to their control and prevention, so I fully expect that the discovery of the basic mechanisms controlling the rate of aging will similarly lead to the development of effective breaks on the downhill course of our lives, so that men and women will remain close to their prime for many more years, measured in decades. Thus, by slowing down the rate of aging we will, at the same time, prevent the degenerative diseases now recognized as being largely manifestations of the aging process, or rather of an accelerated rate of aging.

Pasteur's great discovery was made possible by the availability of the microscope, which enabled him to observe the bacteria associated with infection. The revelation of the secret of age has been made possible by the advent of another weapon, described as "the greatest invention since the microscope"—the radioactive isotopes, miracle products of the atomic oven. These radioactive varieties of the common elements have given man a great variety of wide windows through which to watch life in action as it performs its infinity of functions. For these radioactive substances can be introduced into the living bodies of animals, and their course carefully followed by their radiation as they travel through the great variety of mazes in life's dark labyrinth. Thus, for the first time, man has the means for exploring life's hitherto forbidden interior.

With the aid of this all-seeing cosmic microscope, as it were, by the light emanating from the cores of atoms, inner shrine of the universe, we are beginning to get the first glimpses of the mechanisms controlling the rate of aging. In fact, we are already on the track of one of the basic reasons, if not the basic reason, why some of us are old at fifty or thereabouts, whereas others are still mentally and physically alert in their eighties and even nineties.

It has been known for some time that there are two general types of immunity. One is the acquired or artificial type, which comes as a result of exposure to a specific germ, in which case the individual acquires an immunity against that specific germ for varying periods of time, sometimes for life. But there are other types of immunity that have nothing to do with exposure to any specific germ or disease. They are known collectively as innate immunity, which, rather than being specific, endows the individual possessing it with a high degree of resistance to infections caused by bacteria as well as to viruses in general, and also gives a high degree of protection against noninfectious diseases. As yet, we know very little about these all-important types of natural immunity, which appear to be part of an individual's constitutional make-up, transmitted by heredity.

Years of research on "aging as a physiological process" by Professor Henry S. Simms at the College of Physicians and Surgeons, Columbia University, led to an interesting suggestion about the role played by natural, innate resistance in determining an individual's longevity. "Ninety per cent of the deaths in the United States each year," Professor Simms's studies revealed, "result principally from the progressive loss of resistance to disease with advancing age." The death rate in humans, he found, "is at a minimum at the age of ten, when only one child in 1,200 dies."

These figures brought to light a startling fact. If the death rate remained at this ten-year-old level throughout the whole life span, Professor Simms calculated, "our life expectancy would be over 800 years."

Professor Simms's studies provided one of the first real clues as to the reason why some individuals grow older at a faster rate than others. The rate of "ticking" of the built-in "biological clock," the studies showed, depends on the rate of the gradual loss of the natural, innate resistance. The long-lived individual would thus be one endowed by heredity with "built-in brakes" to check the gradual loss of this general resistance. The more effective the brakes, the slower would be the rate of "ticking" of the "biological clock."

It was the recognition of the role of heredity in an individual's life span that led Oliver Wendell Holmes more than a century ago to present a prescription for longevity. His advice to those who wanted to live long was "to advertise for a couple of parents, both belonging to long-lived families, some years before birth."

Until recently Holmes's longevity formula was still as valid as it was more than a hundred years ago. For while we had learned a great deal about acquired specific immunity and how to induce it artificially by means of vaccines against specific germs, we knew practically nothing about natural immunity.

But in August 1954, a team of investigators at Western Reserve University (Cleveland), headed by Professor Louis Pillemer, announced a dramatic discovery—the isolation of a new protein substance from the serum of animal and man that appears to be one of the key substances in life's all-important general immunity system. The new serum substance, which they have named properdin (from the Latin word *perdire,* to destroy) may turn out to be one of the most important in the catalogue of life, since preliminary studies indicate it may play a significant role in maintaining the body's natural resistance to infectious as well as noninfectious diseases.

Along with the discovery of properdin, we are now watching the development of ever more-refined techniques that are bringing us ever nearer to a sort of chemical fountain of youth, hidden by nature ever since life began. With the light of the electron in the atom's outer shell, harnessed in the electron microscope which magnifies objects 100,000 times, and the light of the atom's inner core, we are now unraveling the structure of the proteins, the primary molecules of life, and are watching life on the elemental molecular level. We are gaining important insights into the chemistry of heredity and the structure of the materials through which heredity is transmitted throughout the realm of life. We are discovering that even in the smallest units of living matter there exists a profound relationship between their architecture and their biological activity, and that even the smallest chemical change may alter the hereditary character of an organism. From the concentrated study of muscle we are beginning to find out how all living things utilize the energy whereby they live. And we are at last beginning to make headway against the formidable blood-brain barrier, which may lead to chemical control and prevention of disorders of the mind and the central nervous system.

By the light from the inner core of atoms we are coming ever closer to the answer of one of life's greatest riddles—the chemical processes that control the rate of aging. When we get the answer— and it is definitely expected to come within a few decades at the most—we shall have found a way to fill Oliver Wendell Holmes's prescription for longevity. Only instead of having to advertise for long-lived parents "sometime before birth" we shall be able to provide the chemical equivalents of long-lived ancestors after we are born.

This is what Dr. Tainter had in mind when he said that "we have consciously evolved a technique and a scientific philosophy that finally enables us to wrestle with death itself, and on increasingly even terms."

While death is an inevitable part of life, and chemical Methuselahs are neither possible nor desirable, all evidence now indicates that the normal human life span could be prolonged in the near future to more than a hundred years.

And more important than adding years to life will be knowledge how to add life to years. By slowing down the rate of aging we shall turn old age into middle age and middle age into the prime of life. No longer will youth be "wasted on the young."

Some twenty years from today we will be some twenty years younger.

CHAPTER THIRTY-TWO

Atomic Plowshares and Magnetic Bottles

A DEEP UNDERGROUND SHOT of a "tiny atomic bomb," with an explosive force on only 1,700 tons of TNT, was fired at 10 A.M., Pacific Daylight Time, Thursday, September 19, 1957, 900 feet under the top of Mount Rainier, a volcanic rock mesa at the atomic-test site near Las Vegas, Nevada. That shot marked a definite turning point in the history of the atomic age, with momentous implications for both the military and the peacetime uses of atomic energy.

The test provided the first definite proof that an atomic bomb, small or large, could be tested underground successfully. It also proved that the radioactivity released by an underground nuclear explosion seals itself in, none of it escaping into the open to increase the natural radioactivity of the atmosphere and of the soil. This, of course, promised to solve once and for all the troublesome problem of radioactive fallout that weighs so heavily on the conscience of mankind.

The discovery that nuclear weapons of all types could be tested without producing any fallout has opened the possibility for the United States and the rest of the free world to renounce forever the testing of nuclear weapons in the open air. Such a renunciation would mean a tremendous psychological victory for the United States in the great battle for the minds of men.

The Rainier test also revealed a vast and revolutionary potential for the peaceful uses of underground atomic explosions in a host of industrial processes. In such explosions enormous quantities of earth can be moved quickly; the "little fellow" in the Rainier shot crushed 400,000 tons of rock. Atomic power, in the form of heat, can be trapped in a mountain and used later to produce steam. Deep harbors can be made by means of such explosions. Old oil fields can be made to flow again. Radioactive rocks, impregnated by an atomic explosion, can be taken out and dissolved to produce isotopes for a vast variety of uses in industry, biology, medicine and agriculture.

All these and many other potential benefits were outlined by Dr. Willard F. Libby, at that time scientist member of the Atomic Energy Commission, before a subcommittee of the Senate's Foreign Relations Committee early in 1958. The other potential benefits include the placing of various materials around a device to be detonated deep underground so as to effect changes in the materials through nuclear reactions; subjecting basic minerals, such as carbon and aluminum oxide, to the tremendous pressures generated in an explosion, and thus creating diamonds, sapphires, rubies, and other precious stones; and further investigations of the make-up of the earth's crust through seismic studies of earth waves resulting from deep underground detonations.

As a result of the dramatic revelations of the underground test in Nevada, the A.E.C. initiated a project to study the feasibility of utilizing the energy of both A-bombs and H-bombs exploded underground. The study, named Project Plowshare, is being carried on by nuclear scientists at the A.E.C.'s laboratory at Livermore, California.

In June 1958 the A.E.C. announced that field studies had been started by the project scientists to determine the practicability of excavating a harbor in northwest Alaska, between Cape Seppings and Cape Thompson, north of the Arctic Circle. The lack of a harbor, it was pointed out, has hampered development of large-scale mineral deposits and fishing grounds in the area.

At that time the scientists at the Livermore laboratory believed that it would be entirely possible to carve a 300-foot-deep harbor and entrance channel in ice-locked northern Alaska by means of four carefully spaced H-bomb blasts. Dr. Gerald Johnson, an asso-

ciate director at Livermore closely associated with Project Plowshare, was quoted in a publication of the Monsanto Chemical Company as stating that the excavation costs for the entire job "might
be about one-tenth the cost of conventional methods."

Project Plowshare included in its aims, as of 1958, the following possible applications of underground nuclear explosions:

(1) *Developing oil deposits*—A hydrogen explosion beneath an
area known to contain tar sands would generate such terrific heat
that the oil trapped there, normally too viscous to be worked, would
flow freely. In one known area, the Athabasca Lake district of northern Canada, there are oil tars worth something like $100 million per
square mile per hundred-foot thickness.

Another vast source of oil is in shale formations. Up to now it has
not been profitable to go after this oil because of the expense of
mining the shale, heating it to extract the oil, and then disposing of
the vast quantity of residue work. But a hydrogen explosion under
oil-bearing shales would heat the formation in place, free the oil for
pumping and eliminate the enormous waste-disposal problem.

(2) *Creating water supplies*—In arid regions where rain runs
off because the ground is impermeable to water, the Plowshare scientists believe, a below-ground hydrogen explosion could crush the
rock, allow water to penetrate the earth and to be stored in huge
underground reservoirs. Dr. Harold Brown, another associate director of Livermore, says that a one-megaton (one million-ton TNT
equivalent) explosion could crush enough rock to allow storage of
as much as 70 billion gallons of water.

(3) *Creating heat reservoirs*—Plowshare scientists point out that
an underground H-bomb explosion generates a tremendous amount
of heat. This heat could either be stored in large underground cav-
ities, in which water could be introduced and drawn off as steam, or
in large quantities of rock shattered by the explosion, from which
the heat could be removed by bubbling a gas through the rock.

There is also the intriguing possibility, still only in the discussion
stage, of extracting fresh water in enormous quantities out of sea
water by using the vast quantities of heat generated in the explosion
of the hydrogen bomb to distill fresh water from the salt.

(4) *Utilizing low-grade ores*—Low-grade ore deposits can be
broken up and made economically usable through a process called
leaching. An underground hydrogen blast could crack the otherwise

impenetrable deposits of copper ore, for example, allowing a leaching fluid to be introduced at the top of the crushed region and drained off at the bottom. The run-off, it is pointed out, would contain soluble compounds of valuable minerals.

(5) *Producing radioactive isotopes*—A great number of radioactive isotopes could be produced by underground hydrogen explosions if suitable "blanket" materials were used. At present such isotopes are produced in nuclear reactors in small quantities, enough to meet our present needs in medicine, biology, agriculture and industry. But underground hydrogen blasts could produce them in such large quantities that they could become an added energy source.

Most of Project Plowshare's ideas, Dr. Brown said, while theoretically attractive, need to be demonstrated. However, he added, even if only one of these ideas is found to work, it will be a multi-billion-dollar project. The heavy hydrogen fuel that would be used in the H-bomb explosions is inexhaustible in supply, being present in all waters, and is comparatively cheap.

The problems that must be solved by Plowshare before its theories can be translated into reality are many and formidable. As Dr. Edward Teller said, "What Project Plowshare is trying to do is to discover how much is only theory and how much will work out in actual practice."

Although only a fraction of the laboratory's total effort now goes into Project Plowshare, the scientists believe that it holds great promise for the future.

Significant progress in the field of research aimed at harnessing the vast power of the hydrogen fusion reaction—now used in the explosion of the hydrogen bomb—in a controlled process that would supply mankind with a virtually limitless source of energy for more than a billion years, was announced at the Second United Nations International Conference on the Peaceful Uses of Atomic Energy, held in Geneva in September 1958, by leading thermonuclear scientists from the United States, Britain and the Soviet Union. The reports, which were the most comprehensive made so far by the three countries, suggested that the taming of the hydrogen bomb is only a matter of time.

In its simplest form the hydrogen fusion reaction—technically known as the thermonuclear reaction—is the fusing of four nuclei of atoms of ordinary hydrogen, the lightest element in nature, into one nucleus of helium, which has an atomic mass slightly less than that of the four hydrogen atoms. This is the process responsible for the immense amounts of energy, in the form of heat and light, given off every second by the sun, which makes possible life on this planet.

When the four nuclei of hydrogen atoms fuse to form one nucleus of helium, a small amount of the mass of the hydrogen nuclei—0.7 of one per cent—is converted into energy. This process goes on in the sun on a colossal scale, 600 million tons of hydrogen being fused every second into 596 million tons of helium.

Because the process of the fusion of light hydrogen in the sun requires a cycle taking millions of years, it is not possible to use the light variety of hydrogen under terrestrial conditions, in which the reaction must be completed within seconds. The type of hydrogen that can be fused on this planet consists of the heavy varieties of the element—deuterium (namely, double-weight hydrogen, of an atomic mass twice that of light hydrogen) and tritium (hydrogen three times the mass of light hydrogen). Deuterium is present in enormous amounts in the world's oceans. Tritium does not exist in nature, but it can be made artificially out of the light element lithium.

There are two major obstacles that stand in the way of fusing the nuclei of deuterium, or of a mixture of deuterium and tritium, to generate electricity on a practical scale. One is the enormous temperature required to bring about the fusion reaction. The second is the problem of creating a vessel to contain the hydrogen gas after it has been raised to the required temperatures.

Furthermore, to light a hydrogen fire that would give out more energy than the energy required to keep it going, that fire must be made to burn on a self-sustaining basis, just as an ordinary fire of coal or wood must continue to burn on its own once it has been ignited with a small amount of kindling.

To build a deuterium fire on a self-sustaining basis requires a temperature of 370 million degrees Centigrade—a temperature twelve to eighteen times the temperature in the interior of the sun. To light a fire consisting of a mixture of deuterium and tritium on a self-sustaining basis would require a temperature of smaller dimensions, about 50 million degrees, but tritium is a rare and much more costly element, since it must be made artificially, and the quantity that can be made must depend on the much more limited supply of lithium in the earth's crust.

The seemingly insurmountable difficulty in the way of creating a miniature sun on earth is the requirement of the enormously high temperature. The temperature in the hydrogen bomb lasts but a fraction of a millionth of a second, long enough to bring about a thermonuclear reaction at an explosive rate but obviously too short to bring about a controlled reaction that would go on at a steady rate. Even if such a temperature could be created, no material exists on earth that would not be vaporized instantly at a temperature above 6,000 degrees. This means that no material vessel could be made to contain hydrogen gas at the required fusion temperature.

Since no material container is possible, scientists have invented a container called a magnetic bottle, in which magnetic lines of force, acting from a distance, literally squeeze the multimillion-degree deuterium gas into a very narrow beam, after the gas has been electrified.

The magnetic bottle takes advantage of three well-known facts. First, a gas such as hydrogen can be broken up into its negative electrons and positive protons by an electrical discharge, such an electrified gas being known as a plasma. Second, electrical currents, fed into such an electrified gas, raise its temperature; the more current fed into it, the higher the temperature, thus making it possible to reach many millions of degrees.

Lastly, such an electrified gas can be confined into a very narrow beam by the application from a distance of magnetic lines of force, which the hot gas particles cannot cross. They are forced instead to travel in spirals inside the powerful magnetic field, without touching the walls of any material vessel. In this manner, it becomes possible to design a vessel in which a narrow beam of gas is raised to a temperature of many millions of degrees, while the walls of the vessel remain cold, since none of the gas particles will escape from their magnetic prison to touch them.

Several types of magnetic bottles have already been designed, but they suffer from one major defect. They are not leakproof.

Thermonuclear burning of one kilogram of deuterium could produce energy equivalent to 100 million kilowatt-hours of electricity. Although only one deuterium nucleus is present in water for every 6,400 nuclei of ordinary hydrogen, the total amount of deuterium available in the oceans and lakes of the world is enormous.

As Professor Lyman Spitzer, Jr., of Princeton, director of the project at that institution, pointed out, "If the energy stored in these deuterium nuclei could be released in a controlled manner and used for generation of electrical power, a virtually inexhaustible supply of power would be available to mankind. Conservatively estimated, the deuterium in the oceans' waters is sufficient to provide many times the present rate of world energy consumption for more than a billion years."

In addition to the use of a fuel of which inexhaustible reserves exist on earth, power production from thermonuclear reactions has three other great advantages: (1) The fuel is available anywhere on earth, so that any nation could become self-sufficient in its power production; (2) there are no fission products emitting huge amounts of radioactivity, as is the case with uranium and plutonium; and (3) there may be less penetrating gamma radiation within the reactor core, and therefore less shielding, and less weight. The fusion process also offers the possibility of creating electricity directly.

Radioactive isotopes were yielding a total of $400 million a year in savings to American industry, the A.E.C. reported to Congress in its semiannual report in the summer of 1957. Professor Libby predicted that by 1960 these savings to industry and agriculture by the peaceful uses of radioactive isotopes "will attain $5 billion a year at a cost to the government not in excess of $20 million."

By mid-1957, the A.E.C. reported to Congress, physicians used radioisotopes in diagnosing or treating the ailments of an estimated one million patients a year.

Radioisotopes have been particularly useful in such diagnostic procedures as analysis of thyroid gland function, determination of blood volume, location of tumors, and liver function. In medical treatment, some of the chief uses are in hyperthyroidism (goiter), thyroid cancer, the blood diseases—polycytemia (too many red cells) and leukemia (too many white cells)—heart disorders, pleural and peritoneal accumulation of liquid, prostate cancer, external whole-body irradiation, and eye lesions. More than one hundred teletherapy (radiation) units are now in operation in the United States.

Radioactive materials are important tools for many types of agricultural studies. Major benefits that have resulted include better placement and application of fertilizer; new and improved growth regulators, herbicides, etc.; improved measures against plant diseases and fungi; better knowledge of animal nutritional needs; improved measures against animal diseases; better insect control through sterilization, insecticides and information on migration and hibernation; and new and improved varieties of plants and breeds of animals.

The measuring, recording and controlling of the thickness of various materials, such as plastic, rubber, aluminum and cigarettes, Professor Libby reported, have already led to savings to American manufacturers of about $120,000,000 a year "which probably will rise to $1 billion a year in two or three years."

A new use for radioisotopes is to facilitate oil well stimulation. Already savings of $180,000,000 a year have been reported. This new use for radioactive tracers, Professor Libby said, "represents a large potential source of profit to the oil industry in terms of getting more oil out of the same piece of ground and doing it more cheaply, and it seems likely that this will come to amount shortly to more than $1 billion annual savings."

An extremely important potential development in the use of isotopes is in radioactive drugs and medicinals as well as organic chemicals. In an isotope farm at the A.E.C's Argonne National Laboratory, near Chicago, various plants yielding important drugs and chemicals are grown in an atmosphere of radioactive carbon dioxide and a soil containing some radioactive minerals. As a result, "we now have a national treasure in a barnful of radioactive plants of many different types, all stored and ready for the chemical extraction and separation needed to produce the desired medicinals and chemicals," Dr. Libby said.

These radioactive farm products have already proved of great value in biochemical and medical research. In addition, Professor Libby said, they may have "great value in ordinary medical practice, and doctors may come to use radioactive pills in normal medical practice for diagnostic purposes."

"The feeding of a radioactive sugar pill to a patient suspected of having an abnormality in his sugar metabolism," he said, "would furnish an easy and particularly illuminating way of testing that metabolism. Perhaps a patient would be asked to blow up a balloon so that the carbon dioxide in his breath at various times after taking the pill could be sampled for radioactive carbon dioxide, and it might also be illuminating to examine the radioactive sugar content of the blood and urine at various times."

Following are some other highlights of the reports presented at the 1958 United Nations Conference at Geneva:

Fission power plants, mainly in Britain and in the United States, have already turned out hundreds of millions of kilowatt-hours of usable electricity. By 1970, it was predicted, nuclear stations will have a capacity of at least fifteen million electrical kilowatts—about fifty times as much as at present. The cost of nuclear power is expected to fall well below conventional power by the late nineteen sixties in the United Kingdom, and to be competitive with conventional power in other countries, including parts of the United States, between 1963 and 1973.

Experiments with a small nuclear system that might be used to propel rockets, ships or aircraft were described in a United States report on work now going on at the Los Alamos Scientific Laboratory and at the University of California Laboratory at Livermore, California. The system would use a highly enriched uranium, graphite-moderated assembly. Experiments show that such a power plant could be "very small and light," consisting of a four-foot cube of some sixty to eighty kilograms (132 to 176 pounds) of uranium 235.

Hydrogen might serve as both coolant and propellant in a nuclear rocket; gas passed through the reactor would be heated and, when ejected, would serve as the propellant.

In assessing some of the hazards associated with the atomic age, speakers indicated that nuclear-power reactors had been performing safely, with few disturbances and no danger to personnel.

Dr. R. H. Chamberlain of the University of Pennsylvania told the conference that radioactive isotopes have now become "precision instruments." For example, he pointed out in a survey report, it is now possible to take "slow-motion pictures" of living processes by injecting radioisotopes into experimental animals, instantly deep-freezing them in liquid nitrogen at fixed intervals, and thus obtaining photographic records of each stage of the process.

A report from the University of California described studies with radioactive tracers of the living processes by which cows, sows, dogs and hens convert foodstuffs into milk and eggs. The studies traced the detailed steps in these processes in the whole animal.

It was also brought out at the conference that new international agreements will be needed to deal with problems raised by mobile reactors, the disposal of wastes in the oceans, and possible damage beyond national boundaries as a result of reactor incidents.

The disposal of wastes from present peaceful uses of atomic energy does not constitute a danger, the speakers agreed. However, when fission reactors come into widespread use throughout the world their radioactive sewage might produce a dumping problem. The chairman of the session on that topic, Dr. Alexander Goldberg of Israel, commented that "tombs" of radioactive waste were becoming as elaborate and as expensive as those of the mummies of Egyptian royalty.

Confidence was expressed that methods now being developed for the solid containment of dangerous atomic by-products for burial —in glass, in concrete and in beads—could be safe and effective. A Canadian report estimated that the cost of storing radioactive wastes in glass would be an important percentage of the price of commercial electricity.

Concern was expressed, by speakers from the U.S.S.R. and the United States, about the possible large-scale dumping of nuclear wastes in the seas, but the consensus was that disposal in the oceans up to now has been within safety limits.

The American Assembly, an organization associated with Columbia University, met at Arden House, Harriman, New York, in October 1957 to discuss United States policy in atomic-energy development.

The conferees, sixty-five nuclear scientists, industrialists, government officials, newspaper editors and publishers, educators and representatives of labor and the utilities, examined present United States policy on the development of atomic power plants and came forth with a set of observations and recommendations which may serve as a guide in the shaping of this country's future course in this vital field.

The United States has today, and will have for some years to come, plentiful low-cost-fuel supplies. Hence, the conferees pointed out, from the point of view of our national power needs, present and projected, an extensive program of construction of large-scale atomic power reactors in this country is not desirable in view of the fact that nuclear reactors cannot now compete on an economic basis in the United States with conventional power plants.

However, the Assembly emphasized that decisions on the type and size and schedule of construction of nuclear reactors cannot be made solely with an eye to national power needs in the United States. They must be influenced by considerations of an international character.

The demand for the rapid development of atomic power, the conference pointed out, is urgently felt in various foreign countries. In the United Kingdom the requirement for energy is far outstripping coal production. In Western Europe comparable needs for increased power resources have been exemplified by the creation of Euratom, a six-nation co-operative venture to encourage the construction of atomic power plants as rapidly as possible. An active reactor development and construction program is under way in the Soviet Union. Atomic-power studies are also being carried on in the less industrialized and underdeveloped countries in Latin America, Asia and the Middle East.

The Assembly's final report states:

The great international significance attached to President Eisenhower's Atoms for Peace speech in the United Nations in December, 1953 gave the United States a moral and psychological lead. It opened new areas for international cooperation. The United States . . . should move with vigor to take full advantage of that lead in countries which are prepared to proceed, or which insist upon proceeding forthwith, to the installation and operation of atomic power plants. From the standpoint of meeting the challenge and the opportunity created by these rising foreign demands, the United States cannot be complacent.

A major effort on the part of American industry and government, the report continued, would provide the American atomic-power program with vitality and purpose and accelerate the development of atomic power at home. Such an effort would assist the aims of American foreign policy in developing the economic strength of the Western European community. It would assist in the establishment of an integrated Western Europe. And it would provide experience in the operation of large-scale reactors of great and immediate benefit to our own development program.

There is "urgent need," the report states, "for a thorough review of the United States atomic power program." Such a review should lead to a "clear formulation of the program's objectives in terms of the national power needs of the United States in the long run as well as the immediate requirements of United States foreign policy."

Prior policies, the conferees pointed out, were adopted in the light of considerations thought valid at the time of their adoption. The relevant factors have changed; policies and programs must be changed to meet them.

In the light of what has been learned since the drafting of the Atomic Energy Act of 1954 about the technical complexity and the cost of the program, and the greater need for international action, it is now apparent, the Assembly holds, "that at this time there is a larger need for Government support and leadership." The desired rate of progress "calls for the Atomic Energy Commission to assume more positive leadership and direction." It should promptly prepare and disseminate a more carefully co-ordinated and scheduled program for both governmental and nongovernmental activity, the conferees urge, and it should provide the financial support needed to make possible such private as well as governmental activity.

It would not be in the public interest to allow the atomic-energy program to be retarded by disagreements over the issue of the relative roles of public and private enterprise in the development of atomic power, the Assembly agreed. For the present, and during the next few years, the report states, "public and private power agencies have a common, not a conflicting, interest in the program." In the circumstances, a truce is therefore possible. Meanwhile, the report adds, "the necessary Government assistance should be available to both private and public power agencies without discrimination."

CHAPTER THIRTY-THREE

Watchman, What of the Night?

Watchman, what of the night?
Watchman, what of the night?
The watchman said, the morning cometh,
and also the night.

—ISAIAH XXI. 11-12

THE YEAR 1954 saw a number of momentous developments in the field of atomic energy. It will be remembered for all time as the year in which the most powerful weapon in history, the fifteen-megaton hydrogen bomb, was successfully tested in the Pacific. That weapon was 750 times more powerful than the original atomic bombs used over Hiroshima and Nagasaki. It can destroy any city in the world. Even bigger hydrogen bombs, concentrating the power of a thousand Hiroshima- or Nagasaki-type bombs, can be built. And as we already know, bombs of this type, if encased in a shell of cobalt, would create radioactive clouds that could travel for thousands of miles and destroy all life in their path. They could turn the earth into a desert for thousands of years.

Yet, by a strange paradox of history, it is the development of these very superweapons, possessed by the United States as well as the Soviet Union, that gives reason for optimism rather than pessimism. For these very earth-destroying weapons make it practically certain that no nation, no matter how powerful, could dare risk an aggressive war, as such a war would mean only suicide for the aggressor. Not even a Hitler would have dared to start a war in which there could be no victor.

Hence, rather than thinking of these superweapons as potential destroyers of civilization, one must look upon them as shields that defend the free world against aggression. Both former President Harry S. Truman and former Prime Minister Winston Churchill have stated that were it not for the possession of the atomic bomb by the United States the Red armies would have long ago overrun the free nations of Europe and of Asia.

"It is certain," Sir Winston said in an address in Boston, Massachusetts, on March 31, 1949, "that Europe would have been communized like Czechoslovakia, and London under bombardment, some time ago but for the deterrent of the atomic bomb in the hands of the United States."

The hydrogen bomb thus has made peace inevitable. It has achieved the realization of one of mankind's most cherished dreams —the abolition of large-scale, total wars of aggression.

World War III, the future historians may find, was the first and last atomic war, in which Russia and the United States—aided by Great Britain, Australia and other members of the NATO alliance —fought with fission and fusion bombs exploded by themselves on their own territory. The actual combatants were just a few scientists and technicians. And the only casualties of that war, possibly the most decisive in history, will turn out to have been one Japanese fisherman dead and some twenty-odd Japanese fishermen suffering from radiation exposure—all innocent bystanders.

The tests of the tactical atomic weapons in Nevada marked the entry upon the stage of history of a new type of weapon, or rather of a whole family of weapons, designed for tactical use against armies in the field, each tailor-made to meet a special situation.

The successful testing of the very first of these weapons heralded the advent of a revolutionary new era in warfare, an era in which vast superiority in men and conventional equipment was no longer of overriding importance. They made it evident that it would be suicidal to launch an aggressive war of the blitzkrieg type which relies on the quick breakthrough by massed mechanized armies, since only a few of these tactical atomic weapons, delivered by air-plane, atomic artillery, guided missiles, rockets, or a combination of these, would turn an army, no matter how great its size, into one vast cloud of radioactive dust soon after it started to march and long before it succeeded in crossing the border of its intended vic-tim.

The advantages of small atomic bombs, which can be used as tactical weapons against armies in the field, are enormous. The big strategic bombs, fission as well as fusion, have strictly limited uses. In the first place, they are suitable only for large industrial centers. Secondly, their use inevitably involves the annihilation of civilian populations, a mass slaughter revolting to the conscience of civilized mankind.

The tactical atomic bombs, on the other hand, have none of these disadvantages. Being small, they do not need large cities for targets. They can be carried in small planes or fired as artillery shells, as guided missiles, or as rockets with atomic warheads. They can be used exclusively against armies in the field to stop a would-be ag-gressor in his tracks.

Equally as important, they can be made in special sizes to wipe out a battalion, a brigade or a division massed in a small area. They can be specially designed to destroy enemy troops sheltered in pill-boxes, foxholes or trenches, or, if desired, to destroy equipment, such as tanks, guns and transports, airfields or oil fields.

Since the radioactivity of these small bombs is negligible, they are merely concentrated versions of the conventional weapons that destroy by their blasting and incendiary powers. This makes their use perfectly legitimate for the purpose for which they are designed —to repel with limited forces an aggressor of vastly superior man-power; or, better still, to deter such an aggressor from marching.

As the late Gordon Dean, onetime chairman of the Atomic En-ergy Commission, said, "It leaves us in a position where we can with complete justification treat the tactical atom—divested of the awesome cloak of destruction which surrounds it in its strategic role—in the same manner as other weapons are treated. In other words, when a situation arises where in our carefully considered judgment the use of any kind of weapon is justified, we are now at the place where we should give serious consideration to the use of an atomic weapon, provided it can be used effectively from the military standpoint and that it is no more destructive than is necessary to meet the particular situation in question."

But, one may ask, would we not risk certain retaliation if we used such weapons, and would not such a risk deter us from using them, so that Russia could still march with impunity, secure in the knowledge that we would not use our tactical atomic weapons against her armies, to avoid the destruction of our cities with strategic atomic bombs?

Such a question fails to recognize that there is a vital distinction between a war of aggression and a defensive battle for survival. The latter offers no choice but to fight with every weapon at one's command for self-preservation. The aggressor, on the other hand, has the choice of whether to move or not. It is therefore inconceivable that any aggressor would decide to move when he knows from the beginning that he would lose infinitely more than he could possibly win.

Indeed, all would have been well in this far from the best possible of worlds were it not for a danger, not from without but from within our own ranks, that could have nullified all the great favors with which destiny had blessed us. That danger was overconfidence, a state of mind that greatly underrated the capabilities of the Soviet Union and her technological and military potential. That dangerous state of mind had bred in our society, up to the highest levels, an attitude of complacency which, if unchecked, might have led to the most dangerous consequences.

Luckily we woke up in time, and, by a strange irony of history, it was Russia that administered the rude shock that quickly brought us to our senses. The day of awakening, which must rank as a great day in history, technologically as well as politically, came on October 4, 1957, when the world was startled by the news that the Russians had launched the first man-made satellite—weighing 184 pounds—into orbit around the earth.

Overnight the world learned a new word, Sputnik, which, translated, means "fellow traveler"; and the American people realized to their chagrin that they had allowed their antagonist to get ahead of them in the development of the most dangerous of all weapons, the intercontinental ballistic missile—best known as the ICBM—which can carry an atomic- or hydrogen-bomb warhead for a distance of 6,500 miles or more in a half hour or less.

The world had hardly recovered from the shock when Soviet scientists launched into orbit around the earth a second satellite—Sputnik II—which weighed 1,120 pounds. To add to the shock, Sputnik II carried a living animal, a little dog named Laika, the first living thing to escape the earth's gravitation, and thus was the forerunner of the man-carrying spaceship.

To add to the chagrin, the American people suffered one humiliation after another as their attempts to launch a satellite much smaller than the sputniks met with one dismal failure after another. The whole world then knew that Russia was considerably ahead of the United States in long-range, intercontinental ballistic missiles.

Fortunately, this chagrin and humiliation was a blessing in disguise, as it was the kind of shock we needed to get us out of our state of complacency—and fast! We realized that we were in a race against time, and that we must move fast in order to catch up. As of this writing, in the spring of 1959, we still have a long way to go, but at the rate we are going it will not take us long.

After the first disheartening failures, we succeeded in launching, in 1958, four small satellites, with instruments much more sophisticated than those of the Russians. We have successfully tested three Atlas missiles, our Air Force's own powerful brand of ICBM, about eighty to ninety feet long, nine feet in diameter, weighing more than ninety tons, and equipped with an engine and two boosters that give it 400,000 pounds of thrust.

After the first successful test of Atlas on December 17, 1957, the Defense Department said that "it flew its prescribed course and landed in its preselected target area." Air Secretary James H. Douglas told a Senate subcommittee at the time that Atlas would be ready for combat within two years, that is, before the end of 1959.

Atlas was fired for the first time at full range on November 28, 1958, when it streaked 6,325 miles from Cape Canaveral, Florida, to its South Atlantic target in one half hour.

The size of Russia's stockpile of ICBMs is, of course, unknown, but since she has had a head start on us we must assume that she has a stockpile of these weapons, armed with atomic warheads, capable of striking targets at a distance of 6,000 to 7,000 miles. We must also resign ourselves to the fact that not until the middle of

1960, and possibly not until early in 1961, may we expect to have a sizable stockpile of ICBMs.

Does that mean that we shall in the meantime be at Russia's mercy? Most certainly not. For the fortunate fact is that we do have a large and highly efficient stockpile of intermediate-range ballistic missiles—better known as IRBMs—armed with atomic- and hydrogen-bomb warheads, with a range of 1,500 to 1,600 miles, that can reach any target in the U.S.S.R. within fifteen minutes from the several hundred bases scattered in many parts of the world, most of which are within a short distance of the Soviet borders.

Since we have bases from which our IRBMs can reach any of Russia's industrial and military centers this means that our stockpile of IRBMs is more than a match for the Russian stockpile of ICBMs. And while some of these bases may be knocked out at the very beginning of hostilities, it would be a mathematical and physical impossibility to knock out all of them, and only a few would be sufficient to deliver fatal retaliation.

All this means, of course, that the Soviet Union's temporary advantage in its stockpile of ICBMs is more than balanced by our advantage of a stockpile of IRBMs together with the bases from which to launch them.

Amidst all the excitement about the sputniks, we—and the rest of the world—have practically lost sight of another truly magnificent achievement of American technology that gives the free world a defensive and offensive weapon on a par with the ICBM. I mean the breathtaking voyages of the American nuclear submarines in 1958.

On August 3, 1958, the *Nautilus,* the world's first atomic submarine, made the first undersea crossing of the North Pole after sailing 1,830 miles under the polar icecap. Eight days later, on August 11, the *Skate,* third nuclear-powered submarine, crossed under the polar icecap from the opposite direction. In March 1958 the *Skate* had set new speed records for underwater crossing of the Atlantic from west to east and from east to west. In October 1958 the *Seawolf* surfaced after having cruised submerged for sixty days.

During the year we launched three new nuclear submarines, bringing the total commissioned and launched by 1958 to eight. All are capable of cruising around the world without surfacing and are able to travel at least 60,000 miles without refueling. One of the three launched, the *Skipjack,* was described as the "fastest and most maneuverable submarine in the fleet." Another, the *Triton,* 447 feet long and displacing 5,900 tons, is the largest known submarine ever built.

And along with all these the Navy has the IRBM Polaris, which can be fired from a submarine while submerged.

What does all this add up to? It means that these few nuclear submarines, and more to come, can drive the Soviet fleet of conventional submarines, estimated to reach as high a figure as five hundred, from the high seas, just as the iron ship drove out the wooden ship.

All of which means a reassuring answer to an old question. To all those who fear the future and anxiously ask, "Watchman, what of the night? Watchman, what of the night?" the answer is still the same as of old:

"The morning cometh, and also the night!"

PART FIVE

Atomic Primer

ATOMIC PRIMER—I

The Universe Within the Atom

THE WORLD of the atom is so fantastic that it requires a complete readjustment in our concepts of space and time.

Atoms are so small that if a drop of water were magnified to the size of the earth the atoms in the drop would be smaller than oranges.

One drop of water is made up of some 6,000 billion billion (6,000,000,000,000,000,000,000) atoms of hydrogen and oxygen, of which 4,000 billion billion are hydrogen atoms.

Yet the atom has a structure analogous to our solar system. In its inconceivably minute center—less than a trillionth of a centimeter in radius—is a relatively gigantic "sun," the atom's nucleus. Around this atomic "sun" revolve tiny "planets" in definite preordained orbits, with the same regularity and obedience to immutable laws as our earth and the other planets revolve around our sun.

The nucleus of the atom is composed of the two fundamental building blocks of the universe, protons and neutrons. Since the two are interchangeable, one into the other, they are known under a common name, the nucleons. When excited, a proton may become a neutron, or a neutron may be transmuted by nature's alchemy into a proton.

On the atomic scale, protons and neutrons have a mass of one atomic unit each. For example, the hydrogen atom, the nucleus of which consists of only one proton, has an atomic mass of one. The helium atom, with a nucleus of two protons and two neutrons, has an atomic mass of four. A twin, or isotope, of hydrogen, known as heavy hydrogen, or deuterium, the nucleus of which consists of one proton and one neutron, has an atomic mass of two, while a third form of hydrogen, named tritium, with a nucleus of one proton and two neutrons, has an atomic mass of three.

An isotope is thus a variant of the same element, in which the number of protons always remains the same, the only difference being the number of neutrons in the nucleus.

For example, the most abundant form of uranium, the heaviest of all the natural elements, has a nucleus of 92 protons and 146 neutrons, or a total of 238, hence it is known as uranium 238. A second form of uranium has a nucleus of the same number of protons, 92, but its quota of neutrons is reduced to 143, or a total of 235 nucleons, and hence it is known as uranium 235, the twin, or isotope, of uranium that has given us the key to the atomic age.

The "planets" revolving in their predetermined orbits around the "sun" in the nucleus are the electrons, entities so infinitesimally minute that it would take nearly 2,000 electrons to balance the scale against just one proton or one neutron. It is this bit of almost nothing, the smallest material entity in the universe, that has made possible radio, television, talking motion pictures, the electron microscope, the giant calculating machines that solve in seconds complex mathematical problems that would require years to solve by the most brilliant of human mathematicians, and the thousand and one other automatic devices that have become commonplace in everyday life.

In fact, as its name implies, it is the electron that has made electricity possible, though electricity has been known for more than 2,500 years and has been harnessed for the uses of man for nearly a century before the very existence of the electron was discovered in 1897. A current of electricity, as we know today, is the flow of electrons in a suitable conductor.

Both the electron and the proton carry a fundamental unit of electric charge. The quantity of the charge in each is exactly the same, differing, however, in sign, the charge in the proton being a charge of positive electricity, whereas the electric charge of the electron is negative. It is the smallest electric charge in nature and hence is known as the "atom of electricity," one of the fundamental constants of the cosmos.

A fifty-watt electric-light bulb uses up in one second a quantity of electricity equal to the charge carried by three billion billion electrons, that is, three billion billion atoms of electricity.

The neutron is the only normal constituent of the nucleus that does not carry an electric charge. Being electrically neutral, as its name implies, it is the most penetrating particle in nature.

It is this ability of the neutron to penetrate the heavy electrical barrier guarding the nuclei of atoms that has provided man with the key to the atom's nucleus and, in the case of uranium 235, has enabled him to split it in halves. It was the neutron, as we already know, that made possible the atomic age.

There are two important facts to keep constantly in mind about protons and neutrons. The first is that the two are interchangeable. A proton, under certain conditions, loses its positive charge by emitting a positive electron (positron) and thus becomes a neutron. Similarly, a neutron, when agitated, emits a negative electron and becomes a proton.

This latter process is taken advantage of in the transmutation of nonfissionable uranium (238) into plutonium, and of thorium into fissionable uranium 233. The transmutation of all other elements, the age-old dream of the alchemists, is made possible by the interchangeability of protons into neutrons, and of neutrons into protons.

The second all-important fact about protons and neutrons, basic to the proper understanding of atomic energy, is that each proton and each neutron in the nuclei of the elements weighs less than it does in the free state outside the nucleus. The loss of weight is balanced by an amount of energy required to bind the proton or the neutron to the other particles within the nucleus.

This loss becomes progressively greater for the nuclei of the elements in the first half of the Periodic Table, reaching the maximum loss per particle in the nucleus of silver, element 47. After that the loss gets progressively smaller.

Hence, if we were to fuse two elements below silver, the protons and the neutrons in the combined element would lose weight if the newly formed nucleus is lighter than silver, but would gain weight if the new nucleus thus formed is heavier than silver.

The opposite would be true if we were to fuse any element heavier than silver with another element. For example, if krypton and barium (with nuclei of 36 and 56 protons) were to be fused into uranium (nucleus of 92 protons), the protons and the neutrons of the uranium nucleus would *gain* weight.

On the other hand, when the uranium nucleus is split into the nuclei of krypton and barium, each proton and each neutron in the nuclei of the two lighter elements will lose weight.

In each case a gain in weight represents a loss in energy, whereas a loss of weight represents a corresponding gain in energy, in exact accord with the Einstein formula for the equivalence of mass and energy. The amount of weight lost represents the force binding proton to proton, neutron to proton, and neutron to neutron in each particular nucleus.

Nuclear energy can thus be released by two diametrically opposed methods. One is fission—the splitting of the nuclei of a heavy element into the nuclei of two lighter elements. The second method is fusion, combining the nuclei of two light elements into one nucleus of a heavier element. In both fission and fusion the resulting elements are lighter than the original elements. And this loss of mass in each case manifests itself in the release of enormous amounts of nuclear energy.

From a practical point of view, fusion on earth is possible only with the two isotopes of hydrogen, deuterium and tritium, while fission can be achieved only with one natural element, uranium 235, and two man-made elements, uranium 233 and plutonium.

It can be seen that in the fusion of two light atoms into one heavier, the addition of one and one yields less than two, and yet half of two will give more than one.

On the other hand, in the case of fission of the heavy elements, the addition of one and one yields more than two, yet half of two makes less than one. Such is the kind of crazy arithmetic one must apply in order to gain understanding of the Alice-in-Wonderland world in the nucleus of the atom.

Einstein's formula showed that matter as well as energy can be both created and destroyed, but only in the sense that matter can be converted into energy and energy into matter.

When coal is burned, a very minute amount, one third of a millionth of a gram per kilogram—one third of a billionth of the total mass burned—is converted into heat energy. Not a single atom in the original mass of the coal has been destroyed, yet every atom in the coal after burning has lost about one third of a billionth of its original mass, which was converted into heat.

Thus in one sense energy is created out of matter, yet, in the true sense, energy is not created at all, since it was there all the time in a frozen form, which we call matter. All that has happened is to convert frozen energy into its fluid form.

When uranium is split, as much as one thousandth of the total mass fissioned is converted into energy, or three million times the mass used up in coal. In this case also not one single proton or neutron has been lost. But every one of the 92 protons and the 143 neutrons has lost a thousandth of the weight it had before it was split.

Similarly, it has more recently been demonstrated by experiment, energy can be transmuted into matter. When atomic particles are speeded up in giant accelerating machines until their velocities approach the velocity of light—186,000 miles per second—and are then made to strike a target of some suitable element, the enormous energy the particles carry is transformed into pairs of material particles known as mesons, a form of matter regarded as serving as the cosmic cement holding the constituents of the atoms together.

But even more spectacular has been the transmutation of pure energy into protons and neutrons, the "cosmic bricks" out of which the material universe is made. This has been achieved in 1955 at the Ernest O. Lawrence Radiation Laboratories of the University of California at Berkeley with the giant accelerator, the bevatron, which speeds up nuclear particles to energies greater than six billion electron-volts, great enough to create the heaviest fundamental particles of matter out of pure energy.

Not only did Emilio Segré, one of Fermi's original collaborators, and his team create the building blocks of matter, they have at the same time also created the building blocks of "anti-matter," the reverse of matter as we know it. Along with the proton, they have created the anti-proton, the elusive particle so far sought in vain in nature, that carries a negative, instead of the normal positive, electrical unit of charge. And with the negative proton they have also created the anti-neutron, which has magnetic and other properties opposite to that of the normal neutron found exclusively in the universe we live in.

In other words, Emilio Segré and his co-workers have succeeded in creating the fundamental building blocks of the "anti-universe," a universe made of atoms of positively charged electrons, negatively charged protons, and anti-neutrons, which, it is now postulated, exists somewhere in the outer reaches of space.

As far as we know the creation of matter in any form has not taken place since Genesis, though there is one modern school of cosmology which holds that Creation is a continuous process.

Such a universe of "anti-matter," if it were to come close enough to our universe of matter, would bring about the instant annihilation of both our universe and its mirror-image, both being transmuted in an infinitesimal time-interval into pure energy.

ATOMIC PRIMER——II

New Dimensions in Space and Time

IN THE atomic world, and particularly in the nucleus, a millionth of a second is a very long time, a billionth of an inch is something very, very long, and a trillionth of a gram is a mass of great weight.

If there be any doubting Thomases around let them consider Hiroshima and Nagasaki and the Pacific island that was blown off the map, for none of these would have happened were it not for precise measurements in terms of fractions of a millionth of a second and billionths of an inch and trillionths of a gram.

We had better learn to be more at home in these new dimensions, for on our knowledge of them greatly depends the shape of things to come.

The radius of the electron, believe it or not, is one tenth of a trillionth of a centimeter, which is about the smallest length known in nature. Its mass is less than one billionth of a billionth of a billionth of a gram. In that one drop of water mentioned earlier there are 20,000 billion billion electrons, 20,000 billion billion protons and 16,000 billion billion neutrons.

And although the mass of the proton and of the neutron is nearly two thousand times that of the electron (actually 1,838 times) their radius is of about the same order as that of the electron. It would take 600,000 billion billion protons or neutrons to make up the weight of one gram. But it would take more than 1.1 billion billion billion electrons to make up the same quantity.

The Alice-through-the-Looking-Glass world of the atom becomes increasingly fantastic as one enters further into the realm of the nucleus. The radius of the atom is one one-hundred millionth of a centimeter, whereas the radius of the nuclei of the naturally occurring elements ranges from fifteen hundredths of a trillionth of a centimeter for the nucleus of common hydrogen, the first and lightest of the natural elements, to nine tenths of a trillionth of a centimeter for uranium, the last and heaviest of the elements.

This means that the volume occupied by the nucleus, and by the electrons surrounding it, is about one-trillionth the volume occupied by the atom as a whole. Which is another way of saying that the atom as a whole consists mostly of empty space, the void in it accounting for 999,999,999,999 parts of the total space occupied by it.

It is this great void that surrounds the forces that could shatter the world of men or "remold it nearer to the Heart's Desire."

Since the matter in the nucleus of the atom occupies but a trillionth of the atom's total space, and since more than 99.98 per cent of the mass of the atom is concentrated in that infinitesimal space of the nucleus, it becomes obvious that the density of matter in the nucleus must be of staggering dimensions.

And, indeed, so it is. The density of matter in the nuclei of atoms is 240 trillion grams per cubic centimeter, as compared with water, the density of which is just one gram per cubic centimeter.

One dime, if its atoms were as densely packed as the protons and neutrons in the nuclei of its silver atoms, would weigh 600 million tons rather than its actual weight of 2.5 grams. At the current rate of 90.5 cents per fine ounce of silver the dime would be worth more than 13 trillion, 32 billion dollars.

The forces within the nucleus holding its particles together are equally staggering. This becomes self-evident when one considers the nature of the electrical charges present.

As everyone knows, like electrical charges repel each other with a force that varies inversely as the square of the distance, the closer the charges the greater the force of repulsion.

Since the distance between the positively charged protons in the nucleus is measured in terms of a tenth of a trillionth of a centimeter, the electrical repulsion force between them, known as the coulomb force, is tremendous. Frederick Soddy, British physicist who won the Nobel Prize for experiments that proved the existence of the atomic twins (isotopes), has calculated that two grams (four-fifths the weight of a dime) of protons placed at the opposite poles of the earth would repel each other with a force of twenty-six tons.

If this force prevailed, all the atoms of the universe, with the exception of the hydrogen atom, which consists of only one proton, would fly apart, transforming the cosmos into one great cloud of hydrogen gas. In fact, the universe of matter, and its great aggregates of stars and galaxies, could never have come into being.

That the universe does exist is therefore absolute proof that there exists within the nuclei of atoms a tremendous force of attraction much greater than the electrical-repulsion force.

As yet we know practically nothing about this force, but we do know that it is by far the greatest in the universe, that it resides within the nucleus of the atoms, and that under certain conditions a small fraction of this force can be harnessed for use either in weapons that could push man back to the cave or as a source of great power that could open the gates to a new Promised Land.

This force is known as the nuclear force. It is the force that holds the universe together, that makes possible the Milky Way and its 100 billion giant suns, of which our sun and its satellites are but an insignificant part, and the millions upon millions of other galaxies, of dimensions of the same order as the Milky Way, in the inconceivable reaches of space.

It is the force that enables the sun to pour out in space every second an amount of energy equal to that of a dozen quadrillion tons of coal, in a process that has been going on for some five billion years, at a rate that will permit it to go on for at least another ten billion years.

And it is a minute portion of that radiance that falls upon our earth and gives it the climate that makes life on it possible.

ATOMIC PRIMER—III

Life Is an Electron

IT IS the electron revolving in the outer orbits of the atom that has made possible all the myriads of chemical permutations and combinations between the elements, all the marvelous chemical reactions responsible for the existence of the infinite variety of substances, living and nonliving, natural and artificial, that make up our world. It is, in fact, responsible for life itself.

Without the electron there could be no such vital substances as water (a chemical combination of hydrogen and oxygen) and carbon dioxide (a combination of carbon and oxygen), the two basic compounds that make possible plants and all other forms of life, including man.

Without the electron there would be no food or clothing, no vitamins, or hormones, or enzymes, or any other substance essential for the maintenance of the chemical processes that keep the fires of life burning.

The functioning of our central nervous system, including the brain, is an electrical process associated with the production of complex chemicals at the nerve endings. These chemicals, like all the others in the vast labyrinth of life, are created through the mediation of the tiny electrical charges of the electron.

Life, insofar as we are able to fathom it, is an electrical phenomenon mediated by an infinite variety of chemical permutations, and the electron is the vital force behind it all.

The growing plant has the ability, one of nature's most marvelous gifts, to store up the energy of sunlight, an ability that provides the food we live by; our clothing; our furniture; building materials for our homes and skyscrapers; our heat, light and electricity; the basic fuels that run our communication and transportation systems; and the great industrial plants that make our civilization what it is.

All these things are created with the energy of sunlight captured by the plant in a process known as photosynthesis. And while the exact mechanism of the process is still one of the greatest of mysteries, we do know the vital force that brings it about—the electron.

It accomplishes this miracle by first creating chlorophyll, the green blood of plants, very similar in its chemical architecture to the red pigment of the blood. The chlorophyll serves as a sunlight trap, and the sunlight captured with it is used by the electron in the creation of a host of supremely important chemicals—sugars, starches, proteins, vitamins, cellulose—out of the water in the soil and the carbon dioxide in the air.

And in this process another of the great miracles of nature takes place—the captured sunlight is converted into chemical energy, which is stored up by the electrons in the plant for future use by animal or man.

It is this trapped sunlight, converted by the electron into chemical energy and stored by it in the body of the plants, that is released as we digest our food and that provides us with the energy for living. The animals may supply us with meat and the land with all manner of fruit and vegetables, but actually it is the electron that feeds us and keeps us alive—with sunbeams.

And all the coal and oil we burn in our furnaces and our engines are also great reservoirs of ancient sunlight, trapped by electrons in the plants that grew on earth some 200 million years ago, when life was still very young and there was not yet even the remotest hint of man as life was slowly evolving all manner of queer fish. For coal is a fossil plant, and oil is also a product of some forms of bacteria, themselves tiny microscopic plants, which in the course of millions of years converted organic matter into liquid fuel.

Thus our great reservoir of oil is bottled sunshine captured by the electron millions of years ago and kept in storage for our use today. We light our lamps, heat our homes, stoke our furnaces, drive our cars and airplanes, and build all the fires that keep the wheels of our civilization running with the ancient beams of sunshine that poured down on the earth millions of years ago, captured and preserved for us by the electron.

And not only our material needs, but our aesthetic and cultural wants are also served by the omnipresent electron. The violins for our music, and indeed all other musical instruments whether of wood or metal; the oils and pigments for our painting; the paper for our poetry and prose, the canvas for our works of art, and a thousand and one other materials, either natural or synthetic, without which man would be no better than his cave-dwelling ancestors, are all either derived directly from plants, or made with the fires of sunlight captured and stored by the electron within the plant.

For all civilization is built on fire, and fire is a chemical reaction, and all chemical reactions are mediated by the outer electrons revolving planetlike in their fixed orbits around the sunlike nucleus of the atoms.

All this is done in one of nature's most marvelous cyclical performances, a cycle that makes life itself possible.

The electrons of the hydrogen in water and of the carbon in carbon dioxide store up sunlight in a host of chemical compounds they create.

When we light a fire, whether of wood, coal or oil, the hydrogen in these substances unites rapidly with oxygen in the air to form water, and the carbon unites rapidly with oxygen to form carbon dioxide, thus ending up with the same substances used by nature at the beginning of the cycle.

In this rapid regeneration of the water and the carbon dioxide, the electrons pour out the sunlight they had stored up, in the form of heat and light.

In every fire we watch the miracle of rebirth, the original building blocks of the plant rising phoenixlike out of flames in which the sun of yesterday brightly shines again.

The electron is thus, indeed, our friend. It began serving us millions of years before man appeared on earth. It gives us fire and it gives us life. It was the electron bursting with sunlight that Prometheus brought down to man from Olympus.

288

And behind the electron, controlling its actions, is the nucleon, in the center of the cosmos—the nucleus of the atom. The number of electrons in an atom is strictly determined by the number of positive electric charges (protons) carried by the nucleons.

With the exception of the nucleus of the lightest variety of hydrogen, nature's first and lightest element, which consists of only one proton, the nuclei of all other atoms contain both protons and neutrons, the neutrons seemingly playing the role of a cosmic balance wheel.

In the lighter elements the ratio of protons to neutrons is about equal, one neutron for each proton. As the elements get progressively heavier, the ratio of neutrons to protons gets progressively larger, reaching a ratio of 92 protons to 146 neutrons in the nucleus of uranium, the last and heaviest of the ninety-two elements found in nature.

The 92 protons are, of course, balanced by 92 electrons, revolving in seven orbits around the nucleus. The seven orbits, named K, L, M, N, O, P and Q, contain, respectively, 2, 8, 18, 32, 21, 9 and 2 electrons, the K orbit being the nearest to the nucleus, corresponding to the planet Mercury in our solar system.

ATOMIC PRIMER—IV

Superbox of Pandora

FERMI AND OTHERS like him throughout the civilized world were not looking for a pot of gold at the end of the rainbow. They were seekers after knowledge that would broaden and deepen man's understanding of his universe.

They knew that within the nucleus of the atom lay the answer to some of the most fundamental riddles of nature, of the vast systems of the stars in their courses in infinite space, and of the equally vast systems of cells of which all living things, plants, animals and men, are constituted. And they were seeking a key, or rather a tiny key-hole, through which they might get a glimpse through the gate guarding that citadel of the cosmos.

In that small glass vessel Fermi had sealed a small quantity of beryllium powder and radon, a natural radioactive gas that, like radium, emanates alpha particles, that is, nuclei of helium atoms. A very few of these helium nuclei, no more than one out of every hundred thousand shot out with terrific energy from the nuclei of the radon gas, strike a nucleus of the beryllium atom.

When this happens there takes place a fusion of the helium and beryllium nuclei, the very same fusion process that takes place on an infinitely larger scale in the explosion of the hydrogen bomb. The tiny glass vessel was thus a miniature prototype of that apocalyptic weapon.

To understand the process requires only simple arithmetic. The helium nucleus consists of two protons and two neutrons. The beryllium nucleus consists of four protons and five neutrons, making a total (with the helium) of six protons and seven neutrons.

When the helium nuclei fuse with the nuclei of beryllium a miracle of creation takes place inside the tiny glass vessel. The two protons and the two neutrons of the helium fuse with four protons and four neutrons of the beryllium, thus creating the life-essential element carbon, which has a nucleus of six protons and six neutrons.

And as the nuclei of the two light elements fuse to form the heavier element, about five hundredths of one per cent of the total mass of the helium and beryllium is converted into an amount of nuclear energy about 1,500,000 times the energy liberated in the burning of an equal quantity of coal, and ten million times the explosive energy of TNT. On a very small scale, of course, since only a very few atoms are fused.

But Fermi and his crew were not interested in the creation of carbon, nor in the release of the energy of fusion. What they were after was the seventh neutron, which is set free in the process of transmutation. They had devised their little fusion contraption for use as a source of free neutrons, very rare items in a cosmos where all neutrons are tightly held within the nuclei of atoms.

The tiny glass vessel containing the mixture of beryllium powder and radon gas was to serve Fermi as a neutron gun to create isotopes of those elements that long ago vanished from nature because of their intense radioactivity, or of entirely new elements that nature never made.

For the neutron is in its way the most remarkable of nature's fundamental substances. Being electrically neutral, it is able to penetrate the gigantic wall of positive electricity surrounding the atom's nucleus, which is composed of the positively charged protons. This property makes it the most powerful tool for entering the citadel of the cosmos to explore its inner secrets.

What is equally remarkable about the neutron is its ability to undergo a profound transmutation. When fired into the nucleus of an atom it may, under given conditions, give off a negative electron and thus change itself into a proton. Or it may cause one of the protons in the nucleus to give up its positive charge of electricity and thus transmute the proton into a neutron.

Now nature has built up her ninety-two elements, from hydrogen at No. 1 (one proton in its nucleus) to uranium at No. 92 (ninety-two protons in its nucleus), out of definite numbers of protons, balanced by a definite, though not always equal, ratio of neutrons. For the stable light elements this ratio is one neutron for each proton. For the heavier elements this ratio of neutrons to protons gets progressively greater than one to one. For example, the nucleus of carbon, as we have seen, contains six protons and six neutrons, whereas the nucleus of uranium, last and heaviest of the natural elements, contains 92 protons and 146 neutrons, a proton-to-neutron ratio of about 1 to 1.6.

When an extra neutron is fired into the nucleus of any element, nature makes frantic efforts to restore the balance. This she may do in a number of ways, including changing a neutron into a proton, thus adding a proton to the nucleus and creating an element one unit higher on the Periodic Table of Elements, or converting a proton into a neutron which, in turn, causes the element to descend one rung on nature's ladder.

With their neutron gun Fermi and his pioneer crew undertook to fire neutrons at the nuclei of all the elements, from the lightest (hydrogen) to the heaviest (uranium). After some initial disappointments, when nothing seemed to happen, they began reaping a rich harvest of new radioactive elements. One by one, the elements exposed to the neutron gun were transmuted by the stream of neutrons that kept emerging from the tiny glass vessel into radioactive elements never seen before.

Then one day in the spring of 1934 Fermi and his crew trained their neutron gun upon the citadel of nature's heaviest element, the nucleus of uranium, and all hell broke loose in atomland.

They had started out with high hopes and great expectations, for here was promise for a grand prize beyond compare. Nature, having created ninety-two elements, of which uranium was the last, had called it a day. If elements heavier than uranium ever existed, they had vanished in the long ago. But here was puny man, with a tiny glass tube shooting out neutrons, making ready to carry on from the point at which nature had stopped. Out of uranium, element 92, they would create an even heavier element, element 93. And after that possibly even element 94. They would add new pinnacles to nature's edifice.

The reason for their great expectations was not based on mere hope but on the results of their experiments with other elements. The nucleus of uranium, they reasoned, was already top-heavy with its 146 neutrons. Shooting an extra neutron into it would most probably cause the transmutation of one of the 147 neutrons into a proton. This would mean that a new element, element 93, with a nucleus of 93 protons and 146 neutrons, an element beyond uranium, would be created artificially by man.

As we know today, this is exactly what happens when a neutron enters the nucleus of uranium 238. One of the neutrons emits a negative electron, thus changing into a proton. The uranium of atomic mass 238 (92 protons, 146 neutrons) is thus transmuted into element 93 (93 protons, 146 neutrons), which, because it is an element beyond uranium, has been named neptunium.

And as we have also learned seven years later, the neptunium lives only a little more than two days. One of its 146 neutrons then shoots off a negative electron, thus becoming a proton, raising the number of protons in the nucleus to 94. In other words, element 93, neptunium, is spontaneously transmuted into element 94, plutonium, the artificial atomic-bomb element used in the test of the first atomic bomb in New Mexico.

There is no question today that these two transuranic elements actually were created in Fermi's crucible. Indeed, not only purely theoretical considerations but preliminary chemical analysis as well seemed to indicate that element 93, the first element beyond uranium, had been created. Yet Fermi was greatly embarrassed when reports in the world press announced it as an established fact that element 93 had been created. ("Italian Produces 93rd Element by Bombarding Uranium," read a two-column headline in *The New York Times*.)

Fermi was looking for more conclusive evidence to establish beyond doubt that element 93 had actually been observed. But the more he looked the more confusing and puzzling were the phenomena. Instead of only one or two elements, a multitude of seemingly new radioactive substances kept appearing, which defied all efforts at identification.

Actually, as was learned some five years later, several events of tremendous importance were taking place in the uranium in Fermi's crucible. Some of the neutrons entered the nucleus of the uranium

238 and transmuted it into element 93 (neptunium), which spontaneously changed itself after about two days into element 94 (plutonium).

But many of the neutrons did not enter the nucleus of the uranium 238. Instead they hit the nucleus of a much rarer form (isotope) of that element, uranium of atomic mass 235, which constitutes only 0.7 of one per cent of every sample of uranium found in nature. And when a neutron enters the nucleus of uranium 235, nature does, indeed, go wild. Instead of the neutron remaining inside the nucleus and transforming it into a heavier element, it splits the nucleus into two uneven parts, thus creating two lighter elements out of one heavy element. In more modern terminology, the nucleus of the uranium 235 undergoes fission, accompanied by the release of a relatively enormous quantity of nuclear energy, the energy that was required to hold the two parts of the U-235 nucleus together.

And since the 92 protons in the U-235 nucleus can be split in many ways (for example, 47-45, 48-44, 49-43, 50-42, 51-41, 56-36, etc.), more than thirty lighter elements can be produced by the splitting of the nucleus of just one heavy element. And since the 143 neutrons of the U-235 nucleus can also be split in many different ways, so that the same number of protons may be combined with different numbers of neutrons, the result is that some ninety radioactive isotopes are actually formed when the nucleus of uranium is fissioned.

Now, when Fermi first performed his pioneer experiments, even the existence of uranium 235 was not known. It was not until 1935, about a year after the Fermi studies, that the existence of this element, the only element that has made the atomic age possible, was first discovered.

This discovery must rank as one of the most important in modern times, for without this element the unlocking of the energy of the atom would have remained forever unattainable. Yet very few people know the name of its discoverer, a modest pioneer in the art of identifying nature's hidden elements, Arthur J. Dempster, a professor of physics at the University of Chicago.

The world took little notice when this Canadian-born physicist died March 11, 1950, at the age of sixty-three. But without his discovery the coming of the atomic age might have been postponed for some years. Someday the free world may build a monument to this modest man of science for his discovery of the key element for the atomic age.

While Fermi did not know of the existence of uranium 235 until a year after his experiments with uranium were carried out, it does not explain, nor lessen in any way, the meaning of the Great Miracle of 1934. For even without knowledge of the existence of uranium 235, means were then available that, if used, would have inevitably led to the discovery of uranium fission as early as 1934.

In laboratories all over the world physicists repeating Fermi's experiments were working frantically to shed light on the tantalizing tricks nature was playing on them.

They suspected that new elements never known to exist were being fashioned out of the uranium in the experimental chamber, but however hard they tried they could not identify these elements, which they believed to be elements heavier than uranium when actually they were elements about half the weight of uranium, the offspring of uranium being fissioned in the manner of living cells.

The Atomic Phoenix

THE DIFFERENCE between a nuclear reactor and an atomic bomb is that the chain reaction in the bomb, which consists of a highly concentrated fissionable material, takes place in about a millionth of a second, all the energy being liberated at a rate more than a thousand times faster than in the explosion of TNT. In a nuclear reactor the neutrons are slowed down by what is known as a moderator, such as graphite, so that the energy is liberated at a slow, controlled rate.

An atomic bomb is thus an uncontrolled nuclear reactor. Conversely, a nuclear reactor is an atomic bomb under control.

Nuclear energy is liberated by the splitting of the nucleus of a heavy element into two lighter elements, with a conversion of about 0.1 per cent of the mass of the heavy atom into energy. An element that can thus be split is known as a fissionable element, or a nuclear fuel.

One pound of nuclear fuel equals 42 billion British thermal units, whereas one pound of good coal yields only 14,000 Btu.

In other words, one pound of nuclear fuel equals three million pounds, or 1,500 tons, of good coal in energy content. As an explosive, one pound of nuclear fuel equals about ten thousand tons of TNT.

Nature has provided us with only one such nuclear fuel, uranium 235 (U 235). In addition there are two artificially produced nuclear fuels, plutonium and uranium 233 (U 233). They are made from two nonfissionable elements, uranium 238 and thorium, respectively.

Uranium as found in nature consists of a mixture of the two variants of the element, uranium 238 (U 238) and uranium 235 (U 235), in the proportion of 140 parts of U 238 to one part of U 235.

In other words, nature provides only 0.7 of one per cent of the fissionable U 235 to 99.3 per cent of the nonfissionable U 238. Thus one ton of natural uranium contains only fourteen pounds of the fissionable U 235.

In a nuclear reactor, also known as an atomic pile, or an atomic boiler, the U 235 is split by a neutron. The initial neutron that splits the first atom is supplied by a cosmic ray coming from outer space. This serves as the spark that lights the nuclear fire.

Each U-235 nucleus, as it splits, liberates an energy, in the form of heat, three million times greater than the energy yielded by an equivalent amount of coal. In addition, it also liberates an average of 2.5 neutrons, which split more atoms, which liberate more neutrons, thus perpetuating a chain reaction. Unlike ordinary combustion, this process does not require oxygen.

In a nuclear reactor only about half of the neutrons liberated in the fission process are used to maintain the chain reaction, i.e., to split other atoms of U 235 and thus liberate heat. The other half goes into the nuclei of the nonfissionable U 238.

When a neutron enters the nucleus of an atom of U 238 it converts it into a new element, plutonium, which does not exist in nature. Thus plutonium is a fissionable element, which, like U 235, undergoes fission by neutrons. Similarly, when a neutron enters thorium, the latter is converted into a fissionable element, uranium 233 (U 233), also not found in nature.

However, in a reactor using natural mixed uranium, only 80 per cent of the neutrons not required to maintain fission are available for the conversion of U 238 into plutonium. This means that when the fourteen pounds of the U 235 in a ton of natural uranium are finally split, they will create only 11.2 pounds of plutonium, and these, in turn, will create only nine pounds, and so on, at an ever decreasing rate of 20 per cent, so that in the end only 3 per cent of the total uranium would be utilized.

Actually, much less than 3 per cent can be utilized in such a reactor, for, after operating for a certain time, the fragments of the split atoms (the fission products, or nuclear ashes) poison the pile, absorbing so many neutrons that not enough are left even to maintain the chain reaction.

This necessitates stopping the reactor, removing the fuel elements and eliminating the fission products, consisting of some ninety radioactive isotopes that must be handled with great care. It is this item that constitutes one of the major expenses in the operation of a nuclear reactor of this type.

There are several types of nuclear reactors, all still in the experimental stage, and many others will no doubt be developed within the next few years. Some use enriched fuels, in which certain quantities of purified U 235 are added to the natural uranium. Another highly promising type is the homogeneous reactor, in which the nuclear fuel is in the form of a solution, from which the fission products are removed in a continuous operation.

But the most promising reactor of all the types so far considered is what is known as a breeder reactor, which creates more nuclear fuel than it uses up on a compound-interest basis.

A breeder reactor is, indeed, one of the present-day wonders. It not only lets you eat your cake and have it, too, it does even more —the more cake you eat the more cake you have.

In the breeder advantage is taken of the fact that fission produces an average of 2.5 neutrons per nucleus. Since only one neutron is needed to keep the chain reaction going, that is, to split other atoms to keep the nuclear fire burning, 1.5 neutrons are left over to transmute U 238 into plutonium. Thus, as each atom of U 235 is used up as fuel, it can be replaced, under ideal conditions, by 1.5 atoms of plutonium, at a compound-interest rate of 50 per cent.

Allowing for losses, let us assume that the interest rate is no more than 10 per cent. This would mean that each pound of U 235 burned as fuel would at the same time be replaced by 1.1 pounds of plutonium, so that when the original fourteen pounds of U 235 in a ton of natural uranium is burned up, yielding the equivalent in heat of 21,000 tons of good coal, we would have 15.4 pounds of the nonfissionable U 238 converted into an equal amount of fissionable plutonium.

This process would go on, at a compound-interest rate of 10 per cent, until the entire ton of natural uranium had been transmuted into plutonium, a gain of 14,000 per cent.

In other words, starting with a ton of natural uranium, containing only fourteen pounds of U 235, we end up, by the breeding process, with a whole ton of fissionable material, equal in heat content to three million tons of good coal.

The Atomic Power Plant of Tomorrow

IN THE SPRING of 1954 the United States Atomic Energy Commission announced a new type of nuclear reactor for the generation of industrial power.

The new reactor is regarded by experts in the field as potentially the reactor of the future, opening vistas of cheap atomic power on a vast scale. It will use thorium instead of uranium as its fuel.

Starting with a small amount of uranium 235, the only nuclear fuel found in nature, it will transmute the thorium into uranium 233, a much more efficient nuclear fuel from a practical point of view than plutonium, or uranium 235.

Thorium is much more abundant than uranium. It is four times as plentiful. It is found in monazite sand, widely distributed in the world, large deposits of it being known in Brazil, India, Indonesia, Malaya and Ceylon. In this country there is thorium on the Florida beaches, in the Carolinas, in Idaho and in many other states, though usually in scattered, low-grade concentrations.

Furthermore, there is evidence that the continental shelf contains five minerals, including monazite, besides petroleum. The evidence indicating the presence of these minerals has been found in the inland sands around Jacksonville, Florida, and along the Gulf Coast of Texas and Louisiana.

It had been known for some time that thorium could be converted into fissionable uranium 233. But it was not known until the Atomic Energy Commission announced it that only a reactor using uranium 233, produced from thorium, can breed more nuclear fuel than it consumes by the use of slow neutrons.

This revelation is of the utmost significance from the point of view of the development of economical atomic power plants for large-scale industrial use. For it is the breeder reactor, the type of atomic power plant that creates more fuel than it consumes—on a compound-interest basis—that is regarded as the reactor of the future, one that will be able to compete more successfully with conventional plants using coal and oil to generate electricity.

There are two types of nuclear reactor. One kind uses fast neutrons, traveling at more than 10,000 miles a second, to split the nuclear fuel and release its energy. The second uses neutrons slowed down, by means of a moderator, to speeds of only one mile a second.

A fast neutron reactor is so concentrated and small, however, that it is difficult to cool and control. For this reason a slow-neutron reactor is much more desirable from a practical engineering standpoint. On the other hand, in such a reactor a considerable quantity of neutrons, vital for keeping the nuclear fire burning, is lost.

It is this loss of neutrons that becomes of vital importance in the breeder reactor, in which more fuel is created than is used up.

In order to breed more fuel than is consumed, the number of neutrons produced in each fission must exceed two by a fair margin. The reason is that some neutrons will always be wasted by absorption in structural materials and other elements in the reactor.

Now it turns out that in the case of the plutonium created in a slow-neutron reactor out of the nonfissionable U 238, the number of slow neutrons per fission is no more than two and may be even less. This means that natural uranium cannot be used, in a slow-neutron reactor, to breed plutonium in larger quantities than the plutonium that is used up.

The U 233 created out of the thorium, on the other hand, releases more than two neutrons even when it is burned in a slow-neutron reactor. Since thorium itself is not fissionable by slow neutrons, it would require a small quantity, say 1 to 5 per cent, of U 235 to start the nuclear fire. The neutrons from the U 235 would convert the thorium into U 233, so that after the initial amount of U 235 is used up, the U 233 would keep breeding more and more U 233 out of the thorium in a reactor using slow neutrons.

Each kilogram of U 235, plutonium or U 233 is equal to three million kilograms (three thousand long tons) of coal. Hence, a thorium breeder reactor containing a ton of thorium, enriched, say, with one per cent of U 235 (ten kilograms, at an estimated cost of $300,000), would yield the equivalent in heat of three million tons of coal. At $10 a ton of coal, this would mean a yield of $30 million in heat energy.

The reactor, known as the homogeneous thorium breeder reactor, is part of the power reactor development program of the Atomic Energy Commission. It is being developed at the Oak Ridge National Laboratory.

It is the homogeneous thorium breeder reactor that appears to hold the most promise for the future. It may prove the most adaptable for the far-reaching "Atomic Marshall Plan," proposed in December 1954, by the late John Jay Hopkins, chairman and president of the General Dynamics Corporation, builder of the first atomic submarines.

Such homogeneous thorium breeder reactors could be provided by the United States, in collaboration with American industry, to the power-starved have-not nations of Europe and Asia and to other underdeveloped areas of the world on a lend-lease basis, under proper supervision and safeguards.

They may, in the long run, prove a much more powerful weapon than any stockpile of hydrogen bombs. For such an atomic lend-lease could beat atomic swords into atomic plowshares and transform the earth into a Promised Land of plenty for all mankind.

ABOUT THE AUTHOR

WILLIAM L. LAURENCE *has been reporting science for* The New York Times *since 1930 and is now the* Times's *Science Editor.*

He has twice been awarded the Pulitzer Prize—the first time, in 1937, for his reporting of the Harvard Tercentenary Conference of Arts and Sciences; the second time, in 1946, for his eyewitness account of the bombing of Nagasaki and the ten subsequent articles he wrote on the development, production and significance of the atomic bomb.

In 1946 he won the George Westinghouse Distinguished Science Writers Award of the American Association for the Advancement of Science. His numerous awards include two citations from the War Department, the University of Missouri Medal for Distinguished Service to Journalism, the Lasker Award and the Grady Gold Medal of the American Chemical Society.

Mr. Laurence has covered all the major medical and scientific meetings of the world, including the Geneva Conference on Peaceful Uses of Atomic Energy in 1955, and has reported on the major tests of atomic and hydrogen bombs in Nevada and the Pacific.

His translation of Maxim Gorky's play At the Bottom *was produced in New York in 1930, and his previous books include* Dawn over Zero *and* The Hell Bomb.